ROMAN SILVER COINS

Vol. IV

GORDIAN III TO POSTUMUS
A.D. 238-268

ROMAN
SILVER COINS

BY

H. A. SEABY

REVISED BY

DAVID R. SEAR

VOL. IV.

GORDIAN III TO POSTUMUS

Arranged according to *Cohen*

2nd edition

London

First edition, 1971

Second (revised) edition, 1982

Published and distributed by
B. A. SEABY LTD.,
Audley House, 11 Margaret Street, London W1N 8AT

also distributed by

M. R. Roberts,
Wynyard Coin Centre, 7, Hunter Arcade,
Sydney, N.S.W. 2000, Australia.

Numismatic Fine Arts, Inc.,
P.O.B. 3788, 342 North Rodeo Drive,
Beverly Hills, California 90210, U.S.A.

Trade Winds Inc.,
P.O. Box 401, Clementon, N.J., 08021,
U.S.A.

ISBN 0 900652 62 4

©
Copyright 1982 by
SEABY PUBLICATIONS LTD.

Printed in England by ROBERT STOCKWELL LTD., London, S.E.1.

PREFACE AND INTRODUCTION TO VOL. IV.

As in the case of the earlier volumes, there is very little original research in this work; and as explained before, the purpose is to give collectors and dealers a quick and ready help in identifying their coins and a guide to present day values. The arrangement is not technically sound as it is alphabetical. The scientific works to which we refer are arranged chronologically and under mints, which makes quick reference difficult. I was criticised for this alphabetical arrangement in a review of Vol. III, so would like to reiterate that the whole idea of these volumes is a reasonably cheap work of easy reference.

I have continued to use Cohen's *Médailles Imperiales* as the basis, as it is still used by most dealers and auction sale cataloguers as a reference. His numbers will be found in black on the left hand side commencing each item. Cohen's system was to list the coins alphabetically according to their reverse legends; where there are a number of pieces with the same legend he started with the old gods and goddesses and then followed with the allegorical personifications (see *Roman Coins and Their Values*, pp. 16-26), the emperor, etc., animals and finally inanimate objects. Where I have varieties not in Cohen I have added them by putting **a, b, c,** etc. to his numbers.

In many cases when there is definitely an error in Cohen I have put it right, sometimes with, but often without any indication. In other cases where it is not certain whether Cohen's coin exists, I have left it in without a price. In some cases a known coin, which may be the piece that Cohen intended, is given an **a** number.

There are other numbers also without prices. This indicates that either I am not certain if the piece exists, that a genuine piece is known or that it is a hybrid.

Hybrids. These are coins that do not fit into the normal series and are for the most part contemporary forgeries, many of which are plated. A few genuine hybrids may have come from the mint, where the moneyer or one of his workmen had used the wrong combination of dies.

Obverses. I have put the obverse legends and types at the beginning of each reign with letters A, B, C, etc. for the legend. For the earlier reigns I have given the head or bust description, a, b, c, etc., but for the later reigns where there is less variety I have put—l. for laureate, d. for draped, etc. In the catalogue I have given Aa, Bc, Ald, etc. as the case may be; this has been done to save space and a lot of repetition.

To overcome the annoyance of having to continually refer back, a folded sheet at the back of the book also gives the obverse legends and types, so that they can be used with any page of the catalogue.

Value. The value given in the right hand column is that which I would have placed on a VF (*very fine*) specimen. By this I mean the price a dealer might reasonably charge, but not the price a dealer would pay for such a piece.

I cannot stress too strongly that the value of any coin depends very largely on its state of preservation and Roman coins are no exception. A poor antoninianus, unless a great rarity, is of little value; on the other hand a coin in superb state of preservation would be worth considerably more than the stated price.

Illustrations. Most of the coins illustrated in the first half of the book are from the collection of Mr. G. R. (Bob) Arnold of Burford (Tom Forrest of the radio series "The Archers"). Most of the other pieces illustrated are British Museum coins. We are greatly indebted to both these sources for allowing their coins to be photographed.

I have to thank Mr. Frank Purvey for his excellent photographs, which were taken by his own specially constructed camera.

In conclusion. My appreciation is due to Mr. David Sear for looking through the mss. and giving me so much help with the pricing of the coins.

February, 1971   H. A. SEABY.

INTRODUCTION TO SECOND (REVISED) EDITION

Eleven years have elapsed since the original publication of this volume, so a thorough revision has been long overdue. The intervening years witnessed a dramatic surge in coin values, up to the mid-70s, followed by a much quieter period during which prices stabilized at their new levels. Only pieces of exceptional quality have continued to appreciate significantly. Nevertheless a comparison between the valuations in this edition and those in the 1971 catalogue provides solid evidence of the growing popularity of Roman coins amongst collectors. Additional interest in the hobby has arisen as a result of metal-detecting which has become so popular over the past few years. A significant proportion of the Roman debased silver coins uncovered by metal-detector users in Great Britain are from the period encompassed by this volume, A.D. 238-268, so this revision has been eagerly awaited by large numbers of the hobby's newest recruits.

Frank Purvey has provided some additional photographic illustrations to augment those which he supplied for the original edition, and my thanks are due to everyone who sent me information on new varieties, all of which have been incorporated in the text.

DAVID R. SEAR
Hawstead, Suffolk

February, 1982

OTHER VOLUMES IN THIS SERIES

ABBREVIATIONS

Æ	= copper	laur.	= laureate
Æ	= silver	O. or *obv.*	= obverse
N	= gold	p.	= page
cuir.	= cuirassed	pl.	= plate
diad.	= diademed	quad.	= quadriga
dr.	= draped	r.	= right
ex.	= exergue	rad.	= radiate
hd.	= head	R. or *rev.*	= reverse
(Hy.)	= hybrid or probable hybrid	stg.	= standing

⌢ indicates that the letters below the sign are ligate.

R.I.C. = Mattingly and Sydenham, *The Roman Imperial Coinage*, Vols. IV-V.

DEITIES AND PERSONIFICATIONS

Unless otherwise stated, they have the following attributes.

Apollo	branch
Juno	patera and sceptre
Jupiter	thunderbolt and sceptre
Mercury	purse and caduceus
Neptune	dolphin and trident
Sol	radiate, holding globe and raising r. hand
Vesta	patera and sceptre
Abundantia	corn-ears and cornucopiae
Aequitas	scales and cornucopiae
Annona	corn-ears and cornucopiae
Clementia	branch and sceptre
Concordia	patera and cornucopiae
Felicitas	caduceus and cornucopiae
Fortuna	rudder and cornucopiae
Indulgentia	patera and sceptre
Laetitia	wreath and anchor
Liberalitas	tessera (tablet) and cornucopiae
Libertas	pileus (pointed cap) and sceptre
Moneta	scales and cornucopiae
Nobilitas	palladium and sceptre
Pax	olive-branch and sceptre
Pietas	patera and sceptre
Providentia	baton pointing to globe at feet and sceptre
Pudicitia	sceptre
Spes	flower and slightly raising the drapery of her dress
Uberitas	cornucopiae and purse or bunch of grapes
Victory	wreath and palm
Bonus Eventus	patera and cornucopiae
Genius	patera and cornucopiae
Virtus	Victory and spear

GORDIAN III

A.D. 238-244

Marcus Antonius Gordianus was the grandson of Gordian I and was adopted as heir to the throne by Balbinus and Pupienus, with the rank of Caesar. After the massacre of these joint-emperors in July 238, Gordian, then probably not more than fifteen years old, was proclaimed Augustus and unanimously confirmed by the Senate. Little is known about his reign. In 240 Sabinianus led a revolt in Africa, but this was promptly suppressed. In the following year the Persians invaded Mesopotamia and Gordian married Sabinia Tranquillina. In 242 Gordian set out for the East to direct the Persian campaign in person and he was so successful that in 243 he drove them out of Mesopotamia. At about this time his father-in-law Timisitheus, the prefect of the praetorian guards, died and was succeeded by M. Julius Philippus. This ambitious man irritated the army against their emperor and Gordian was assassinated at Zeila, on the Euphrates, in Feb. 244.

Obverse legends.

As Emperor.

A.	IMP . CAES . GORDIANVS PIVS AVG.	A.D. 240
B.	IMP . CAES . M . ANT . GORDIANVS AVG.	A.D. 238-240
C.	IMP . C . M . ANT . GORDIANVS AVG.	A.D. 238-240
D.	IMP . GORDIANVS PIVS FEL . AVG.	A.D. 240-244
E.	IMP . GORDIANVS PIVS FELIX AVG.	A.D. 240-244

Obverse types.

As Emperor.

ldc. Laureate bust draped and cuirassed on right shoulder.

lc. Laureate bust cuirassed.

rdc. Radiate bust draped and cuirassed seen from the side or slightly from the back.

rc. Radiate bust cuirassed seen from the back, except for those facing **left** which are seen from the front.

All coins show the emperor facing to **right** *unless otherwise catalogued—***to left.**

(A) *Roman Imperial Coinage attribute the pieces marked thus after the obv. description to Eastern mints, probably Antioch. R.I.C. nos. 168-219 (pp. 33-36).*

17 Antoninianus. Brdc. ℞. AEQVITAS AVG., Aequitas stg. half-left. *R.I.C. 34* £15

17a Brdc(A). ℞. — As last, but Aequitas stg. l. *R.I.C. 177 (a)*		18
18 Brdc **to left** (A). ℞. — As last. *R.I.C. 177 (b)*		150
22 Ardc. ℞ — As **17**. *R.I.C. 51*		18
25 Drdc. ℞. — As last. *R.I.C. 63*		15
28a Drdc. ℞. AEQVITAS AVGG. As **17a** (Hy.; *rev of Philip I*). *R.I.C. 230* (*Verulamium Theatre*)		20

29 Medallion. Elc, seen from front. ℞. AEQVITAS AVGVSTI, the three
Monetae stg. l.; at feet of each, pile of metal or coins. *R.I.C.* 133 (a)

Extremely rare

31 Dldc, seen from front. ℞. — As last. *R.I.C.* 133 (b) ..   *Extremely rare*

32 E, laur. bust in lion's skin l., holding spear (*Cohen*, with aegis covering
shoulder and holding sceptre). ℞. — As before, but central Moneta
stg. front. *R.I.C.* 134 (a) ..   ..   *Extremely rare*

33 Eldc, seen from front. ℞. — As last. *R.I.C* 134 (b) ..   .. *Extremely rare*

34 Bldc, seen from front? ℞. — As before, but all the Monetae stg. front,
looking l. *R.I.C.* 47 ..   .. *Extremely rare*

39   40

39 Denarius. Dldc. ℞. AETERNITATI AVG., Sol stg. front, hd. l. *R.I.C.* 111   £25

40 Quinarius. Dldc. ℞. — As last. *R.I.C.* 117   150

41 Antoninianus. Drdc. ℞. — As last. *R.I.C.* 83   15

42 As last (*base, plated or Æ*). *R.I.C.* 83*   ..   ..

46 Drdc. ℞. ANNONA AVG., Annona stg. l., modius at her feet (Hy.; *rev. of
Philip I*). *R.I.C.* 231   20

46a Brdc. ℞. APOL . CONSERVAT., Apollo stg. l., resting lyre on tripod (Hy.;
rev. copied from a coin of Aemilian). *R.I.C.* 245 (*Hull Museum*) ..   ..

48 Brdc. ℞. CONCORDIA AVG., Concordia seated l. on throne. *R.I.C.* 35* ..   18

48a Brdc(A). ℞. — As last. *R.I.C.* 180 (*Vienna*)   18

50 As **48,** but double cornucopiae. *R.I.C.* 35   15

52 Drdc. ℞. — As last. *R.I.C.* 64   15

53 Ardc. ℞. — As last. *R.I.C.* 52   18

57 Brdc. ℞. — Concordia seated l., holding patera only. *R.I.C.* 48 (*this
could be as next*)   20

57a Brdc(A). ℞. — As last. *R.I.C.* 181 (*Vienna*)   20

58 Brdc(A). ℞. — Concordia stg. l. before altar. *R.I.C.* 178 (a)   20

58a Brc **to left** (A). ℞. — As last. *R.I.C.* 178 (b) (*Vienna*)   150

59 Drdc(A). ℞. — As last. *R.I.C.* 208   25

60a Brdc(A).   ℞. — Concordia or Providentia stg. l., holding globe and
transverse sceptre. *R.I.C.* 179 (*Vienna*)   25

60b Drdc. ℞. CONCORDIA AVGG., Concordia seated l. (Hy.; *rev. of Volusian*).
R.I.C. 244 (*Ashmolean*)   ..   ..

61 Drdc. ℞. CONCORDIA MILIT, as last. *R.I.C.* 65*   15

62 As last, but double cornucopiae. *R.I.C.* 65   15

62   71

62a **Antoninianus.** Brdc. ℞. — As last (Hy). *R.I.C.* 49 (*B.M.: base metal*) and 219A (*Dorchester*) .. ..

62b Ardc. ℞. — As last. *R.I.C.* 52 note (*B.M.; ex Dorchester*) £20

63 **Quinarius.** Dldc. ℞. — As last. *R.I.C.* 75 150

67 **Antoninianus.** Drdc. ℞. CONCORDIA MILITVM, as last. *R.I.C.* 65* 18

69 **Denarius.** Dldc. ℞. DIANA LVCIFERA, Diana stg. r., holding flaming torch. *R.I.C.* 127 30

71 **Antoninianus.** Drdc. ℞. FELICIT . TEMP., Felicitas stg. l. *R.I.C.* 140 15

71a **Quinarius.** Dldc. ℞. — As last. *R.I.C.* 167 (*Trau*) 175

72 **Antoninianus.** Drdc. ℞. FELICIT . TEMPOR., as last. *R.I.C.* 141 .. 15

79 **Denarius.** Dldc. ℞. FELICITAS PVBLICA, Felicitas stg. l., holding caduceus and leaning against column. *R.I.C.* 128 (*It has been suggested that the specimen Cohen quotes from is false*) .. ..

81 **Antoninianus.** Drdc. ℞. FELICITAS TEMPORVM, as **71**. *R.I.C.* 142 15

83 Drdc. ℞. FIDES EXERCITVS, Fides stg. l., holding two standards (Hy.; *rev. of Philip I*). *R.I.C.* 232 20

83a As last, but she holds four standards (Hy.; *rev.* of Ph. I). *R.I.C.* 233 (*Dorchester*) 22

86   98a

86 Brdc. ℞. FIDES MILITVM, Fides stg. half-left, holding standard and transverse sceptre. *R.I.C.* 1 15

90 Brdc(A). ℞. — Fides stg. l., holding standard and cornucopiae. *R.I.C.* 183 (a) 18

90a Brdc. **to left** (A). ℞. — As last. *R.I.C.* 183 (b) (*Vienna*) 150

91 Brc **to left** (A). ℞. — As last. *R.I.C.* 183 (c) 150

91a Brdc **to left** (A). ℞. — Fides stg. l., holding standard. *R.I.C.* 182 (*Vienna*) 150

92 Drdc(A). ℞. — Fides stg. l., holding two standards. *R.I.C.* 209 .. 20

92a Drdc. ℞. — As last. *R.I.C.* 234 (Hy.; *rev. of Philip I*) 20

92b Drc(A). ℞. — As last. *R.I.C.* 209 (*Vienna*) 20

92c Brdc(A). ℞. — As last. *R.I.C.* 184 (*B.M., ex Dorchester*) 20

93 Brdc(A). ℞. — Fides seated l., holding standard and cornucopiae. *R.I.C.* 185 (*Vienna*) 20

95 Drdc. ℞. FORT . REDVX, Victory stg. l., holding palm and leaning on shield; at feet, seated captive. *R.I.C.* 247A (*A most peculiar rev.*)
Excessively rare if genuine

97 Drdc. ℞. — Fortuna seated l.; under seat, wheel. *R.I.C.* 143 .. 15

97a Drdc. ℞. FORTVNA AVG., Fortuna stg. l., holding globe and cornucopiae. *R.I.C.* 248 20

98 Drdc (*Cohen has laur. in error*). ℞. FORTVNA REDVX, as **97**. *R.I.C.* 144 15

98a As last, but without the wheel under seat (A). *R.I.C.* 210 15

98b Drdc **to left** (A). ℞. — As last. *R.I.C.* 210 (*perhaps a printer's error for obv.* Drc to r.) .. ..

102 Antoninianus. Brdc. ℞. IOVI CONSERVATORI, Jupiter seated l., eagle at feet. *R.I.C.* 50 .. .. £20

103 Drdc. ℞. — Jupiter stg. l., naked but for cloak on l. shoulder. *R.I.C.* 136 (*this could be the next piece*) 20

103a Drc(A). ℞. — As last. *R.I.C.* 211 (*Vienna*) 20

105 Brdc. ℞. — Jupiter stg. half-left; before, small figure of Gordian III stg. l. *R.I.C.* 2 15

105a As last, but Gordian III seems to be like Spes, holding up flower and gathering up his robe. *R.I.C.* 2‡ 18

109 Drdc. ℞. IOVI STATORI, Jupiter stg. facing, hd. r. *R.I.C.* 84 15

110 As last (*base, plated or Æ*). *R.I.C.* 84* .. ..

113 Denarius. Dldc. ℞. IOVIS STATOR, as last. *R.I.C.* 112.. 30

114 Quinarius. As last. *R.I.C.* 118 150

115 Antoninianus. Drdc. ℞. — As last. *R.I.C.* 85 15

118 Brdc. ℞. LAETITIA AVG . N., Laetitia stg. l. (Hy.). *R.I.C.* 221 20

118a As last (Hy.; *plated*). *R.I.C.* 221 (*Vienna*) .. ..

118b Ardc. ℞. — As before. *R.I.C.* 222 (*Vienna*) 20

120 Denarius. Dldc. ℞. — As last. *R.I.C.* 113 30

121 Antoninianus. Drdc. ℞. — As last. *R.I.C.* 86 15

124a Drdc. ℞. LAETIT . FVNDAT., Laetitia stg. l., holding wreath and rudder(?) (Hy.; *rev. of Philip I*). *R.I.C.* 235 (*B.M., ex Dorchester hoard; poor Æ*)

125 Medallion (barbarous). IMP . GORDIANVS PIVS LALVAO, rdc. ℞. LAHTITIA AVG . N., as **118**. *R.I.C.*, p. 29 .. .. ..

126 Antoninianus. Brdc(A). ℞. LIBERALITAS AVG., Liberty stg. l. *R.I.C.* 187 (a) 25

127 Brdc **to left** (A). *R.I.C.* 187 (b) 150

127a Brdc(A). ℞. — Liberalitas stg. half-left. *R.I.C.* 186 (*B.M.*) 22

130 Brdc. ℞. LIBERALITAS AVG . II, as last. *R.I.C.* 36 15

131 Denarius. Cldc. ℞. — As last. *R.I.C.* 45 35

132 Antoninianus. Drdc. ℞. — As last. *R.I.C.* 66 22

133 Ardc. ℞. — As last. *R.I.C.* 53 20

141 Ardc. ℞. LIBERALITAS AVG . III, as last, but double cornucopiae. (Hy.). *R.I.C.* 223 25

142 Drdc. ℞. — As **127a**. *R.I.C.* 67 (*Cohen gives as last, probably in error*) .. 15

145a Drdc. ℞. — Philip I and II seated l. on curule chairs and raising their r. hands. (Hy.; *rev. of Philip II*). *R.I.C.* 241A (*B.M.*) 35

147 Drdc. ℞. LIBERALITAS AVG . IIII, as **127a**. *R.I.C.* 137 20

154a Drdc. ℞. LIBERTAS AVGG., Libertas stg. l. (Hy.; *rev. of Treb. Gallus*). *R.I.C.* 242 .. ..

113   160

155 Drdc. ℞. MARS PROPVG., Mars walking r., holding transverse spear and shield. *R.I.C.* 145 15

156 Drdc. ℞. MARS PROPVGNAT., as last. *R.I.C.* 146 20

160 Drdc. ℞. MARTEM PROPVGNATOREM, as last. *R.I.C.* 147.. 15

162 **Antoninianus.** Drdc(A). ℞. MARTI PACIFERO, Mars walking or running l., holding branch, reversed spear and shield. *R.I.C.* 212 .. .. £22
162a Drc(A). ℞. — As last. *R.I.C.* 212 (*B.M.*) 22
167 Drc(A). ℞. ORIENS AVG., Sol stg. l. *R.I.C.* 213 15
167a As last (*base*). *R.I.C.* 213* (*Ashmolean*) .. ..
168 Drdc. ℞. PAX AETERNA, Pax hurrying l. (Hy.; *rev. of Philip I*). *R.I.C.* 237 20
172a Drdc. ℞. PAX AVGG., Pax stg. l. *R.I.C.* Addenda (*B. A. Seaby Ltd*, 1947; *very base*) 20
173 Brdc. ℞. PAX AVGVSTI, Pax stg. half-left. *R.I.C.* 3 (*Cohen,* AVGVST, *a slip ?*) 15
174 Brdc **to left**. ℞. PAX AVGVST., Pax stg. l. *R.I.C.* 188 (AVGVS) 150
174a Brdc. ℞. PAX AVGVSTI, as last. *R.I.C.* 189 (a) (*Vienna*) 18
174b Brdc **to left**. ℞. — As last. *R.I.C.* 189 (b) (*Trau*) 150
177a Ardc. ℞. — As last (Hy.). *R.I.C.* 62 (*B.M., ex. Dorchester*) 20
178 Drdc(A). ℞. — As last. *R.I.C.* 215 (*perhaps not* (A), *but* Hy.) .. 25

167 179

179 Drdc(A) ℞. — As before, but Pax running l. *R.I.C.* 214 20
179a Drc(A). ℞. — As last. *R.I.C.* 214 20
180 Brdc **to left** (A). ℞. — Mars (Virtus, Peace or Warrior) stg. l., holding olive-branch and reversed spear. *R.I.C.* 191 (*Vienna*) 150
180a Brdc(A). ℞. — As last, but at feet, shield. *R.I.C.* 190 (*B.M.; Vienna*) 22
181 Brdc(A). ℞. PAX AVGSTI, as **180**. *R.I.C.* 192 30
181a Brdc. ℞. PIETAS AVGG., Pietas stg. facing, hd. l., raising both hands. (Hy.; *rev. of Treb. Gallus*) *R.I.C* 243 .. ..
182 **Denarius.** M . ANT . GORDIANVS CAES, his bare-headed bust dr. r. ℞. PIETAS AVGG., augur's wand, sacrificial knife, patera, sacrificial jug, simpulum and sprinkler. *B.M.C.*, Balbinus and Pupienus 62-3; *R.I.C.* 1 .. 175
186 Dldc. ℞. PIETAS AVGVSTI, Pietas, veiled, stg. facing, hd. l., raising both hands. *R.I.C.* 129 25
186a **Antoninianus.** Brdc(A). ℞. P . M . TRI . P . CON . P . P., Sol stg. l. *R.I.C.* 168 (*Vienna*) 25
187 Brdc(A). ℞. — Gordian, veiled, stg. l., holding sceptre and sacrificing over altar out of a patera. *R.I.C.* 169 25
189 Brdc. ℞. P . M . TR . P . II COS . P . P., Jupiter stg. half-left; before, small figure of Gordian stg. l. *R.I.C.* 16 20
190 Brdc(A). ℞. — Jupiter seated l.; at his feet, eagle. *R.I.C.* 27 and 170 (*Vienna*) 18
191 Brdc. ℞. — Serapis stg. l., holding transverse sceptre and raising r. hand. *R.I.C.* 30 30
192 Brdc. ℞. — Mars stg. facing, hd. r., r. foot drawn back to l., holding transverse spear and shield. *R.I.C.* 28 (*B.M.*) 30
192a Brdc. ℞. — Mars advancing r., holding spear and trophy. (Hy.? *with rev. of Sev. Alexander*). *R.I.C.* 29 .. ..
192b Brdc. ℞. — Sol stg. l. *R.I.C.* 31 (*Smederevo hoard*) 30

194 Antoninianus. Brdc. ℞. P . M . TR . P . II COS . P . P., Virtus in military dress, stg. half-left, holding vertical spear and with r. hand on shield resting on ground. *R.I.C.* 20 .. .. £18

196 Brdc. ℞. — Providentia stg. half-left, holding globe and transverse sceptre. *R.I.C.* 18 15

196a Brdc(A). ℞. — As last. *R.I.C.* 172 (*Vienna*) 18

197 Brc **to left.** ℞. — As last. *R.I.C.* 172 150

197a Brdc. **to left.** ℞. — As last. (*British Museum*) 150

199 Brdc. ℞. — Victory advancing l. *R.I.C.* 19 18

203 Brdc. ℞. — Pax stg. half-left. *R.I.C.* 17 15

204 Brdc. ℞. — Concordia stg. l. *R.I.C.* 32 30

205 Brdc. ℞. — Fides stg. half-left, holding standard and transverse sceptre. *R.I.C.* 15 15

206 Quinarius. Cldc. ℞. — As last. *R.I.C.* 26 (*Trau; Cohen describes this as a denarius in error*) 175

205   210

206a Antoninianus. Brdc(A). ℞. — Libertas stg. l. *R.I.C.* 33 and 171 (*Vienna*) 20

210 Brdc. ℞. — Gordian, veiled and togate, stg. half-left, sacrificing over altar from patera and holding wand. *R.I.C.* 37 15

210a Quinarius. Cldc. ℞. — As last. *R.I.C.* 46 (*De Moustier*) 175

212 Antoninianus. Ardc. ℞. — As last. *R.I.C.* 54 18

215 Quinarius. Dldc. ℞. — As last. *R.I.C.* 76 175

216 Antoninianus. Drdc. ℞. — As last. *R.I.C.* 68 15

219 Brdc. ℞. — Gordian on horseback r., raising r. hand. *R.I.C.* 50A .. 30

219a Brdc(A). ℞. — As last. *R.I.C.* 174 30

220 Brdc. ℞. — Gordian seated r. in slow-moving quadriga, holding eagle-headed sceptre. *R.I.C.* 50B 200

220a Brdc(A). ℞. — As last. *R.I.C.* 173 200

223 Brdc. ℞. — Gordian seated l., on curule chair, receiving branch from Pax stg. before him and being crowned by Victory behind, holding palm. *R.I.C.* 50C 200

223a Brdc(A). ℞. — As last. *R.I.C.* 175 200

224 Quinarius. *Obv.*? ℞. P . M . TR . P . III COS . P . P., Apollo or Peace seated, holding branch and resting l. elbow on seat. *R.I.C.*, p. 24 (*needs confirmation; expect* COS . II *on rev.*) .. ..

226 Antoninianus. Drdc. ℞. — Gordian sacrificing, as **210**. *R.I.C.* 69 .. 18

228 Quinarius. Dldc. ℞. — As last. *R.I.C.* 77 175

230a Antoninianus. Brdc. ℞. — As last (Hy.). *R.I.C.* 224 (*Ashmolean*) .. 18

230b Ardc. ℞. — As last (Hy.). *R.I.C.* 225 (*Vienna*) 18

232a Drdc. ℞. — Gordian seated l., holding globe and sceptre. *R.I.C.* 82 (*Vienna*) 25

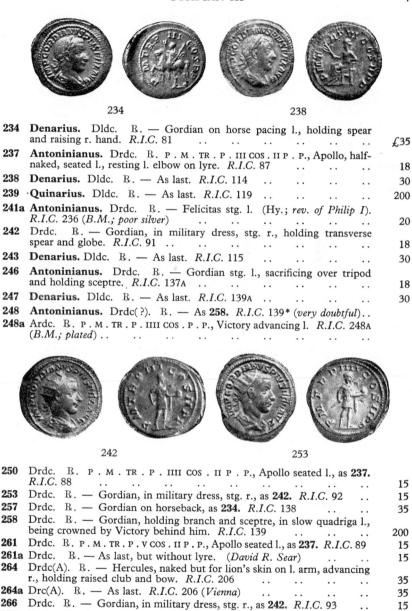

234   238

234 **Denarius.** Dldc. ℞. — Gordian on horse pacing l., holding spear
and raising r. hand. *R.I.C.* 81 .. .. £35

237 **Antoninianus.** Drdc. ℞. P . M . TR . P . III COS . II P . P., Apollo, half-
naked, seated l., resting l. elbow on lyre. *R.I.C.* 87 18

238 **Denarius.** Dldc. ℞. — As last. *R.I.C.* 114 30

239 **·Quinarius.** Dldc. ℞. — As last. *R.I.C.* 119 200

241a **Antoninianus.** Drdc. ℞. — Felicitas stg. l. (Hy.; *rev. of Philip I*).
R.I.C. 236 (*B.M.; poor silver*) 20

242   Drdc. ℞. — Gordian, in military dress, stg. r., holding transverse
spear and globe. *R.I.C.* 91 18

243 **Denarius.** Dldc. ℞. — As last. *R.I.C.* 115 30

246 **Antoninianus.** Drdc. ℞. — Gordian stg. l., sacrificing over tripod
and holding sceptre. *R.I.C.* 137A 18

247 **Denarius.** Dldc. ℞. — As last. *R.I.C.* 139A 30

248 **Antoninianus.** Drdc(?). ℞. — As **258**. *R.I.C.* 139* (*very doubtful*)..

248a   Ardc. ℞. P . M . TR . P . IIII COS . P . P., Victory advancing l. *R.I.C.* 248A
(*B.M.; plated*) .. ..

242   253

250   Drdc. ℞. P . M . TR . P . IIII COS . II P . P., Apollo seated l., as **237**.
R.I.C. 88 15

253   Drdc. ℞. — Gordian, in military dress, stg. r., as **242**. *R.I.C.* 92 .. 15

257   Drdc. ℞. — Gordian on horseback, as **234**. *R.I.C.* 138 .. 35

258   Drdc. ℞. — Gordian, holding branch and sceptre, in slow quadriga l.,
being crowned by Victory behind him. *R.I.C.* 139 200

261   Drdc. ℞. P . M . TR . P . V COS . II P . P., Apollo seated l., as **237**. *R.I.C.* 89 15

261a   Drdc. ℞. — As last, but without lyre. (*David R. Sear*) 15

264   Drdc(A). ℞. — Hercules, naked but for lion's skin on l. arm, advancing
r., holding raised club and bow. *R.I.C.* 206 35

264a **Drc(A).** ℞. — As last. *R.I.C.* 206 (*Vienna*) 35

266   Drdc. ℞. — Gordian, in military dress, stg. r., as **242**. *R.I.C.* 93 .. 15

269a   Drdc. ℞. P . M . TR . P . V COS . III P . P., Apollo seated l., as **237**. *R.I.C.*
114* (*Hollscheck coll., Vienna; plated*) .. ..

269b   Drdc. ℞. P . M . TR . P . VN COS . III P . P., Gordian stg. r., as **242**.
R.I.C. 248B (*Vienna*) 20

272 Antoninianus. Drdc. ℞. P . M . TR . P . VI COS II . P . P., Apollo seated
         l., as **237**. *R.I.C.* 90 ..   £18
276 Drdc. ℞. — Gordian, in military dress, stg. r., as **242**. *R.I.C.* 94 ..   18
280 Drdc. ℞. P . M . TR . P . VII COS . II P . P., Mars walking r., holding spear
         and shield. *R.I.C.* 167A   20
280a Drdc(A). ℞. — As last. *R.I.C.* 207   20
281a Drdc. ℞. — Gordian stg. r., as **242**. *R.I.C.* 248C *(B.M.; poor Æ)* ..   15
282a Brdc(A). ℞. POMAE AETERNAE, accidental variant of **312a**. *R.I.C.* 200*
         (Vienna)   18
293 Drdc. ℞. PRINCIPI IVVENT, Philip II stg. l., holding globe and sceptre
         (Hy.; *with rev. of Philip II*). *R.I.C.* 241 *(B.M.)*   25
296 Drdc. ℞. PROVID . AVG., Providentia stg. half-left. *R.I.C.* 148 ..   15
297 Brdc. ℞. PROVIDENT . AVG., Providentia stg. half-left, holding globe
         and transverse sceptre. *R.I.C.* 4*   15
298 Drdc. ℞. — Providentia, as **296**. *R.I.C.* 149   15
299 Drdc. ℞. PROVIDENTIA AVG., as last. *R.I.C.* 150   15
299a Brdc(A). ℞. — As last. *R.I.C.* 194 *(Dorchester)*   15
299b As before, but Providentia points finger, in place of baton, at globe. *R.I.C.*
         195 *(Vienna)*   20

302   314

302 Brdc. ℞. — Providentia, as **297**. *R.I.C.* 4   15
302a Brdc(A). ℞. — As last. *R.I.C.* 193 *(Vienna)*   15
303 Drdc *(Cohen has* laur.). ℞. — As last (Hy.). *R.I.C.* 227 *(B.M.* 314)   18
306 Brdc(A). ℞. — Providentia (or Fortuna) stg. l., holding rudder and
         cornucopiae. *R.I.C.* 196   20
307 Brdc(A). ℞. — Providentia (or Annona) stg. l., holding corn-ears over
         altar and cornucopiae. *R.I.C.* 197   20
307a Brdc(A). ℞. — As last, but corn-ears over modius. *R.I.C.* 198
         (Smederevo hoard)   20
308 Brdc(A). ℞. — Providentia stg. l., holding corn-ears over modius and
         anchor. *R.I.C.* 199 (a)   20
309 Brdc **to left** (A). ℞. — As last. *R.I.C.* 199 (b)   150
309a Brdc(A). ℞. PROVIDENTI . AVG., Providentia, as **306**. *R.I.C.* 196*
         (Vienna)   25
310 Drdc. ℞. PVDICITIA AVG., Pudicitia (*Cohen says*, Tranquillina), veiled,
         seated l., r. hand to veil (Hy.; *rev. of Otacilia Severa*). *R.I.C.* 240   ..
311 Drdc. ℞. RESTITVTIR ORBIS, emperor raising kneeling female (Hy.; *rev.* ⋛
         of Valerian I). *R.I.C.* 246   ..
311a Drdc. ℞. ROMA AETERNE, Roma, in military dress, seated l. on shield,
         holding Victory and spear. *R.I.C.* 70* *(Trau sale)*   20
311b Brdc. ℞. ROMAE AERMAE, as last. *R.I.C.* 38* *(Gnecchi)*   20
312 Brdc. ℞. ROMAE AETERNAE, as last. *R.I.C.* 38   15
312a Brdc(A). ℞. — As last. *R.I.C.* 200 *(Vienna)*   15
313 Ardc. ℞. — As last. *R.I.C.* 55   15
314 Drdc. ℞. — As last. *R.I.C.* 70   15
314a Denarius. Dldc. ℞. — As last. *R.I.C.*, p, 23, * *(Vienna; plated)* ..
315 Quinarius. Dldc. ℞. — As last. *R.I.C.* 78   175

318a Antoninianus. Drdc. ℞. SAECVLARES AVG, lion walking r.; in ex., I
(Hy.; *rev. of Philip I*). *R.I.C.* 238 (*B.M.*) £30
319 Drdc(A). ℞. SAECVLI FELICITAS, Gordian, laur., stg. r., holding transverse spear and globe. *R.I.C.* 216 15
319a Antoninianus. Drc(A). ℞. — As last. *R.I.C.* 216 (*Vienna*) .. 18
319b Denarius. Dldc. ℞. — Felicitas stg. l., sacrificing out of patera over
altar, and holding caduceus; in field to r., *. (*British Museum*).. .. 75
319c Antoninianus. Drdc. ℞. SALVS AVG., Salus stg. l., feeding snake held
in both arms (Hy.; *rev. of Philip I*). *R.I.C.* 239 25
325 Denarius. Dldc. ℞. SALVS AVGVSTI, Salus stg. r., feeding snake held in
both arms. *R.I.C.* 129A 25
327 Antoninianus. Drdc. ℞. SECVRIT . PERP., Securitas stg. l., legs
crossed, holding sceptre and resting l. arm on column. *R.I.C.* 151 .. 15
328 Drdc. ℞. SECVRIT . PERPET., as last. *R.I.C.* 152.. 18
328a Ardc. ℞. — As last (Hy.). *R.I.C.* 228 (*B.M.*) 18
335 Drdc. ℞. SECVRITAS PERPETV., Securitas (or Felicitas) stg. l., holding
caduceus and cornucopiae (Hy ?). *R.I.C.* 248D 25
336 Drdc. ℞. SECVRITAS PERPETVA, Securitas stg. l., as **327.** *R.I.C.* 153 .. 15

327   340

340 Denarius. Dldc. ℞. SECVRITAS PVBLICA, Securitas seated l., holding
sceptre and supporting hd. on l. hand. *R.I.C.* 130 25
340a Antoninianus. Brdc(A). ℞. SPES PVPLICA, Spes walking l. *R.I.C.*
201 20
347 Denarius. Dldc. ℞. VENVS VICTRIX, Venus stg. l., holding helmet and
sceptre and leaning on shield. *R.I.C.* 131 25
348 Antoninianus. Drdc. ℞. VICTOR . AETER., Victory stg. l., holding
palm and leaning on shield which is resting on a captive. *R.I.C.* 154 .. 15
349 Drdc. ℞. VICTORIA AETER., as last. *R.I.C.* 155 18
353 Drdc. ℞. VICTORIA AETERNA, as last. *R.I.C.* 156 15
357 Brdc. ℞. VICTORIA AVG., Victory advancing l. *R.I.C.* 5 15
357a Brdc(A). ℞. — As last. *R.I.C.* 202 (*Vienna*) 18
361 Quinarius. Cldc. ℞. — As last. *R.I.C.* 13 150
362 Antoninianus. Drdc(A). ℞. — Victory running r. *R.I.C.* 217 .. 20
362a Drc(A). ℞. — As last. *R.I.C.*-217 (*B.M.*) 20
366 Brdc(A). ℞. — Gordian on horseback r., holding spear and raising r.
hand. *R.I.C.* 203 150
375 Drdc(A). ℞. VICTORIA AVGVSTI, Victory r., as **362.** *R.I.C.* 218 .. 20
375a Drc(A). ℞. — As last. *R.I.C.* 218 (*B.M.*) 20
376 Brdc(A). ℞. — Gordian on horseback, as **366.** *R.I.C.* 204 150

380 Drdc(A). ℞. VICTORIA GORDIANI AVG., Victory r., as **362.** *R.I.C.* 219 22
380a Drc(A). ℞. — As last. *R.I.C.* 219 (*B.M.*) 22

381 Antoninianus. Brdc. ℞. VIRTVS AVG., Virtus, in military dress, stg.
      half-left, holding spear and resting r. hand on shield. *R.I.C.* 6 ..   ..   £15
381a Drdc. ℞. — As last (Hy.). *R.I.C.* 229 (*Dorchester*) and 71* (*B.M.*) ..   18
383 Brdc. ℞. — As before, but Virtus holds branch and spear, and shield
      rests against r. foot. *R.I.C.* 39   15
386 Ardc. ℞. — As last. *R.I.C.* 56   18
388 Drdc. ℞. — As last. *R.I.C.* 71   15
389 Quinarius. Dldc. ℞. — As last. *R.I.C.* 79   175
403 Denarius. Dldc. ℞. VIRTVTI AVGVSTI, Hercules, naked, stg. r., r. hd. on
      hip and resting l. on club set on rock; lion's skin beside club. *R.I.C.* 116   25
403a As last, but *plated*. *R.I.C.* 116* (*Ashmolean*)   ..   ..

404 Antoninianus. Drdc. ℞. — As **403**. *R.I.C.* 95   15
405 Quinarius. Dldc. ℞. — As last. *R.I.C.* 120   150
408 Denarius. Dldc. ℞. — As **403,** but club rests on lion's hd. *R.I.C.* 116*   35
409 Antoninianus. Brdc. ℞. VOTIS / DECENNA / LIBVS in laurel-wreath.
      R.I.C. 14   200

TRANQUILLINA

*Furia Sabinia Tranquillina was the daughter of Timisitheus the Praetorian Prefect,
and married Gordian III in 241. Stephenson writes "Young, beautiful and intelligent, she
graced by sweetness of her disposition and the purity of her morals, the elevation to which
Gordian had raised her . . . congenial tributes and public testimonies of love, respect and
admiration". She survived her husband and nothing further is known of her.*

Obverse legend.

SABINIA TRANQVILLINA AVG

1 Antoninianus. Diad. bust dr. r. on crescent. ℞. CONCORDIA AVGG.,
   Concord seated l., holding patera and double-cornucopiae. *R.I.C.*
   Gordian III 249   3500

1a Denarius. Diad. bust dr. r. ℞. — As last. *R.I.C.* 252   3500
1b As last, but single-cornucopiae. *R.I.C.* 252* (*Bachofen von Echt*)   ..   3500
2 Quinarius. — ℞. — As **1.** *R.I.C.* 253   3500
4 Antoninianus. As **1,** but *rev*. type, Gordian III and Tranquillina standing
   hand in hand; the former holds roll. *R.I.C.* 250   3500
9 — ℞. PIETAS AVGG., standing figure. *R.I.C.* 251 (*needs confirmation*) ..

PHILIP I

A.D. 244-249

M. Julius Philippus was a native of Arabia, but little is known of his early life. It is said he was the son of a celebrated bandit chief. He became Praetorian Prefect on the death of Timisitheus, during the Persian campaign of Gordian III, whose murder he is thought to have instigated. The army saluted Philip as emperor and his elevation was confirmed by the Senate. He then concluded a rather unsatisfactory peace with the Persians, founded the city of Philippopolis, and returned to Rome. The chief event of his reign was the celebration, in 248, of the thousandth anniversary of the founding of Rome. There were magnificent games with numerous wild beasts and many of his coins have legends or types alluding to these events.

The latter part of Philip's reign was troubled by numerous pretenders and rebellions. In 249 he had to take the field with his army against the rebellious legions of Trajan Decius. He was killed either in battle or by his own troops near Verona, and his son was killed at the same time.

Obverse legends.

A.	IMP . CAES . M . IVL . PHILLIPVS AVG.	A.D. 247
B.	IMP . C . M . IVL . PHILLIPVS P . F . AVG . P . M.	A.D. 247
C.	IMP . IVL . PHILIPPVS PIVS FEL . AVG . P . M.	A.D. 247
D.	IMP . M . IVL . PHILIPPVS AVG.	A.D. 244-9
E.	IMP . PHILIPPVS AVG.	A.D. 247-9

Obverse types.

Unless otherwise stated all are draped and cuirassed to right, with the antoniniani radiate and the others laureate.

(A) Coins attributed by *R.I.C.* (nos. 69-87; pp. 76-79) to the mint at Antioch.

3   12a

3	**Antoninianus.** D. ℞. ADVENTVS AVGG, Philip on horseback l., holding spear and raising r. hand. *R.I.C.* 26 (b)							18
4	D, bust to **left** (A). ℞. — As last. *R.I.C.* 81							125
5	**Denarius.** D. ℞. — As last. *R.I.C.* 26 (a)							450
8	**Antoninianus.** D, bust to **left** (A). ℞. AEQVITAS AVGG. (*Cohen has* AVG. *in error*), Aequitas stg. l. *R.I.C.* 82							125
9	D. ℞. — As last. *R.I.C.* 27 (b)							16
12	E. ℞. — As last. *R.I.C.* 57							16
12a	**Denarius.** D. ℞. — As last.							450
14	**Medallion.** A. ℞. AEQVITAS AVGVSTI, the three Monetae stg. half-left; at their feet, heaps of metal or coins. *R.I.C.* 54							*Very rare*
16	A (*Cohen reads* PHILLIPVS *in error*). ℞. AEQVITAS PVBLICA, as last. *R.I.C.* 55							*Very rare*

17 Antoninianus. E. ℞. AETERNITAS AVGG, elephant walking l., bearing driver who holds goad and wand. *R.I.C.* 58 .. .. £24

22 D. ℞. AETERNIT . IMPER. (*Cohen*) or IMPERI (*R.I.C.*), Sol, rad., advancing l., holding whip and raising r. hand (Hy.; *rev. of Philip II*). *R.I.C.* 112 (*not in B.M.*) 22

22a E. ℞. AETERNITATI AVGG, Sol stg. half-right (Hy.; *varied from Gordian III*). *R.I.C.* 90 (*B.M.*) 22

24 Quinarius. D. ℞. ANNONA AVGG, Annona stg. half-left; before, modius. *R.I.C.* 28 (b) 400

25 Antoninianus. D. ℞. — As last. *R.I.C.* 28 (c) 16

32 D. ℞. — As last, but prow for modius. *R.I.C.* 29 16

33 E. ℞. — As last. *R.I.C.* 59 16

33a D. ℞. CONCORDIA AVG., as next. *R.I.C.* 83* (*note in B.M.*) .. 20

34 D. ℞. CONCORDIA AVGG, Concordia seated l. *R.I.C.* 83* (? A) and 109 (Hy.; *rev. of Otacilia*) 22

35 D, bust to **left** (A). ℞. — As last. *R.I.C.* 83 (scales *in error ?*) .. 125

36 D. ℞. — As before, but seated before altar (Hy.; *rev. of Otacilia*). *R.I.C.* 110 22

25   72

37 D. ℞. COS . II P . P., Apollo seated l., resting elbow on lyre (Hy.; *type of Gordian III*). *R.I.C.* 91, also p. 69 note 22

39 E. ℞. FELI / CITAS / IMPP within laurel-wreath. *R.I.C.* 60 30

40 D, but without M. before IVL. ℞. — As last (Hy.). *R.I.C.* 103 35

41 D, bust to **left** (A). ℞. — As last. *R.I.C.* 84 150

43 D. ℞. FELICITAS TEMP., Felicitas stg. half-left. *R.I.C.* 31 16

43a E, bust to **left** (A). ℞. — As last. *R.I.C.* 87 125

46 D. ℞. FELICIT. TEMPOR., as last (Hy.; *rev. of Gordian III*). *R.I.C.* 31* and 92 22

49 E. ℞. FIDES EXERCITVS, Fides stg. l., holding vexillum and transverse standard. *R.I.C.* 61 18

50 E. ℞. — Four standards, one of which is a legionary eagle. *R.I.C.* 62 .. 20

50a D(A). ℞. — As last. *R.I.C.* 84A (*B.M., ex Dorchester*) and 103A (Hy.) 22

50b E. ℞. — As before, but none is legionary eagle. *R.I.C.* 62* (*B.M.*) .. 22

54 D. ℞. FIDES MILIT., Fides stg. l., holding sceptre and standard. *R.I.C.* 33 18

55 D. ℞. — Fides stg. l., holding two standards. *R.I.C.* 32 (b) 18

58 D. ℞. FIDES MILITVM, as last. *R.I.C.* 34 (b) 18

61a D. ℞. — As **54.** *R.I.C.* 34A (*Dorchester*) 22

65 E. ℞. FORTVNA REDVX, Fortuna seated l., wheel under seat. *R.I.C.* 63 (b) 18

69 E. ℞. As *obv. R.I.C.* 67 350

70 E. ℞. IOVI STATORI, Jupiter stg. facing (Hy.; *rev. of Gordian III*). *R.I.C.* 93 25

72 D. ℞. LAET . FVNDATA, Laetitia stg. l., holding wreath and rudder. *R.I.C.* 35 (b) 18

72a D. ℞. — As last, but sceptre for rudder. *R.I.C.* 35* (*Dorchester*) .. 25

80 Antoninianus. D. ℞. LAETIT . FVNDAT., Laetitia stg. l., as **72.** *R.I.C.* 36 (b) £16

81 D. ℞. — Laetitia stg. l., foot on prow, holding patera and rudder. *R.I.C.* 37 (b) 18

82 D. ℞. LAETITIA AVG . N., Laetitia stg. l. (Hy.; *rev. of Gordian III*). *R.I.C.* 94 22

82a D. ℞. LIBERALITAS AVG., Liberalitas stg. half-left. *R.I.C.* 37A (*B.M.,* *ex Dorchester*) 40

82b As last, but AVGG. (Hy.; *plated*). *R.I.C.* 38* .. ..

87 D. ℞. LIBERALITAS AVGG . II, as last. *R.I.C.* 38 (b) 16

91 E. ℞. LIBERALITAS AVG . III, as last (Hy.; *rev. of Gordian III*). *R.I.C.* 95 25

98 E. ℞. NOBILITAS AVGG., Nobilitas stg. r., holding sceptre and globe; in field, z (*Cohen*, G or S). *R.I.C.* 8 (stg. l. *in error*) 22

101 D. ℞. PACE FVNDATA, Pax stg., holding ? and rudder. *R.I.C.* 40* (*perhaps Antioch*) 75

102 D. ℞. PAX AETERN., Pax running l. *R.I.C.* 41 16

103 D. ℞. — Pax stg. half-left. *R.I.C.* 40 (b) 18

103a E. ℞. — As last (Hy.). *R.I.C.* 105B (*Dorchester*) 22

109 D. ℞. PAX AETERNA, as **102.** *R.I.C.* 42 18

112 M . IVL . PHILIPPVS P . F . AVG. ℞. PAX AVGVSTI (*R.I.C.* gives AVG), as **103** (Hy.; *rev. of Gordian III*). *R.I.C.* 100 and 69 note 25

112a D. ℞. — As **102** (Hy.; *rev. of Gordian III*). *R.I.C.* 99 22

113 B(A). ℞. PAX FVNDATA CVM PERSIS, as **103.** *R.I.C.* 69 35

114 C(A). ℞. — As last. *R.I.C.* 72 45

114a C, but FELIX for FEL. (A). ℞. — As last. *R.I.C.* 72* 45

87   120

117 D. ℞. P . M . TR . P , II COS . P . P., Minerva stg. l., foot on helmet, holding branch. *R.I.C.* 1 25

117a As last, but Minerva holds branch and sceptre. *R.I.C.* 1* 25

118 D. ℞. — Felicitas stg. half-left. *R.I.C.* 3* (*very doubtful*) .. ..

120 D. ℞. — Philip seated l. on curule chair, holding globe and short sceptre. *R.I.C.* 2 (b) 18

122a D. ℞. — Woman stg. facing, hd. l., foot on globe, holding branch and rudder. *R.I.C.* 88 (*B.M., uncertain Eastern mint*) 150

123 E. ℞. P . M . TR . P . III COS . P . P., as **118** (Hy.). *R.I.C.* 3* and 105; also 75* (*B.M.; probably Antioch*) .. ..

124 D. ℞. — As last. *R.I.C.* 3 16

129 D, bust to **left** (A). ℞. P . M . TR . P . III COS . II P . P., as last. *R.I.C.* 75 125

129a D. ℞. P . M . TR . P . III (or IIII ?) COS . P . P., Apollo seated l., resting elbow on lyre (Hy.; *rev. of Gordian III*). *R.I.C.* 96 (*B.M.*) .. 22

130 D(A). ℞. P . M . TR . P . IIII COS . P . P., Felicitas, as **118.** *R.I.C.* 75A .. 25

131 E(A). ℞. — As last. *R.I.C.* 76A (but COS II) 25

132 D(A). ℞. — Philip, veiled, stg. l. sacrificing over tripod and holding wand. *R.I.C.* 75B 28

134 **Antoninianus.** E, bust to **left** (A). R . P . M . TR . P . IIII COS . II P . P., Concordia, veiled, stg. l., holding patera and wand. *R.I.C.* 77 .. .. £125

135 D, bust to **left** (A). R. — Felicitas, stg. half-left. *R.I.C.* 76 125

136   145

136 D. R. — As last. *R.I.C.* 4 16

137 E. R. — As last. *R.I.C.* 5 18

144 E. R . P . M . TR . P . IIII COS . III (*sic*) P . P., woman (Minerva or Mars) stg. l., holding branch and leaning on shield, spear against l. arm. *R.I.C.* p. 69, * (*irregular and uncertain*) .. ..

144a D. R . P . M . TR . P . V COS . II P . P., Apollo, as **129a** (Hy.; *rev. of Gordian III*). *R.I.C.* 97 22

145 E. R . P . M . TR . P . V COS . III P . P., Mars stg. l., holding branch and resting l. hand on shield, spear against l. arm; A in field. *R.I.C.* 7 .. 18

147 E. R. — Felicitas stg. half-left. *R.I.C.* 6 22

147a D (A). R. — As last. *R.I.C.* 77A (*B.M., ex Dorchester*) 35

147b D. R. — As last (Hy.). *R.I.C.* 105A (*Dorchester*) 22

154 D. R . P . M . TR . P . VI COS . P . P., Apollo, as **129a** (Hy.; *rev. of Gordian III*). *R.I.C.* 98 (*rev.* COS II ?) 22

155 D(A). R. — As **147**. *R.I.C.* 78 25

156 D(A). R. — Philip sacrificing, as **132**. *R.I.C.* 79 (a) 28

156a E(A). R. — As last. *R.I.C.* 79 (b) (*B.M., ex Dorchester*) 30

157 D(A). R. — Lion, rad., walking r. *R.I.C.* 80 35

161 E. R. PROVID . AVG., Providentia stg. l., holding sceptre; at her feet, globe (Hy., *rev. of Gordian III*). *R.I.C.* 101 22

161a D. R. PROVIDENT . AVG., as last. *R.I.C.* 101A (*Dorchester; base*) ..

162 D. R. PROVIDENTIA AVG., as last. *R.I.C.* 102 22

163 As last (*base, plated or Æ*). *R.I.C.* 102* .. ..

164a E. R. ROMAE AETERNAE, Roma seated l., holding Victory and spear; at side, shield. *R.I.C.* 106 and 65*.. 22

165 D. R. — As last. *R.I.C.* 44* and 106A 18

166 As last (*base, plated or Æ*). *R.I.C.* 44* .. ..

167 D, bust to **left** (A). R. — As last. *R.I.C.* 85 125

169 D. R. — As before, but sceptre for spear. *R.I.C.* 44(b) 16

170 D. R. — Similar, but with altar on l. *R.I.C.* 45 16

171 E. R. — As last. *R.I.C.* 65* 18

171a E. R. — As **164a**. *R.I.C.* 65 18

173 178

172	**Antoninianus.** E. R. SAECVLARES AVGG., lion walking l., I in ex. R.I.C. 13	40
173	E. R. — Lion walking r.; I in ex. R.I.C. 12	24
173a	As last, but star in ex. R.I.C. 12*	35
175	E. R. — As **172** or **173**/ II in ex. R.I.C. 12*	40
177	E. R. — She-wolf stg. r., suckling the twins (Romulus and Remus); II in ex. R.I.C. 16	40
178	As last, but she-wolf l. R.I.C. 15	25
180	D. R. — Gazelle walking r.; III in ex.	25
180a	E. R. — Gazelle walking l.; III in ex. R.I.C. 17	25
180b	E. R. — Antelope walking l.; IIII in ex. R.I.C. 18 (B.M.)	35
181	E. R. — Hippopotamus stg. r.; IIII in ex. (Hy.; *rev. of Otacilia*). R.I.C. 111	30
182	E. R. — Stag walking r.; V or U in ex. R.I.C. 19	22
185	E. R. — Similar, but walking l. R.I.C. 20	40
186	E. R. — Gazelle; V in ex. R.I.C. 19*	
187	E. R. — Goat or hind walking l., horns not sunk over back; VI in ex. R.I.C. 23 (*perhaps the same as a B.M. coin with rev., stag with long straight horns, upright, walking l.*)	30
188	E. R. — Antelope walking r.; VI or UI in ex. R.I.C. 22	40
189	E. R. — Similar, but antelope walking l. R.I.C. 21	22
192	**Quinarius.** E. R. — Low column inscribed cos / III. R.I.C. 24 (b)	450
193	**Antoninianus.** E. R. — As last. R.I.C. 24 (c)	20
194	D. R. — As last (Hy.). R.I.C. 107	22

189 205

198	E. R. SAECVLVM NOVVM, temple of six columns; in centre, statue half-left, holding sceptre. R.I.C. 25 (b)	25
199	D. R. — As last (*Antioch mint or* Hy.). R.I.C. 25*, 86*, 86 (b) (B.M., ex Dorchester) and 108	28
200	D, bust to **left** (A). R. — As last. R.I.C. 86 (a)	125
205	D. R. SALVS AVG., Salus stg. l., holding rudder, and feeding snake coiled around altar. R.I.C. 47	18
209	D. R. — Salus stg. r., feeding snake held in both arms. R.I.C. 46 (b)	16
210	**Quinarius.** D. R. — As last. R.I.C. 46 (a)	400
212a	**Antoninianus.** D. R. SALVS AVGG., as last. R.I.C. 47A (Dorchester)	25

214 Denarius. D. ℞. SECVRIT . ORBIS, Securitas seated l., propping-up
head on l. hand and holding sceptre. *R.I.C.* 48 (a) £450

215 Antoninianus. D. ℞. — As last. *R.I.C.* 48 (b)   16

217 D. ℞. SECVRITAS ORBIS, as last. *R.I.C.* 48*   22

218 B, but without P . M. (A). ℞. SPES FELICITATIS OBIS, Spes advancing l.
R.I.C. 70* (*doubtful*) ..   ..

219 IMP . M . IVL . PHILIPPVS PIVS FEL . AVG. (A). ℞. — As last. *R.I.C.* 73*
(*confirmation required*)..   ..   ..

220 C(A). ℞. — As last. *R.I.C.* 73   30

221 B(A). ℞. — As last. *R.I.C.* 70   26

222 D. ℞. SPES PVBLICA, as last (Hy.; *rev. of Philip II*). *R.I.C.* 113 ..   22

223 E. ℞. TRANQVILLITAS AVGG., Tranquillitas stg. l., holding capricorn
(?; *Cohen*, two-footed dragon) and sceptre; B in field. *R.I.C.* 9   22

225 Medallion. *Obv.?* ℞. VICTORIA AVG., Victory walking. *R.I.C.* 88*
(*possibly Eastern mint, but quite uncertain*) ..   ..

227 Antoninianus. D. ℞. — Victory advancing r. *R.I.C.* 49 (b)..   ..   16

231 Similar, but Victory advancing l. *R.I.C.* 50   18

235 D. ℞. VICTORIA AVGG., as last, but Victory stg. l. *R.I.C.* 51   16

238 E. ℞. VICTORIA CARPICA, as before, but Victory running r. *R.I.C.* 66   125

227　　　　　　　　　　　　　241a

239 D. ℞. VIRTVS AVG., Virtus (*Cohen*, Pallas) stg. l., foot on helmet, holding
branch and spear. *R.I.C.* 52..   18

239a E. ℞. — Virtus stg. r., holding spear and resting hand on shield (?)
(Hy.). *R.I.C.* 114 (*B.M.*; *poor workmanship*)   20

240 D. ℞. — Virtus seated l. on cuirass, holding branch and spear. *R.I.C.* 53   16

240a As last, but shield behind the cuirass. *R.I.C.* 53   16

241 E. ℞. VIRTVS AVGG., Philip I and Philip II galloping r., each raising r.
hand; Є (*Cohen* E or G) in ex. *R.I.C.* 10   30

241a As last, but one of them holds spear (*Cohen*, sceptre). *R.I.C.* 10   ..   30

243 B(A). ℞. VIRTVS EXERCITVS, Virtus stg. r., foot on helmet, holding spear
and resting r. hand on shield. *R.I.C.* 71   25

244 As last, but foot not on helmet. *R.I.C.* 71   22

245 C(A). ℞. — As **243.** *R.I.C.* 74   28

245a D. ℞. VOTIS / DECENNA / LIBVS in laurel-wreath. *R.I.C.* 53A (*Dorchester;
new rare type or* Hy., *with rev. of Gord. III*)   200

PHILIP I and OTACILIA SEVERA

2 Antoninianus. D. ℞. MARCIA OTACIL. SEVERA AVG., her diad. bust dr. r.
with crescent. *R.I.C.* Philip I 39 ..   ..   *Extremely rare*

6 ? ℞. PIETAS AVGG., bust of Otacilia. *R.I.C.* 64* (*quite uncertain*) ..   ..

PHILIP I, OTACILIA SEVERA and PHILIP II

1 Antoninianus. D. ℞. DE PIA MATRE PIVS FILIVS, laur. bust of Philip II dr. and cuir. r. facing diad. bust of Otacilia dr. l. *R.I.C.* Philip I 30 *Extremely rare*

4 D. ℞. PIETAS AVGG., similar, but bust of Philip II is bare-headed. *R.I.C.* 43 (b) .. .. *Extremely rare*

5 Denarius. D. ℞. — As last. *R.I.C.* 43 (a) .. .. .. *Extremely rare*

PHILIP I and PHILIP II

4 Antoninianus. E. ℞. As *obv.*, but bust of Philip II (*Cohen gives* head *instead of* bust *for each side*). *R.I.C.* Philip I 68 .. .. .. *Extremely rare*

8 M . IVL . PHILIPPVS AVG . M . IVL . PHILIPPVS N . C., rad. bust of Ph. I and Ph. II dr. and cuir. facing each other, crowned by Victory between them. ℞. LIBERALITAS AVGG . II, Liberalitas stg. l., holding abacus and cornucopiae. *R.I.C.* 56 .. .. *Extremely rare*

OTACILIA SEVERA, PHILIP I and PHILIP II

2a Antoninianus. M. OTACIL . SEVERA AVG., her diad. and dr. bust r., on crescent. ℞. IMPP . PHILIPPVS COSS., laur., dr. and cuir. busts of Philip I r. and Philip II l., face to face. (*British Museum*) .. .. .. *Extremely rare*

OTACILIA SEVERA

Marcia Otacilia Severa, the daughter of Severus, Governor of Pannonia, married Philip I, about 234, by whom she had Philip II in 237. The latter was slain in her arms by the Praetorians. She passed the remainder of her days in retirement.

Obverse types.

A. MARCIA OTACIL SEVERA AVG.   A.D. 244-246
B. M . OTACIL . SEVERA AVG.   A.D. 246-248
C. OTACIL SEVERA AVG.   A.D. 248-249
D. MARC . OTACIL . SEVERA AVG.   *Antioch, later issues*

Obverse legends.

Diademed bust draped right (denarii and quinarii).
Diademed bust draped right, on crescent (antoniniani).
(A) Attributed by *R.I.C.* to the Antioch mint (nos. 132-5; pp. 84-5).
All *R.I.C.* numbers are under Philip I.

0 Antoninianus. A. ℞. AETERNITATI AVG., Sol. stg. l. (Hy.; *rev. of Gordian III*). *R.I.C.* 137 (*Vienna*); *Cohen*, p. 151 note 30

0a B. ℞. AEQVITAS AVG., Aequitas stg. l. (Hy.; *rev. of Philip I*). *R.I.C.* 138 (*Hoffman sale*) 30

1 B. ℞. ANNONA AVG. (*probably should be* AVGG.), Annona stg. l.; before, modius (Hy.; *rev. of Ph. I*). *R.I.C.* 139 30

3 Denarius. B. ℞. CONCORDIA AVGG., Concordia seated l., holding patera and double cornucopiae. *R.I.C.* 125 (b) 500

4 Antoninianus. B. ℞. — As last. *R.I.C.* 125 (c) 22

8 Quinarius. A. ℞. — As last. *R.I.C.* 119 (a) 400

16   20

9   **Antoninianus.** A.   R.   CONCORDIA AVGG., Concordia seated l., holding
    patera and single cornucopiae. *R.I.C.* 119 (b)   24
14 C.   R. — As before, but single cornucopiae (Hy.). *R.I.C.* 143   ..   24
16 C.   R. — As last, but with altar before her. *R.I.C.* 129   22
17 B.   R. — As last. *R.I.C.* 126   22
18 D(A).   R.   FECVNDITAS TEMPORVM, Tellus seated l., holding corn-ears
    and cornucopiae, between two children. *R.I.C.* 132   200
20 B.   R.   IVNO CONSERVAT., Juno, veiled, stg. l. *R.I.C.* 127 (*probably
    Antioch*)   24
21 B.   R.   IVNO CONSERVATRIX, as last. *R.I.C.* 128 (*probably Antioch*) ..   35
23 A, without diadem.   R.   IVNO LVCINA, Juno (in goat's skin head-dress ?)
    stg. r. (Hy.). *R.I.C.* 136   ..   ..
24 D(A).   R.   As *obv.* (*Cohen quotes this without crescent so it may be a
    Denarius*). *R.I.C.* 135   500
28 C.   R.   As *obv.* *R.I.C.* 131   450
28a C.   R.   PAX AVGG., Pax stg. l. (Hy.). *R.I.C.* 147 (*B.M.; rev. of Treb.
    Gallus ?; Eastern style ?*)   30
28b B.   R. — As last (Hy.). (*D. E. Ward*)   30

34   43

30 A.   R.   PIETAS AVG., Pietas stg. half-left, holding box of perfume and
    raising r. hand. *R.I.C.* 120 (b)   35
34 A.   R. — As before, but lighted altar before her. *R.I.C.* 121   35
37 A.   R. — As 30, but child stg. before her. *R.I.C.* 122 (b)   35
39 C.   R.   PIETAS AVGG., as 34, but ⏆ added in field. *R.I.C.* 115   ..   24
39a A.   R. — As 37. *R.I.C.* 122* (*Dorchester*)   35
42 D(A).   R.   PIETAS AVG . N., Pietas stg. l., child before her. *R.I.C.* 133 ..   35
42a D(A).   R. — As last, but holds globe instead of patera. *R.I.C.* 134
    (*B.M.*)   40
43 C.   R.   PIETAS AVGVSTAE, as 30. *R.I.C.* 130   22
45 A.   R. — As last (Hy.). *R.I.C.* 144 (b) (*gives it with altar, in error ?*) ..   30
45a B.   R. — As 34 (Hy.). *R.I.C.* 144 (a) (*Dorchester*)   30
49 C.   R.   PIETAS AVGVSTE (*sic*), as 30. *R.I.C.* 130*   24
50a C.   R.   P . M . TR . P . IIII COS . II P . P., Pietas stg. l., sacrificing over
    altar (Hy.). *R.I.C.* 146 (*? copied from coin of Sev. Alex.*)   ..   ..

52 Denarius. A. ℞. PVDICITIA AVG., Pud'citia, veiled, seated l., drawing
veil with r. hand, transverse sceptre in l. *R.I.C.* 123 (b) £500

53 Antoninianus. As last. *R.I.C.* 123c 22

54 Double antoninianus (?) As last. *R.I.C.* 123* .. ..

54a Antoninianus. B. ℞. — As last. *R.I.C.* 128A (*B.M.*) and 145 (Hy.;
B.M.) 30

61 B. ℞. ROMAE AETERNAE, Roma seated l. before altar, holding Victory
and sceptre; at side, shield (Hy.). *R.I.C.* 140 35

53 63

63 C. ℞. SAECVLARES AVGG., Hippopotamus stg. r., looking down; IIII in ex.
R.I.C. 116 (b) 30

64 As last, but looking up. *R.I.C.* 116 (b) 30

72 B. ℞. SALVS AVG., Salus stg. l., holding sceptre and feeding snake coiled
around altar (Hy.). *R.I.C.* 141 30

74 A, but without diadem. ℞. SECVRIT . ORBIS, Securitas seated l., propping
hd. on hand and holding sceptre (Hy.). *R.I.C.* 142 (b) 35

74a A. ℞. — As last. *R.I.C.* 124 (b) (*Vienna*) 35

PHILIP II

A.D. 247-249

*M. Julius Severus Philippus was the son of Philip I and Otacilia. On his father's
accession, at the age of seven, he was given the title of Caesar and elevated to the rank of
Augustus in 247. He was assassinated by the praetorian guard in his mother's arms after
his father had been killed in 249.*

Obverse legends.

As Caesar.

| A. | M . IVL . PHILIPPVS CAES. | A.D. 244-7 |
| B. | M . IVL . PHILIPPVS NOBIL . CAES, | A.D. 244 |

As Augustus.

C.	IMP . CAES . M . IVL . PHILIPPVS AVG.	A.D. 247
D.	IMP M . IVL . PHILIPPVS AVG.	A.D. 247
E.	IMP PHILIPPVS AVG.	A.D. 247-9

Obverse types.

a. Bare-headed bust draped right.

b. Radiate bust draped and cuirassed right (*on some the cuirassing is rather
vague and Cohen omits the* et cuirassé).

c. Laureate bust draped and cuirassed right.

d. Radiate bust draped and cuirassed **left.**

(A) Placed against coins attributed in *R.I.C.* to Antioch (nos. 232-245, pp. 98-99)·
The *R.I.C.* numbers start with 213, having carried on after Philip I and Otacilia.

1   Antoninianus. Db(A). R. AEQVITAS AVGG. (*Cohen has* AVG. *in error*),
Aequitas stg. l. *R.I.C.* 240 (a) and 246 (Hy.; *rev. of Philip I*) £25
2   Dd(A). R. — As last. *R.I.C.* 240 (b)   125
3   Medallion. Cc. R. — The three Monetae stg. half-left; at their feet,
piles of metal. *R.I.C.* 228 ..   .. *Extremely rare*
4   Antoninianus. Ab. R. AETERNITAS AVG., elephant walking l., with
rider who holds goad and wand (Hy.; *rev. of Philip I*). *R.I.C.* 246A (b)   30
- **5   Db.** R. — As last (Hy.). *R.I.C.* 246A (a)   30
6   Db. R. AETERNIT . IMPER., Sol advancing l., holding whip and raising r.
hand. *R.I.C.* 226 (IMPERI *in text in error*)   22
7   ? ? R. ANNONA AVGG., Annona stg.; at her feet, modius ? (Hy.). *R.I.C.*
p. 100 (ANNON).   ..   ..
7a Dd(A ?). R. As next, but AVG   125
8   Dd(A). R. CONCORDIA AVGG., Concordia seated l. *R.I.C.* 241   125
10 Db. R. FELI / CITAS / IMPP within laurel-wreath (Hy.; *rev of Ph. I*).
R.I.C. 247 (Hy. *or of Antioch ?*)   35
11 Dd(A). R. — As last. *R.I.C.* 242..   150
12 Db. R. FIDES EXERCITVS, four standards (Hy.; *rev. of Ph. I*). *R.I.C.* 248   35
13 Ab. R. IOVI CONSERVAT., Jupiter stg. half-left, naked, cloak hangs from
l. shoulder. *R.I.C.* 213 (*perhaps of Antioch*)   25
13a As last, but CONSERVATORI. *R.I.C.* 214 (*perhaps of Antioch*)   25
14 Ab. R. IVNO CONSERVAT., as last (Hy.; *rev. legend of Otacilia*). *R.I.C.* 253   35
15 ? ? R. LIBERALITAS AVGG . II, the two emperors seated (*probably a misreading or die-engraver's mistake for* 17) ..   ..

17   23

17 Eb. R. LIBERALITAS AVGG . III, Philip I, holding short sceptre, and Ph. II
seated l. on curule chairs. *R.I.C.* 230   25
19 Eb(A). R. LIBERALITAS AVGG . IIII, as last. *R.I.C.* 245 (*B.M.*)   35
22 Quinarius. Ec. R. PAX AETERNA, Pax stg. l. *R.I.C.* 231 (b) (*obv. a in
error*)   400
23 Antoninianus. Eb. R. — As last. *R.I.C.* 231 (c)   22
24 Db. R. — As last. *R.I.C.* 227   22
29 Db. R. — As before, but Pax running l. (Hy.; *rev. of Ph. I*) *R.I.C.*
250   25
30a Quinarius. Aa. R. PIETAS AVGG., sacrificial implements. (*British
Museum*)   400
32 Antoninianus. Ab. R. PIETAS AVGVSTOR., sprinkler, simpulum, jug,
knife and lituus. *R.I.C.* 215   30
33 Db. R. P . M . TR . P . II COS . P . P., Philip I seated l. on curule chair,
holding globe and sceptre (Hy.; *rev. of Ph. I*). *R.I.C.* 249 (*not in B.M.*) ..   25
33a Db(A). R. P . M . TR . P . IIII COS . P . P., Felicitas stg. l. *R.I.C.* 232
(*B.M.*)   30
34 Db(A). R. P . M . TR . P . IIII COS . II P P., as last. *R.I.C.* 233 (*? this
mint*)   30
34a Dd(A). R. — As last. (*G. Brosi*)   125
35 Db(A). R. Legend as **33a,** Philip II, veiled, stg. l., holding sceptre and
sacrificing out of patera over lighted tripod. *R.I.C.* 234   35

40   48

38 **Antoninianus.** Db(A). ℞. P . M . TR . P . VI COS . P . P., Felicitas stg. l.,
as **34** (*Cohen has the wrong type, referring back to 36 instead of 34*). *R.I.C.*
235 (*B.M.*)   28
39 **Dd**(A). ℞. — As last. *R.I.C.* 235 (*B.M.*)   125
40 **Db**(A). ℞. — Philip stg. l., sacrificing as **35.** *R.I.C.* 236 ..   30
41 **Db**(A). ℞. — Philip, veiled, stg. l., holding globe and reversed spear;
at his feet, seated captive. *R.I.C.* 237   30
42 **Dd**(A). ℞. — Lion, rad., walking r. *R.I.C.* 238   150
43 **Db**(A). ℞. — Lion, rad., walking l. *R.I.C.* 239   40
47 **Quinarius.** Aa. ℞. PRINCIPI IVVENT., Philip, in military dress, stg. l.,
holding globe and reversed spear (*R.I.C. standard in error*). *R.I.C.* 218 (c) 400
47a **Denarius.** Aa. ℞. — As last. *R.I.C.* 218 (b)   500
48 **Antoninianus.** Ab. ℞. — As last. *R.I.C.* 218 (d)   22
51 D, but without IMP., b. ℞. — As last (Hy.). *R.I.C.* 254 (*is obv. correct ?*),
also p. 96 ..   ..
53 **Denarius.** Aa. ℞. — As before, but Philip r. and spear or sceptre
transverse. *R.I.C.* 216 (b)   500
54 **Antoninianus.** Ab. ℞. — As last. *R.I.C.* 216 (c)   22
57 Ab. ℞. — As **47,** but at his feet a captive. *R.I.C.* 219   25
57a Eb. ℞. — As last (Hy.). *R.I.C.* 254A (*Dorchester*)   25
58 Ab. ℞. — As **53,** but definitely spear and with soldier stg. behind
Philip, holding spear. *R.I.C.* 217   30
59 Ab. ℞. — As last, but soldier does not hold spear. *R.I.C.* 217* ..   30
61 Ab. ℞. PRINCIPI IVVENTVTIS, Philip stg. l., holding standard and spear.
R.I.C. 220 (b)   25
69 Ab. ℞. ROMAE AETERNAE, Roma seated l. on shield, holding Victory and
spear (Hy.; *rev. of Ph. I*). *R.I.C.* 251 (b)   25
70 Db(A ?) ℞. — As last. *R.I.C.* 243* and 251 (a) (Hy. ?)   25
71 **Dd**(A). ℞. — As last. *R.I.C.* 243   125

61   72

72 Eb. ℞. SAECVLARES AVGG., goat walking l.; III in ex. *R.I.C.* 224 ..   28
81 **Dd**(A). ℞. SAECVLVM NOVVM, temple of six columns, with facing statue
(of Roma ?) in centre, holding spear or long sceptre. *R.I.C.* 244 ..   150
83 Ab. ℞. SPES AVGVSTOR., Spes walking l. *R.I.C.* 221* (*doubtful*) ..
84 Ab. ℞. SPES PVBLICA, as last. *R.I.C.* 221   30
86 **Denarius.** Aa. ℞. VICTORIA AVG., Victory advancing l., holding
wreath or palm (Hy.). *R.I.C.* 252 (*or should it be obv.* b, *an antoninianus*)

87 Antoninianus. ?? ℞. VIRTVS AVG., Roma seated on a cuirass, holding
branch and spear. *R.I.C.* p. 100   ..   ..

88 Eb. ℞. VIRTVS AVGG., Mars advancing r., holding spear and trophy;
in field, r. *R.I.C.* 223   ..   ..   **£22**

88a As last, but O in field. *R.I.C.* 223* **25**

PHILIP II, PHILIP I and OTACILIA SEVERA

1 Antoninianus. Db. ℞. AVG . PATRI AVG . MATRI, laur. bust of Philip I
dr. and cuir. r. facing diad. bust of Otacilia dr. l. *R.I.C.* 229   .. *Extremely rare*

2 Medallion. Ba. ℞. CONCORDIA AVGVSTORVM, as last. *R.I.C.* 222   *Extremely rare*

PACATIAN
c. A.D. 248-249

*Ti. Claudius Marinus Pacatianus was a usurper who seized power in Upper Moesia,
and is practically unknown except from his coins, which were probably struck at Viminacium.
He is believed to have been murdered by his own troops.*

Obverse legends and type.

A.   IMP . TI . CL . MAR . PACATIANVS AVG.
B.   IMP . TI . CL . MAR . PACATIANVS P . F . AVG.
C.   IMP . TI . CL . MAR . PACATIANVS P . F . AV.

Radiate bust draped and cuirassed right.

1 Antoninianus. B. ℞. CONCORDIA MILITVM, Concordia seated l., holding
patera and double cornucopiae. *R.I.C.* 1 (b) **2500**

2 A. ℞. — As last. *R.I.C.* 1 (a) (*not in B.M.; confirmation required*)   ..

3 A. ℞. FELICITAS PVBL., Felicitas stg. l. *R.I.C.* 2..   ..   ..   **2500**

4 B. ℞. FIDES MILITVM, Fides stg. l., between two standards and holding
two more. *R.I.C.* 3   ..   ..   **2500**

5 A. ℞. FORTVNA REDVX, Fortuna seated l., wheel under seat. *R.I.C.* 4   **2500**

6 C. ℞. PAX AETERNA, Pax stg. l. *R.I.C.* 5 ..   ..   **2500**

6a A. ℞. — As last. *R.I.C.* 5 (*Bourgey sale*, 1926) **2500**

6b B. ℞. — As last. *R.I.C.* 5 (*B.M.*) **2500**

N.B.—*A Becker forgery exists of this type and another with* PROVIDENTIA
AVG., *Providentia stg. l. against column* (*obv.* A).

7 A. ℞. ROMAE AETER . AN . MILL . ET PRIMO, Roma seated l. on shield,
holding Victory and spear. *R.I.C.* 6   ..   ..   **3500**

8 A. ℞. VICTORIA AVGG., Victory advancing l. (Hy.; *plated; rev. of Philip I*)

N.B.—*Another Becker forgery*, C. ℞. VIRTVS AVG., *Hercules wrestling
with lion.*

JOTAPIAN

c. A.D. 248-249

M. Fulvius Rufus Jotapianus was a usurper about whom little is known. The troops revolted in Syria and Cappadocia and proclaimed him emperor. His reign was very short lived and he was killed by his own men.

2

1 Antoninianus. IMP . M . F . R . IOTAPIANVS A., his rad. bust cuir. r.
℞. VICTORIA AVS. (*sic*), Victory advancing l. *R.I.C.* 2* (*Paris*) 3500

1a — — ℞. VICTORIA AVG., as last. *R.I.C.* 2 (a) (*Levis sale*) 3500

1b As last, but *obv.* ends AV. *R.I.C.* 2 (b) (*Bachofen von Echt*) 3500

2 IM . C . M . F . RV . IOTAPIANVS — ℞. — As last. *R.I.C.* 2 (c) (*B.M.*) 3500

3 IMP . M . F . R . IOTAPIANVS — ℞. — As before, but Victory advancing
r. *R.I.C.* 1 (*Cohen, a small medallion or double antoninianus; probably only
an unusually heavy specimen*) 3500

MAR. SILBANNACUS

An unknown ruler

1 (*Not in Cohen*) **Antoninianus.** IMP . MAR . SILBANNACVS AVG., rad. bust
cuir. r. ℞. VICTORIA AVG., Mercury, naked, stg. half-left, holding
Victory and caduceus. *R.I.C.* 1 (*B.M.; believed to have been found in
Lorraine*) .. .. *Unique*

TRAJAN DECIUS

A.D. 249-251

C. *Messius Quintus Traianus Decius was born, about* A.D. *201, at Bubalia, in Lower Pannonia. Descended from an Illyrian family of rank, he proved himself an able statesman and a great captain and was governor of Lower Moesia 234-8. When the legions in Upper Moesia revolted, Decius was in Rome, in favour with Philip, who despatched him to restore order, but the rebels forced him, under the threat of death, to declare himself emperor and march upon Italy. In a battle in 249, near Verona, he was the victor and Philip and his son were slain. Decius was now undisputed master of the empire and accepted as emperor by the Senate and people.*

Most of his short reign was spent in defending the northern frontiers. Late in 251 he was fighting the Goths and in a battle at Abrittus he was defeated and lost his life and his eldest son, Herennius Etruscus was also killed. His reign is best known for his persecution of the Christians, in which Pope Fabian lost his life.

Obverse legends.

A.	IMP . CAE . TRA . DEC . AVG. (*only Milan*)	A.D. 250-1 ?
B.	IMP . CAE . TRA . DECIVS AVG (*only Milan*)	A.D. 250-1 ?
C.	IMP . C . DECIVS AVG. (*only Milan*)	A.D. 250-1 ?
D.	IMP . C . M . Q . TRAIANVS DECIVS AVG.	A.D. 249-251
E.	IMP . TRAIANVS AVG. DECIVS	A.D. 249 ?

Obverse type.

Bust draped and cuirassed right; radiate on the antoniniani and laureate on denarii and quinarii.

(A) Those attributed to Antioch by *R.I.C.* (nos. 44-8 and pp. 125-6).

(M) Those attributed to Milan by *R.I.C.* (nos. 33-43 and pp. 124-5).

2 6

2 Antoninianus. D. ℞. ABVNDANTIA AVG., Abundantia stg. half-right, emptying cornucopiae held in both hands *R I.C.* 10 (b) 22

2a A(M). ℞. — As last. *R.I.C.* 33 (a) (*B.M., Dorchester*).. 30

2b B(M). ℞. — As last. *R.I.C.* 33 (b) (*B.M., Dorchester*).. 30

4 D. ℞. ADVENTVS AVG., Decius on horse pacing l., holding sceptre and raising r. hand. *R.I.C.* 11 (b) 22

6 E ℞. — As last. *R.I.C.* 1 (b) 25

6a A(M). ℞. — As last. *R.I.C.* 34 (*B.M., Dorchester*) 30

9 D(A). ℞. AEQVITAS AVG, Aequitas stg. half-left. *R.I.C.* 44 (a) .. 30

9a D, .. below bust (A). ℞. — As last. *R.I.C.* 44 (b) 30

9b As **9,** but AVGG. on *rev.* (A). *R.I.C.* 45 30

13 Antoninianus. E. ℞. DACIA, Dacia stg. l., holding staff surmounted
with hd. of ass. *R.I.C.* 2 (b) £25
14 Quinarius. C(M). ℞ —. As last. *R.I.C.* 35 (a) 200
15 Antoninianus. A(M). ℞. — As last. *R.I.C.* 35 (b) 30
15a B(M). ℞. — As last. *R.I.C.* 35 (c) (*B.M.*) 30
16 D. ℞. — As last. *R.I.C.* 12 (b) 22
17 Quinarius. D. ℞. — As last. *R.I.C.* 12 (a) 200
25 Antoninianus. A(M). ℞. — Dacia stg. l., holding standard. *R.I.C.*
36 (a) 30
26 B(M). ℞. — As last. *R.I.C.* 36 (b) 30
27 D. ℞. — As last. *R.I.C.* 13 25
32 B(M). ℞. DACIA FELIX, as last. *R.I.C.* 37 (c) 30
33 A(M). ℞. — As last. *R.I.C.* 37 (b) 30
34 D. ℞. — As last. *R.I.C.* 14 (b) 25
38a B. ℞. FECVNDITAS AVG., Fecunditas stg. l., holding cornucopiae and
stretching out r. hand over child stg. r. (Hy.; *rev. of Her. Etruscilla*).
R.I.C. 52A (*Dorchester*) 30
43 A(M). ℞. GEN . ILLVRICI, Genius, wearing polos on hd., stg. l. *R.I.C.*
38 (a) 25
N.B.—*On nos. 43-64 the* V *in* ILLVRICI, ILLVRICIANI *is sometimes a* Y.
44 B(M). ℞. — As last. *R.I.C.* 38 (b) 30
45 E. ℞. — As last. *R.I.C.* 9 (Hy. ?) 30
46 D. ℞. — As last. *R.I.C.* 15 (b) 25
49 D. ℞. GENIVS EXERC . ILLVRICIANI, as before, but with standard on r.
R.I.C. 16 (c) 22
50 E. ℞. — As last. *R.I.C.* 3 (b) 25
51 A(M). ℞. — As last. *R.I.C.* 39 (a) 30
51a B(M). ℞. — As last. *R.I.C.* 39 (b) (*Paris*) 30
51b Denarius. As **49.** *R.I.C.* 16 (b) (*B.M.*) 550

33   56

56 Antoninianus. D. ℞. — As before, but standard is on l., as is an altar.
R.I.C. 17 (b) 25
57 A(M). ℞. — As last. *R.I.C.* 40 30
58 Quinarius. D, but IMP . C . Q (*no* M *as given by Cohen*). ℞. — As last.
R.I.C. 17 (a) 200
63 Antoninianus. E. ℞. GENIVS EXERCITVS ILLVRICIANI, as **49.** *R.I.C.*
4 (b) 25
64 D. ℞. — As last. *R.I.C.* 18 25
77 A(M ?). ℞. LIBERTAS AVGG., Uberitas stg. l. *R.I.C.*, p. 125 35
77a A(M ?). ℞. — Libertas stg. l. *R.I.C.*, p. 125 (*Dorchester hoard*) .. 35
77b D. ℞. MERITAS AVG., as **77.** *R.I.C.* 28* (*Springhead hoard*) .. 35
79 E. ℞. PANNONIAE, Pannonia, veiled, stg. front or half-left, looking r.,
holding standard and raising r. hand. *R.I.C.* 5 25
80 D. ℞. — As last. *R.I.C.* 20 30

81 Antoninianus. D. R. PANNONIAE, the two Pannoniae, veiled, stg. r.
and l. facing each other, clasping hands in front of a standard in the centre.
R.I.C. 26 ..   ..   £25
82 A(M). R. — As last. *R.I.C.* 41 (a)   30
83 B(M). R. — As last. *R.I.C.* 41 (b)   30
84 A(M). R. — As before, but a male on l. and female on r. *R.I.C.* 41*   30
84a B(M). R. — As last. *R.I.C.* 41*   30

86   92

86 D. R. — The two Pannoniae, veiled, stg. half-left, but looking in
opposite directions away from each other, each holds a standard; the one
on r. raises r. hand. *R.I.C.* 21 (b)   22
89a D. R. — Similar, but both look l. *R.I.C.* 23 (*Dorchester*)   35
89b D. R. — The same type, but they stand close together with standard
between them; the one on l. has no standard. *R.I.C.* 24 (*Dorchester*) ..   40
89c A. R. — As **86,** but the one on l. holds standard in l. hand instead of
r. hand. *R.I.C.* 25 (*Dorchester*)   35
90 D. R. PAX AETERN., Pax running l. (Hy.; *rev. of Philip I*). *R.I.C.* 49..   30
90a As last, but AETERNA. *R.I.C.* 49*   30
90b As **90a,** but Pax stg. l. (Hy.; *rev. of Philip II*). *R.I.C.* 51 (*B.M., base*)..   30
91 E. R. PAX AVGVSTI, as last. *R.I.C.* 6   30
92 D. R. — As last. *R.I.C.* 27   25
96 D. R. PIETAS AVGG., Mercury stg. l., holding purse and caduceus (Hy.;
rev. of Herennius). *R.I.C.* 53..   30
96a As last (Hy.; *plated*). *R.I.C.* 53* (*Berlin*) ..   ..
98 D(A). R. PVDICITIA AVG., Pudicitia, veiled, seated l., holding sceptre
and r. hand up to veil. *R.I.C.* 46 (a)   35
98a As last, but pellet below bust. *R.I.C.* 46 (b) (*B.M.*)   35
99 D(A). R. ROMAE AETERNAE, Roma seated l., holding Victory and spear
(*Cohen*, sceptre), shield at side. *R.I.C.* 47   35

105   111

103 D. R. SECVRITAS AVG., Securitas or Uberitas stg., holding purse and
cornucopiae (Hy.). *R.I.C.* 54   30
105 D. R. VBERITAS AVG., Uberitas as last. *R.I.C.* 28 (b)   22
105a D. R. VBERTAS AVG., as last. *R.I.C.* 28* (*Budapest; base*)   25
106 D. R. VERITAS AVG., as last. *R.I.C.* 28* (*Antioch mint ?*)   25
111 E. R. VICTORIA AVG., Victory running l. *R.I.C.* 7 (c)   25

112 Quinarius. C(M). ℞. VICTORIA AVG., Victory running l. *R.I.C. 29**
and 42 (b) *(confirmation required)* ..   ..
112a D. ℞. — As last. *R.I.C.* 29 (b) *(Vienna)*..   ..   .. £200
113 Antoninianus. IMP . CAES . Q . TRAIANVS DECIVS AVG. ℞. — As last.
R.I.C. 29(c), *note (confirmation required)* ..   ..
113a D. ℞. — As last. *R.I.C.* 29 (c) *(B.M.)* 22
113b D, · · · below bust (A). ℞. — As last. *R.I.C.* 48   25
122 B(M). ℞. VICTORIA GERMANICA, Decius on horse pacing l., holding
sceptre and raising r. hand; horse is led by Victory walking l., holding
wreath and palm. *R.I.C.* 43 ..   ..
122a D. ℞. — As last. *R.I.C.*, p. 123 *(Vierordt sale)*   150
123 E. ℞. VIRTVS AVG., Virtus seated l. on cuirass, holding branch and
reversed spear *(Cohen,* sceptre*). R.I.C.* 8 *(B.M.)* 150
129 D. ℞. VOTIS / DECEN / NALI / BVS in laurel-wreath. *R.I.C.* 30   22
                                                                               200

TRAJAN DECIUS, ETRUSCILLA, HERENNIUS and HOSTILIAN

1 Antoninianus. D. ℞. CONCORDIA AVG., diad. bust of Etruscilla dr. on
crescent r., facing conjoined busts of her two sons, rad. and di. l. *R.I.C.* 31
Extremely rare

TRAJAN DECIUS, HERENNIUS and HOSTILIAN

1a Antoninianus. D. ℞. PIETAS AVGG., busts of the two sons, dr., facing
each other. *R.I.C.* 32 *(DeQuelen sale)*   ..   .. *Extremely rare*

HERENNIA ETRUSCILLA

*Herennia Cupressenia Etruscilla was the wife of Trajan Decius and the mother of
Herennius and Hostilian. She is practically unknown to history except from her coins.*

Obverse legend and type.

HER . ETRVSCILLA AVG., her diademed bust draped to right; in the case of
the antoninianus, with a crescent beneath.
The *R.I.C.* numbers are of Trajan Decius.
(A)   Attributed to Antioch in *R.I.C.* (nos. 62-70, pp. 128-9).
1 Antoninianus. ℞. ABVNDANTIA AVG., Pudicitia, veiled, stg. l., holding
sceptre *(Cohen,* spear*)* and r. hand drawing veil. *R.I.C.* 74   30
1a — Abundantia stg. r., emptying cornucopiae held in both hands (Hy.;
rev. of Decius). *R.I.C.* 73 (stg. l.)   30
2 (A). ℞. ADVENTVS AVG., Decius on horse pacing l., holding sceptre and
raising r. hand. *R.I.C.* 62 (a)   35
2a (A). As last, but · · · below bust. *R.I.C.* 62 (b) *(Vienna)*   35
2b (A). Similar, but · · · · below bust. *R.I.C.* 62 (c) *(Vienna)*   35
3 (A). AEQVITAS AVG., Aequitas stg. l. *R.I.C.* 63 (a)   30
3a (A). As last, but · below bust. *R.I.C.* 63 (b) *(doubtful)* ..   ..
3b (A). Similar, but · · below bust. *R.I.C.* 63 (c) *(B.M.)* 30
3c (A). Similar, but · · · · below bust. *R.I.C.* 63 (d) *(Vienna)*   30
3d (A). AEQVITAS AVGG., as **3.** *R.I.C.* 64   ·   30

 5 **Antoninianus.** R. CONCORDIA AVGG., Concordia seated l., holding
    patera and double cornucopiae (Hy.; *rev. of Otacilia Severa*). *R.I.C.* 72 ..   £28

 8 R. FECVNDITAS AVG., Fecunditas stg. half-left, holding cornucopiae and
    with r. hand above child who stands r. before her with hands raised.
    R.I.C. 55 (b)   26
11 R. FECVNDITAS AVGG., as last. *R.I.C.* 56   26

14   19

14 R. IVNO REGINA, Juno stg. half-left, holding patera and sceptre; peacock
    at her feet. *R.I.C.* 57..   26
17 R. PVDICITIA AVG., Pudicitia stg., as **1**. *R.I.C.* 58 (b)   24
19 R. — Similar, but Pudicitia seated. *R.I.C.* 59 (b)   24
19a (A). As last. *R.I.C.* 65 (a)   28
19b (A). As last, but with IV below bust. *R.I.C.* 65 (b) (*Vienna*)   28
20 As **19**, but ETVSCILLA (*sic*). *R.I.C.* 59*   28
24a R. PVDICITIA AVGG., as **19**. *R.I.C.* 60 (*Dorchester*)   35
27 (A). ·· below bust. R. ROMAE AETERNAE AVG., Roma seated l. on shield,
    holding Victory and spear. *R.I.C.* 66 (a)   65
27a (A). IV below bust. R. — As last. *R.I.C.* 66 (b) (*Vienna*)   65
28 (A). R. SAECVLVM NOVVM, temple of six columns; in centre, figure stg. r.,
    holding spear or sceptre. *R.I.C.* 67 (a)   65
29 (A). Similar, but ·· below bust. *R.I.C.* 67 (b)   65
29a (A). Similar, but IIV below bust. *R.I.C.* 67 (c) (*B.M.*)   65
30 R. SECVRIT . ORBIS, Securitas seated l., resting hd. on l. hand (Hy.;
    rev. of Philip I). *R.I.C.* 71 ·..   30
31 (A). R. VBERITAS AVG., Uberitas stg. l. *R.I.C.* 68 (a)   30
31a (A). Similar, but . below bust. *R.I.C.* 68 (b) (*B.M.*)   30
31b (A). Similar, but .. below bust. *R.I.C.* 68 (c) (*Vienna*)   30
31c (A). Similar, but IV below bust. *R.I.C.* 68 (d) (*Vienna*)   30
32 (A). R. VERITAS AVG, same type. *R.I.C.* 69 (a)   35
32a (A). Similar, but ··· below bust. *R.I.C.* 69 (b) (*B.M.*)   35
34 (A). R. VICTORIA AVG., Victory running l. *R.I.C.* 70 (a)   30
34a (A). Similar, but ·· below bust. *R.I.C.* 70 (b) (*B.M.*)   30
34b (A). Similar, but ···· below bust. *R.I.C.* 70 (c) (*Vienna*)   30
34c R. VICTORIA GERMANICA, as **34**, but Victory running r. (Hy.; *rev. of
    Herennius*). *R.I.C.* 76 (*Rosenburg sale*, 1932)   45

HERENNIUS ETRUSCUS
A.D. 251

Quintus Herennius Etruscus Messius Decius was the elder son of Trajan Decius and Etruscilla and was given the rank of Caesar in 250. He was made Augustus in the following year and fully associated with his father in the empire. He perished with his father at the battle of Abrittus in the same year.

Obverse legends.

As Caesar.

A.	HEREN . ETRV . MES . QV . DECIVS CAESAR	Antioch
B.	HEREN . TRV . MES . QV . DECIVS CAESAR	Antioch
C.	Q . HER . ETR . MES . DECIVS NOB . C.	Rome

As Augustus.

D.	IMP . C . Q . HER . ETR . MES . DECIO AVG
E.	IMP . C . Q . HER . ETR . MES . DECIVS AVG
F.	Q . HER . ETR . MES . DECIVS AVG.

Obverse types.

Radiate bust draped r. for all the antoniniani, and bare-headed bust draped r. for the other denominations, which are all rare and only occur with the Caesar obverse legends.

(A) is placed against pieces attributed to the Antioch mint by *R.I.C.* (nos. 156-161). The *R.I.C.* numbers carry on from Trajan Decius.

	4	6

1	**Antoninianus.** A(A). ℞. ADVENTVS AVG., emperor on horseback l., holding spear and raising r. hand. *R.I.C.* 156	£65
2	A(A). ℞. AEQVITAS AVG., Aequitas stg. l. *R.I.C.* 157*	
2a	(A). As last, but with · in ex. on *rev.* *R.I.C.* 157 (a) (*Budapest*) ..	55
2b	(A). As **2**, but ···· below bust. *R.I.C.* 157 (b) (*Budapest*)	55
2c	B(A). As **2**. *R.I.C.* 157 (c) (*B.M.*)	55
2d	(A). As last, but ··· below bust. *R.I.C.* 157 (d)	55
3	C. ℞. CONCORDIA AVG., two clasped r. hands. *R.I.C.* 138* (*confirmation required*)	
4	C. ℞. CONCORDIA AVGG., as last. *R.I.C.* 138	50
5	Q . HERE . TRAIANVS DECIVS NOB . C. (*probably a misreading of C*). ℞. As last. *R.I.C.* 138* (*very doubtful*)	
6	C. ℞. GENIVS EXERC . ILLYRICIANI, Genius stg. l.; to r., standard (Hy.; *rev. of Decius*). *R.I.C.* 163	50
7	D. ℞. MAR . PROP., Mars advancing r., holding spear and shield. *R.I.C.* 150A (*confirmation required*)	
7a	C. ℞. — As last. *R.I.C.* 139 (*Dorchester hoard*)	60
7b	C. ℞. MARS PROPVG., as last. *R.I.C.* 140 (*Budapest*)	60
8	C. ℞. MARTI PROPVGNATORI, as last. *R.I.C.* 141	55

9 Antoninianus. A, with . below bust (A). ℞. PANNONIAE, Pannonia,
veiled, stg. half-left, looking r., holding helmet and standard. *R.I.C.*
158 (b) £65
9a B (with . below bust ?) (A). ℞. — As last. *R.I.C.* 158 (a) (*B.M.*) ..   65
11 C.   ℞. PIETAS AVGG., Mercury stg. half-left. *R.I.C.* 142 (b)   45
13a D.   ℞. — As last. *R.I.C.* 151 (a) (*Dorchester*)..   150
13b E.   ℞. — As last. *R.I.C.* 151 (b) (*Vienna*)   150
13c C.   ℞. — Pietas stg. half-left before altar, raising both hands (Hy.; *rev.
of Treb. Gallus*). *R.I.C.* 165 (*B.M.; plated*)   ..   ..   ..
13d Q . HERINNIVS ETR . MES . DECIVS NOB . C.   ℞. — Sprinkler, simpulum, jug,
patera and lituus. *R.I.C.* 143* (*Trau sale; regular mintage ?*) ..   ..
14 C.   ℞. PIETAS AVGVSTORVM, as last. *R.I.C.* 143   45
16 D.   ℞. — As last. *R.I.C.* 152   150
17 Q . HERENNOS ME . DECIVS NO . C.   ℞. P . M . TR . P . II CONS . V, prince
stg. l., sacrificing over altar (*plated*). *R.I.C.* 166 (*ancient forgery ?*) ..

14   40b

19 D. ℞. PRINC . IVVENT., Apollo seated l., resting elbow against lyre,
holding laurel-branch. *R.I.C.* 153 (b)   150
20 C. ℞. — As last. *R.I.C.* 144 (b)   45
20a Denarius. C. ℞. — As last. *R.I.C.* 144 (a)   750
22 Antoninianus. C. ℞. PRINC . IVVENTVTIS, as last. *R.I.C.* 145   ..   45
24a C. ℞. PRINCIPI IVVENTVTIS, as last. *R.I.C.* 146 (*B.M.*)..   50
26 C. ℞. — Herennius stg. l., in military dress, holding wand and transverse spear. *R.I.C.* 147 (c)   45
27 Quinarius. C. ℞. — As last. *R.I.C.* 147 (b)   300
33 Antoninianus. C. ℞. — As before, but he holds standard and spear.
R.I.C. 148 (b)   45
33a F. ℞. — As last. *R.I.C.* 153A (*Dorchester hoard*)   150
35 A(A). ℞. PVDICITIA AVG., Pudicitia, veiled, seated l., drawing veil and
holding sceptre. *R.I.C.* 159 (a)   55
35a As last, but . . . . below bust. *R.I.C.* 159 (b) (*Vienna*)   55
36 C. ℞. SAECVLARES AVGG., goat stg. (Hy.; *rev. of Philip II*). *R.I.C.* 162   50
37 D. ℞. SECVRITAS AVGG., Securitas stg., leaning against column, r. hand
to head. *R.I.C.* p. 140 (*very deoubtful*)   ..   ..
38 C. ℞. SPES PVBLICA, Spes advancing l., raising skirt and holding flower.
R.I.C. 149   45
39 Medallion. C. ℞. — Herennius stg. l., holding spear, in six-column
temple. *R.I.C.* 150 ..   .. *Extremely rare*
40 Antoninianus. A(A). ℞. VBERITAS AVG., Uberitas stg. l. *R.I.C.* 160 (a)   55
40a As last, but . below bust. *R.I.C.* 160 (b) (*Vienna*)   55
40b A, with . . . below bust (A). ℞. VICTORIA AVG., Victory running l.
R.I.C. 161 (a) (*B.M.*)   55
40c A but ETR for ETRV, and · below bust (A). ℞. — As last. *R.I.C.* 161 (b)
(*Vienna*)   55
40d C. ℞. — As last (Hy.). *R.I.C.* 164 (*Trau*)   50

41 Antoninianus. D. ℞. VICTORIA GERMANICA, as before but Victory
running r. *R.I.C.* 154 175
42 D. ℞. VOTIS DECENNALIBVS in laurel-wreath. *R.I.C.* 155 (a) 200
42a E. ℞. — As last. *R.I.C.* 155 (b) (*Vienna*) 200

HOSTILIAN
A.D. 251

Caius Valens Hostilianus Messius Quintus was the younger son of Trajan Decius and
Etruscilla and created Caesar at the same time as his brother. On the deaths of Decius and
Herennius he was proclaimed emperor by the Senate and reigned in association with Treboni-
anus Gallus, whom the troops had elected. The joint reign only lasted a few months before
Hostilian died of the plague.

Obverse legends and types.

As Caesar.

A.   C . OVAL . OSTIL . MES . COVINTVS CAESAR   *Antioch*
B.   C . OVL . OSTIL . MES . COVINTVS CAESAR   *Antioch*
C.   C . VALES HOS . MES . QVINTVS N . C.
D.   C . VAL . HOS . MES . QVINTVS N . C.
E.   C . VAL . HOST . MES . QVINTVS N. C.   *Antioch*
F.   C . VAL . HOSTIL . MES . QVINTVS N . C.   *Antioch*
G.   C . VALENS . HOSTIL . MES . QVINTVS N . C.

As Augustus.

H.   C . OVAL . OSTIL . MES . COVINTVS AVG.   *Antioch*
I.   IMP . CAE . C . VAL . HOS . MES . QVINTVS AVG.
J   IMP . C . MES . QVINTVS AVG.

All the antoninani have—radiate bust draped right.
The rare quinarius has—bare-headed bust draped right.
(A) attributed to the mint of Antioch by *R.I.C.* (nos. 193-209; pp. 146-8).
The *R.I.C.* numbers carry on after Herennius under Trajan Decius.

1 Antoninianus. G. ℞. ADVENTVS AVG., emperor on horseback l., holding spear and rasing r. hand. *R.I.C.* 210 (Hy. *or Eastern; confirmation*
required) 75
2 B, with . . . below bust (A). ℞. — As last. *R.I.C.* 193 (a) (*B.M.*) .. 75
2a B, with IIV below bust (A). ℞. — As last. *R.I.C.* 193 (b) 75
3 H(A). ℞. AEQVITAS AVG., Aequitas stg. l. *R.I.C.* 202 (a) 125
3a H, and . . . below bust (A). ℞. — As last. *R.I.C.* 202 (b) (*Vienna*) .. 125
3b H, and IV below bust (A). ℞. — As last. *R.I.C.* 202 (c) (*Vienna*) .. 125
·4 E(A). ℞. — As last. *R.I.C.* 194* 75
4a E, with . . . below bust (A). ℞. — As last. *R.I.C.* 194 (c) (*Vienna*) .. 75
4b A(A). ℞, — As last. *R.I.C.* 194 (a) (*DeQuellen sale*) 75
4c A, with . below bust (A). ℞. — As last. *R.I.C.* 194 (b) (*Vienna*) .. 75
5 D. ℞. CONCORDIA AVGG., two clasped r. hands. *R.I.C.* 174 (a) .. 75
6 G. ℞. — As last. *R.I.C.* 174 (b) 75
7 I (*Cohen gives* HOST). ℞. — As last. *R.I.C.* 186 125
8 I. ℞. IVNONI MARTIALI, Juno seated facing, with peacock beside her, in
distyle temple. *R.I.C.* 190 150
9 H(A). ℞. — As last. *R.I.C.* 202A 140

10 Antoninianus. G. R. MAR . PROP., Mars advancing r., holding spear
and shield. *R.I.C.* 175 (b) 65
11 D. R. — As last. *R.I.C.* 175 (a) 65
12 D. R. MARS PROPVG., as last. *R.I.C.* 176 (a) 65
12a C. R. — As last. *R.I.C.* 176 (b) (*Dorchester*) 65
13 G. R. — As last. *R.I.C.* 176 (c) 65
15 G. R. MARTI PROPVGNAYORI, as last. *R.I.C.* 177 (b) 65
15a J. R. — As last. *R.I.C.* 187 (*R. It.* 1902, p. 277) 125
15b As last (base metal). *R.I.C.* 187 (*B.M.*, *ex Dorchester*) .. ..
16 C . VALENS HOSTIL . MES . QVINTVS AVG. *R.I.C* 177* ('*confirmation urgently
needed*') .. ..
17 E(A). R. PANNONIAE, Pannonia stg. l., holding helmet and standard.
R.I.C. 195 75
20 D. R. PIETAS AVGG. (*Cohen* AVG. *in error*), Mercury stg. l. *R.I.C.* 178 (b) 65
21 G. R. — As last. *R.I.C.* 178 (c) (*obv.* C *in error ?*) 65
22 J. R. — As last. *R.I.C.* 188 125
25 G. R. PIETAS AVGVSTORVM, simpulum, sprinkler, jug, patera and lituus.
R.I.C. 179 (*obv.* D, *in error ?*) 65

15   34

26a Q . . . MOS . ME . DECIVS NO . C. R . P . M . TR . P . II CONS . V, prince stg. l.
sacrificing over altar out of patera. *R.I.C.* 211 (*Paris; ancient forgery ?*)
29 I (*Cohen gives* HOST, *in error ?*). R. PRINCIPI IVVENTVTIS, Apollo seated l.,
resting elbow on lyre, holding branch. *R.I.C.* 189 125
30 G. R. — As last. *R.I.C.* 180 65
34 G. R. — Hostilian, in military dress, stg. l., holding standard and
reversed spear. *R.I.C.* 181 (d) 65
34c C. R. — As last. *R.I.C.* 181 (c) 65
36 D, but AVG. for N .C. (*?in error*). R. — As before, but transverse spear.
36a G. R. — As last. *R.I.C.* 182 65
38 G. R. — As **34**, but he holds wand and transverse spear. *R.I.C.* 183 (e) 65
39 D. R. — As last. *R.I.C.* 183 (d) 65
39a Quinarius. G. R. — As last. *R.I.C.* 183 (c) (*R. It.*, 1914) 400
43 Antoninianus. A(A). R. PVDICITIA AVG., Pudicitia seated l., drawing
veil and holding sceptre. *R.I.C.* 196 (a) 70
43a A, but .. below bust (A). R. — As last. *R.I.C.* 196 (b) (*Berlin*) .. 70
43b A, but . . . below bust (A). R. — As last. *R.I.C.* 196 (c) 70
43c A, but IV below bust (A). R. — As last. *R.I.C.* 196 (d) 70
43d H(A). R. — As last. *R.I.C.* 203 (a) (*R. It.* 1896, p. 184) 125
43e H, but . below bust (A). R. — As last. *R.I.C.* 203 (b) (*Vienna*) .. 125
43f H, but . . below bust (A). R. — As last. *R.I.C.* 203 (c) 125
43g H, but . . . below bust (A). R. — As last. *R.I.C.* 203 (d) 125
43h H, but IV below bust (A). R. — As last. *R.I.C.* 203 (e) 125

45 Antoninianus. H(A). ℞. ROMAE AETERNAE, Roma seated l., holding
Victory and spear; at her side, shield. *R.I.C.* 204 (a) £125
45a H, but · · · below bust (A). ℞. — As last. *R.I.C.* 204 (b) (*Vienna*) .. 125
46 A, but COVINVS (*sic*) (A). ℞. — As last. *R.I.C.* 198 (a) 70
46a A, but · · below bust (A). ℞. — As last. *R.I.C.* 198 (b) (*Vienna*) .. 70
46b A, but · · · below bust (A). ℞. — As last. *R.I.C.* 198 (c) (*Vienna*) .. 70
52 B(A). ℞. ROM . AETERNAE AVG, as last. *R.I.C.* 197 70
53 F, with · · · · below bust (A). ℞. SAECVLVM NOVVM, temple of six
columns, with standing figure (?Roma) in centre. *R.I.C.* 199 (d) .. 75
54 A, with · · · · below bust. ℞. — As last. *R.I.C.* 199 (b) 75
54a A, with IIV below bust. ℞. — As last. *Arnold Col.* 75
54b A, with · below bust. ℞. — As last. *R.I.C.* 199 (a) (*Ashmolean*) .. 75
54c A, with IV below bust. ℞. — As last. *R.I.C.* 199 (c) (*B.M.*) 75
55 C . VALENS HOSTIL. MES . COVINTVS AVG. (A). ℞ — As last. *R.I.C.* 205*
(*confirmation required*).. .. ..
55a H(A). ℞. — As last. *R.I.C.* 205 (a) 125
55b H, with · · · below bust (A). ℞. — As last. *R.I.C.* 205 (b) (*Vienna*) .. 125
57 I. ℞. SECVRITAS AVGG., Securitas stg. half-left, legs crossed and
leaning l. elbow on column and r. hand on hd. *R.I.C.* 192 (Pl. 12, 2) .. 125
58 J. ℞. — As last, but hd. r. *R.I.C.* 191 (b) 125

54a   59

59 I. ℞. — Similar. *R.I.C.* 191 (a) 125
N.B.—*R.I.C. is a little confused on these last three as his* 191 (a) *and* 192
are similar; we have followed Cohen.
61 G. ℞. SPES PVBLICA, Spes walking l. *R.I.C.* 184 (b) 65
61a D. ℞. — As last. *R.I.C.* 184 (a) (*Budapest*) 65
62 C . VAI (*sic*.) HOS . M . OVINT (*sic*.) AVG. (A). ℞. — As last. *R.I.C.* 206 .. 125
63 B, with one or more dots under bust (A). ℞. VBERITAS AVG., Uberitas
stg. l. *R.I.C.* 200 (a) 70
63a A, with · under bust (A). ℞. — As last. *R.I.C.* 200 (b) 70
63b A, with · · · under bust (A). ℞. — As last. *R.I.C.* 200 (c) .. 70
63c A, with IV under bust (A). ℞. — As last. *R.I.C.* 200 (d) (*Vienna*) .. 70
63d E, with · · under bust (A). ℞. — As last. *R.I.C.* 200 (e) (*Berlin*) .. 70
64 H, with · · · under bust (A). ℞. — As last. *R.I.C.* 207 (a) 125
64a H, with IV under bust (A). ℞. — As last. *R.I.C.* 207 (b) (*Vienna*) .. 125
65 B, with VII below bust (A). ℞. VICTORIA AVG., Victory running l. *R.I.C.*
201 70
66 H, with · · below bust (A). ℞. — As last. *R.I.C.* 208 125
66a H, with IV under bust (A). ℞. — Victory running r. (*British Museum*) 125
67 H, with · below bust (A). ℞. — Victory stg. r. on globe. *R.I.C.* 209 (a) 125
67a Similar, but · · (A). *R.I.C.* 209 (b) (*B.M.*).. 125
67b Similar, but · · · · (A). *R.I.C.* 209 (c) (*Vienna*) 125
67c Similar, but IV (A). *R.I.C.* 209 (d) (*B.M.*).. 125
70 D. ℞. VICTORIA GERMANICA, as **65.** *R.I.C.* 185 150

TREBONIANUS GALLUS

A.D. 251-253

Caius Vibius Trebonianus Gallus held high command in the army which was routed by the Goths at Arbrittus. Nothing is known of his birth and previous history. With the deaths of Decius and Herennius, which may have been partly due to treachery by Gallus, the empire was left without a ruler. Gallus was chosen by the army and confirmed by the Senate. Hostilian, the surviving son of Decius, was made joint-emperor and Volusian, son of Gallus, given the title of Caesar.

He concluded peace with the Goths, on terms that Rome felt were disadvantageous and his reign was troubled by invasions on both the Northern and Eastern frontiers. At the same time a devastating plague swept the empire.

In 252 Aemilian, governor of Moesia, was fighting the Goths and severely defeated them; his troops were so delighted by this that they proclaimed him emperor. In the following year he invaded Italy and whilst Gallus and his son were advancing to deal with this rebellious force, they were murdered by their own soldiers.

Obverse legends and types.

A. GALLVS PIVS AVG.
B. IMP . CAES . C . VIBIVS TREBONIANVS GALLVS AVG.
C. IMP . CAE . C . VIB . TREB . GALLVS AVG.
D. IMP . C . C . VIB . TREB . GALLVS AVG.   *Milan*
E. IMP . C . C . VIB . TREB . GALLVS P . F . AVG.   *Antioch*
F. IMP . C . GALLVS AVG.

All the antoniniani have radiate bust draped and cuirassed to right. The few quinarii and medallions are similar, but the bust is laureate.
(A) Is placed against pieces attributed in *R.I.C.* to the Antioch mint (nos. 79-96 pp. 167-9).
(M) ditto for Milan mint (nos. 69-78, pp. 166-7).

The mintmarks, dots or pellets or Roman numerals, of Antioch are below th bust on the *obv.* and in the exergue on the *rev.*

2 Antoninianus. E(A). ℞. ADVENTVS AVG., emperor on horseback l., holding sceptre and raising r. hand. *R.I.C.* 79 ..   ..   £3
2a As last, . below bust. *R.I.C.* 79*   3
2b — · in ex. on *rev.* *R.I.C.* 79*   3
2c — · each side. *R.I.C.* 79*   3
2d — ·· in ex. on *rev.* *R.I.C.* 79*   3
2e — ·· each side. *R.I.C.* 79*   3
3 — ··· each side. *R.I.C.* 79*   3
3a — IV each side   ..   ..
3b — IV below bust. *R.I.C.* 79*   3
3c — ···· each side. *R.I.C.* 79*   3
3d — VI each side. *R.I.C.* 79*   3
3e — VII each side. *R.I.C.* 79*   ..   ..

6 Antoninianus. E(A). ℞. AEQVITAS AVG., Aequitas stg. l. *R.I.C.* 80 .. £24
6a As last, ···· below bust. *R.I.C.* 80* 24
6b — VI below bust. *R.I.C.* 80* 24
6c — ·· each side. *R.I.C.* 80* 24
6d — ··· each side. *R.I.C.* 80* 24
6e — ···· each side. *R.I.C.* 80* 24
6f — VI each side. *R.I C.* 80* 24
6g — VII each side. *R.I.C.* 80* 24
6h — IIII below bust; VII in ex. *R.I.C.* 80* 26
6i — IV below bust; IIV in ex. *R.I.C.* 80* 26
6j — VI below bust; IIV in ex. *R.I.C.* 80* 26
6k — VI below bust; VII in ex. *R.I.C.* 80* 26
7 As **6,** but extra heavy (*Cohen suggests* double antoninianus). *R.I.C.* 80*
  (*probably only an exceptionally heavy* antoninianus) 45
9 E(A). ℞. AEQVITAS AVGG., as **6.** *R.I.C.* 81 24
9a As last, · below bust. *R.I.C.* 81* 24
9b — ·· below bust. *R.I.C.* 81* 24
9c — ·· each side. *R.I.C.* 81* 24
9d — ··· below bust. *R.I.C.* 81* 24
9e — ···· each side. *R.I.C.* 81* 24
9f — VI each side. *R.I.C.* 81* 24
11 C. ℞. AETERNITAS AVG., Aeternitas stg. l., raising skirt and holding
  phoenix on globe. *R.I.C.* 30* (*confirmation required*) .. .. ..
13 C. ℞. AETERNITAS AVGG., as last. *R.I.C.* 30 .. 28
15 C. ℞. ANNONA AVG., Annona stg. l.; before modius (Hy.; *rev. type of
  Philip I*). *R.I.C.* 62 30
17 C. ℞. ANNONA AVGG., Annona stg. r., l. foot on prow, holding rudder and
  corn-ears. *R.I.C.* 31 24

13   20

20 C. ℞. APOLL . SALVTARI, Apollo stg. l., holding branch and lyre resting
  on rock. *R.I.C.* 32 28
25a C. ℞. CONCORDIA AVGG., Concordia seated l., holding patera and double
  cornucopiae, star in field. *R.I.C.* 53 (*Dorchester; poor metal*) 28
25b As last, but without star. *R.I.C.* 52 (*Dorchester; poor metal*) 28
29 C. ℞. — As last, but Concordia stg. l. *R.I.C.* 51 (*poor metal*) .. 28
29a As last, but good Roman style. *R.I.C.* 51* (*Dorchester*) 35
29b C. ℞. CONCORDIA AVGG., two clasped r. hands. (*British Museum*—
  Hy.; *rev. type of Etruscus*) 35
33 C. ℞. FELICITAS AVGG., Felicitas stg. facing, looking l., star in field.
  R.I.C. 33* (*confirmation required*) .. ..
34 E(A). ℞. FELICITAS PVBL., Felicitas stg. l. *R.I.C.* 82 24
34a As last, · below bust. *R.I.C.* 82* 24
34b — · in ex. on *rev.* *R.I.C.* 82* 24
34c — · both sides. *R.I.C.* 82* 24
34d — ·· both sides. *R.I.C.* 82* 24
34e — ··· both sides. *R.I.C.* 82* 24
34f — ···· below bust. *R.I.C.* 82* 24
34g — ···· in ex. *R.I.C.* 82* 24

34h **Antoninianus.** E(A), · · · · below bust. ℞. FELICITAS PVBL., Felicitas
   stg. l., · · · · in ex. *R.I.C.* 82* £24
34i As last, IV both sides. *R.I.C.* 82* (*Cohen gives* IV *in ex.*).. 24
34j — VI both sides. *R.I.C.* 82* 24
34k — IIV both sides. *R.I.C.* 82* 24
34l — VII both sides. *R.I.C.* 82* 24
34m — IIV below bust; IV in ex. *R.I.C.* 82* 26
34n — VI below bust; IV in ex. *R.I.C.* 82* 26
34p — VII below bust; IIV in ex. *R.I.C.* 82* 26
34q — Star in ex. *R.I.C.* 82* 28
35 C. ℞. As before, but nothing below bust or in ex. *R.I.C.* 59 35
35a D(M). ℞. — As last. *R.I.C.* 75 (*B.M., ex Dorchester*) 35
37 C. ℞. FELICITAS PVBLICA, as last. *R.I.C.* 33 24
37a C. ℞. — As last, but with star in field. *R.I.C.* 34 28
38 E(A). ℞. — As **37**. *R.I.C.* 82* (*doubtful*) .. .. ..

39 **Quinarius.** F (*Cohen omits the* AVG., *in error ?*). ℞. — As **37**. *R.I.C.* 27 200
39a As last, but with star in field on *rev. R.I.C.* 28 200

39   41

41 **Antoninianus.** C. ℞. — Felicitas stg. l., leaning against column,
   holding short caduceus and transverse sceptre. *R.I.C.* 34A 24
42 **Quinarius.** F. ℞. — As last. *R.I.C.* 29 200
45 **Antoninianus.** C. ℞. IOVI STATORI, Jupiter stg. front, head r. (Hy.;
   plated; rev. of Gordian III). *R.I.C.* 60 .. ..
46 D(M). ℞. IVNO MARTIALIS, Juno seated l., holding corn-ears(?) and
   transverse sceptre. *R.I.C.* 69 28
46a C. ℞. — As last. *R.I.C.* 35 35
47 E(A). ℞. — As last, with IV in ex. *R.I.C.* 83* 28
47a As last, but VII in ex. *R.I.C.* 83* 28
47b — · · · · both sides. *R.I.C.* 83* 28
47c — · · · · below bust. *R.I.C.* 83* 28
47d — · both sides. *R.I.C.* 83* 28
47e — · · both sides. *R.I.C.* 83 28
47f — · · · both sides. *R.I.C.* 83* 28
47g — IV both sides. *R.I.C.* 83* 28
47h — VI both sides. *R.I.C.* 83* 28
47i — VI below bust; IV in ex. *R.I.C.* 83* 30
47j — VII both sides. *R.I.C.* 83* 28
48 **Quinarius.** D(M ?). ℞. — As **46**. *R.I.C.* 78 200
49 **Antoninianus.** C. ℞. IVNONI MARTIALI, Juno seated facing in distyle
   round temple. *R.I.C.* 54 60
53 **Medallion.** B. ℞. — As last, but the temple has four columns.
   R.I.C. 25 .. .. *Extremely rare*

56 Antoninianus. C. ℞. LIBERALITAS AVGG., Liberalitas stg. l. *R.I.C.* 36   £40
59 D(M). ℞. LIBERALITAS AVGG . III, as last (Hy.). *R.I.C.* 77   35
63 C. ℞. LIBERTAS AVGG., Libertas stg. half-left, her sceptre long. *R.I.C.* 37   24
63a As last, but with star in field on *rev.* *R.I.C.* 38   26
67 C. ℞. — As **63,** but Libertas has her legs crossed and leans against
  column. *R.I.C.* 39   24
68 D(M). ℞. LIBERTAS PVBLICA, As **63,** but transverse sceptre. *R.I.C.* 70   24
69 C. ℞. — As last. *R.I.C.* 50   ..   ..   .:   30
70 E(A). ℞. MARTEM PROPVGNATOREM, Mars walking r., holding spear
  and shield. *R.I.C.* 84   30

    63   72a

71 C. ℞. MARTI PACIFERO, Mars running l., holding branch and spear
  (*Cohen,* sceptre, *in error*). *R.I.C.* 40   30
72 E(A)., VII below bust. ℞. — As last. *R.I.C.* 85 (*Cohen also gives obv.* D;
  doubtful)   28
72a As last, · both sides. *R.I.C.* 85*   28
72b — · · both sides. *R.I.C.* 85*   28
72c — · · · both sides. (*Dorchester*)   28
72d — · · · · both sides. *R.I.C.* 85*   28
72e — IV both sides. *R.I.C.* 85*   28

74 Medallion. B. ℞. MONETA AVGG., the three Monetae stg. l.; at the feet
  of each, a pile of metal. *R.I.C.* 26 ..   .. *Extremely rare*
75 As last, but larger size. *R.I.C.* 26 ..   .. *Extremely rare*
75a Antoninianus. IMP . C . C . VIB . TREB . CILLVS . AV. ℞. PAT . AVGG.,
  Pax stg. l. *R.I.C.* 97 (*Budapest; barbarous and base metal*)   ..   ..
76 D(M). ℞. PAX AETERNA, as last, but sceptre is transverse. *R.I.C.* 7 ..   24
76a E(A). ℞. PAX AVG . AVG., as last. *R.I.C.* 86* (*Budapest—accidental
  variant of* **80** *?*)   28
77 C. ℞. PAX AVGG., as last. *R.I.C.* 55   30
77a As last, but vertical sceptre. *R.I.C.* 55* (*B.M.*)   30
77b As **77,** but with star in field. *R.I.C.* 56 (*Dorchester*)   30
79a E(A). ℞. PAX AVG . VG., as **76,** but with · · in ex. *R.I.C.* 86* (*Dorchester—
  accidental variant ?*)   28
80 E(A). ℞. PAX AVGVS., as last. *R.I.C.* 86   24
80a As last, · both sides. *R.I.C.* 86*   24
80b — · · both sides. *R.I.C.* 86*   24
80c — · · · both sides. *R.I.C.* 86*   24
80d — · · · · both sides. *R.I.C.* 86*   24
80e — IIV both sides. *R.I.C.* 86*   24
80f — IV both sides. *R.I.C.* 86*   24
80g — VII both sides. *R.I.C.* 86*   24
80h — · below bust. *R.I.C.* 86*   24
80i — · · below bust. *R.I.C.* 86*   24
80j — · · · · below bust. *R.I.C.* 86*   24
80k — VI below bust. *R.I.C.* 86*   24

81 Antoninianus. E(A). ℞. PAX AVGVS . S . C., Pax stg. l. *R.I.C.* 87 (*B.M.*,
ex Dorchester, etc.) £45

84 C. ℞. PIETAS AVGG., Pietas, veiled, stg. half-left, raising both hands.
R.I.C. 41 24

84a As last, but with star in *rev.* field. *R.I.C.* 42 26

85 D(M). ℞. — As last. *R.I.C.* 73 (*Confirmation required*) ..

88 D(M). ℞. — As **84**, but lighted altar before Pietas. *R.I.C.* 72 .. 24

88a C. ℞. — As last. *R.I.C.* 41* (*B.M., ex Dorchester*) 30

91 C.? (*Cohen gives*, IMP . CAES . TREBONIANVS AVG.). ℞. P . M . TR . POT .
COS . P . P., emperor seated, holding globe (Hy. ?). *R.I.C.* 66 .. ..

93 C. ℞. P . M . TR . P . IIII COS . II, emperor stg. l., holding laurel-branch
and transverse sceptre. *R.I.C.* 2 (*rev. of Volusian*) 30

95 C. ℞. — Emperor stg. l., holding short sceptre, and sacrificing over
lighted tripod. *R.I.C.* 3 (*rev. of Volusian*) 30

100 C. ℞. PROVIDENT . AVG., Providentia stg. l., holding wand over globe and
sceptre (Hy.; *rev. of Gordian III*). *R.I.C.* 61 30

102 C. ℞. PROVIDENTIA AVG., Providentia stg. l., holding globe and transverse
sceptre. *R.I.C.* 43 30

103 C. ℞. PROVIDENTIA AVGG., as last. *R.I.C.* 44 30

103a As last, but vertical sceptre. *R.I.C.* 44* (*B.M., ex Dorchester*) .. 30

103b D(M). ℞. — As **103**. *R.I.C.* 74 (*B.M., ex Dorchester*) 30

104 E(A). ℞. PVDICITIA AVG., Pudicitia, veiled, seated l., raising veil. *R.I.C.* 88 28

104a As last, · · · · below bust. *R.I.C.* 88* 28

104b — IV below bust. *R.I.C.* 88* 28

104c — VI below bust. *R.I.C.* 88* 28

88   108e

105 C. ℞. ROMAE AETERNAE, Roma seated l., holding Victory and spear,
shield at her side. *R.I.C.* 63 (*rev. of Philip I*) 30

107 E(A). ℞. ROMAE AETERNAE AVG., as last. *R.I.C.* 89 26

108 As last · · · · in ex. *R.I.C.* 89* 26

108a — IIV in ex. *R.I.C.* 89* 26

108b — IV in ex. *R.I.C.* 89* 26

108c — · below bust. *R.I.C.* 89* 26

108d — ·· below bust. *R.I.C.* 89* 26

108e — IV below bust. *R.I.C.* 89* 26

108f — · each side. *R.I.C.* 89* 26

108g — ·· each side. *R.I.C.* 89* 26

108h — ··· each side. *R.I.C.* 89* 26

108i — ···· each side. *R.I.C.* 89* 26

108j — IIV each side. *R.I.C.* 89* 26

108k — IV each side. *R.I.C.* 89* 26

108l — VI each side. *R.I.C.* 89* 26

108m — VII each side. *R.I.C.* 89* 26

108p — VII below bust; VI in ex. *R.I.C.* 89* 28

110 Antoninianus. E(A). ℞. SAECVLVM NOVVM, temple of six columns,
figure (? Roma) in the centre. *R.I.C.* 90 ..   ..   £30
110a As last, · in ex. *R.I.C.* 90*   30
110b — ·· in ex. *R.I.C.* 90*   30
110c — ··· in ex. *R.I.C.* 90*   30
110d — ···· in ex. *R.I.C.* 90*   30
110e — VI in ex. *R.I.C.* 90*   30
110f — VII in ex. *R.I.C.* 90*   30
110g — ·· below bust. *R.I.C.* 90*   30
110h — ···· below bust. *R.I.C.* 90*   30
110i — · both sides. *R.I.C.* 91*   30
110j — ·· both sides. *R.I.C.* 90*   30
110k — ··· both sides. *R.I.C.* 90*   30
110l — ···· both sides. *R.I.C.* 90*   30
110m — IIV both sides. *R.I.C.* 90*   30
110n — IV both sides. *R.I.C.* 90*   30
110p — VI both sides. *R.I.C.* 90*   30
110q — IV below bust; ····· in ex. *R.I.C.* 90*   32
110r — VI below bust; IIV in ex. *R.I.C.* 90*   32

111   125

111 As **110**, but SAECVLLVM, IV both sides. *R.I.C.* 91*   35
11a — — IIV both sides. *R.I.C.* 91*   35
111b — — VI both sides. *R.I.C.* 91*   35
111c — — · both sides. *R.I.C.* 91*   35
111d — — · both sides. *R.I.C.* 91*   35
111e — — ··· both sides. *R.I.C.* 91*   35
111f — — ·· in ex. only. *R.I.C.* 91*   35
114 C. ℞. SALVS AVGG., Salus stg. r., feeding out of patera a snake held in
her arms. *R.I.C.* 45   35
117 C. ℞. — Salus stg. l., holding sceptre and feeding snake coiled around
altar. *R.I.C.* 46 (a)   30
118 A. ℞. — As last. *R.I.C.* 46 (b)   90
121 C. ℞. SALVS AVGVS., as last. *R.I.C.* 47   35
125 E(A). ℞. VBERITAS AVG., Uberitas stg. l. *R.I.C.* 92   26
125a As last, ·· in ex. *R.I.C.* 92*   26
125b — ··· in ex. *R.I.C.* 92*   26
125c — ···· in ex. *R.I.C.* 92*   26
125d — IIV in ex. *R.I.C.* 92*   26
125e — IV in ex. *R.I.C.* 92*   26
125f — · below bust. *R.I.C.* 92*..   26
125g — ··· below bust. *R.I.C.* 92*   26
125h — ···· below bust. *R.I.C.* 92*   26
125i — · both sides. *R.I.C.* 92* ..   ..   ..   ·   26
125j — ·· both sides. *R.I.C.* 92*   26

125k Antoninianus. E, · · · below bust (A). R. VBERITAS AVG., Uberitas
stg. l., · · · in ex. *R.I.C.* 92* £26
1251 — · · · · both sides. *R.I.C.* 92* 26
125m — IIV both sides. *R.I.C.* 92* 26
125n — IV both sides. *R.I.C.* 92* 26
125p — VI both sides. *R.I.C.* 92* 26
125q — VII both sides. *R.I.C.* 92* 26
125r — · · · · below bust, · · · in ex. *R.I.C.* 92* 28
125s C. R. VBERTAS AVGG., Uberitas l., leaning against column, holding
purse and sceptre (Hy). *R.I.C.* 64 30
125t E(A). R. As **125,** but VDERITAS AVG. *R.I.C.* 92* (*Budapest*) 28
126 E(A). R. VICTORIA AVG., Victory running l. *R.I.C.* 93 24
126a As last, · · below bust. *R.I.C.* 93* 24
126b — · · · below bust. *R.I.C.* 93* 24
126c — · · in ex. *R.I.C.* 93* 24
126d — · · · in ex. *R.I.C.* 93* 24
126e — · · · · in ex. *R.I.C.* 93* 24
126f — IIV in ex. *R.I.C.* 93* 24
126g — IV in ex. *R.I.C.* 93* 24
126h — · both sides. *R.I.C.* 93* 24
126i — · · both sides. *R.I.C.* 93* 24
126j — · · · both sides. *R.I.C.* 93* 24
126k — · · · · both sides. *R.I.C.* 93* 24
1261 — IIV both sides. *R.I.C.* 93* 24
126m — VI both sides. *R.I.C.* 93* 24
126n — VII both sides. *R.I.C.* 93* 24
127 E(A). R. — VICTORIA AVG., Victory walking r. *R.I.C.* 95 35
127a As last, · · · below bust. *R.I.C.* 95* 35
127b As **126,** but Victory stg. r. on globe. *R.I.C.* (49 *B.M.*) 40

128 C. R. VICTORIA AVGG., Victory stg. l. *R.I.C.* 48 (a) 24
129 A. R. — As last. *R.I.C.* 48 (b) 90
131 C. R. VIRTVS AVGG., Virtus stg. r., leaning on shield and holding spear.
R.I.C. 57 (*has* stg. l., *in error ?*) 30
131a C. R. — As last, but with star in field. *R.I.C.* 58 30
132 E(A). R. — As **131.** *R.I.C.* 96 35
133 D(M). R. — As last. *R.I.C.* 76 35
136 C. R. VOTIS / DECENNA / LIBVS within laurel-wreath. *R.I.C.* 49 .. 150

TREBONIANUS GALLUS and VOLUSIAN

6 **Antoninianus.** C. R. IMP . C . C . VIB . VOLVSIANVS AVG., rad. bust of
Volusian dr. and cuir. r. *R.I.C.* 68 *Extremely rare if genuine*
6a **Medallion.** C. R. IMP . CAE . C . VIB . VOLVSIAN . AVG., as last. *R.I.C.*
67 (*Vierordt sale,* 1923) .. .. *Extremely rare if genuine*

VOLUSIAN

A.D. 251-253

Caius Vibius Afinus Gallus Vendumnianus Volusianus was the son of Trebonianus Gallus, who on his succession in 251 A.D., made him Caesar. On the death of Hostilian he was created Augustus and reigned jointly with his father until they were both assassinated.

Obverse legends and types.

As Caesar.

A. c . VIBIO VOLVSIANO CAES.   Radiate bust draped right.

As Augustus.

B. IM . C . AF . GAL . VEND . VOLVSIANO AVG.   *Antioch*
C. IM . C . V . AF . GAL . VEND . VOLVSIANO AVG.   *Antioch*
D. IM . C . V . AF . G . M . VEND . VOLVSIANO AVG.   *Antioch*
E. IMP . CAE . C . VIB . VOLVSIANO AVG.
F. IMP . C . C . VIB . VOLVSIANVS AVG.   *Milan, Antioch*
G. IMP . C . VOLVSIANO AVG.
H. IMP . C . V . AF . GAL . VEND . VOLVSIANO AVG.   *Antioch*
I. IMP . C . V . AF . GAL . VEND . VOLVSIANVS AVG.   *Antioch*
J. IMP . C . V . AF . GAL . VAL . VEND . VOLVSIANVS AVG. *Antioch*
K. IMP . C . V . AF . G . M . VOLVSIANO AVG.   *Antioch*
L. VOLVSIANVS PIVS F . AVG.

Radiate bust draped and cuirassed right on the antoniniani, and on other denominations the same, but laureate.

(A) Put against coins attributed in *R.I.C.* to *Antioch*.
(M) Put against coins attributed in *R.I.C.* to *Milan*.

In *R.I.C.* the numbers run on from Trebonianus Gallus. starting at 129

1 Antoninianus. F(A). R. ADVENTVS AVG., Volusian on horseback l., raising r. hand and holding spear. *R.I.C.* 214		£34
2 B, · · · below bust (A). R. — As last. *R.I.C.* 224 (b)		36
2a As last, but VI below bust. *R.I.C.* 224*		36
2b H, · · · below bust (A). R. — As last. *R.I.C.* 224 (a) (*B.M.*)		36
2c As last, but VI below bust. *R.I.C.* 224*		36
2d B, but VOLVSINO (A). R. As **1.** *R.I.C.* 224 (c) (*Budapest*)		36
4 F(A). R. AEQVITAS AVG., Aequitas stg. l. *R.I.C.* 215		28
4a As last, · · · below bust. *R.I.C.* 215*		28
4b — · · · both sides. *R.I.C.* 215*		28
4c — IV both sides. *R.I.C.* 215*		28
4d — VI both sides. *R.I.C.* 215*		28
5 H(A). R. — As **4**, but · · · · in ex. *R.I.C.* 225		30
5a As last, · · · · each side (A). *R.I.C.* 225*		30
5b As **5**, but · below bust (A). *R.I.C.* 225*		30
8 E. R. AEQVITAS AVGG., as **4.** *R.I.C.* 166		26
8a As **4a**, but AEQVTAS (*sic.*) AVG. *R.I.C.* 215* (*Vienna*)		30

8   25

12 Antoninianus. *Obv.* ? R. ANNONA AVGG., Annona stg. .. ..

14 E. R. APOLL . SALVTARI, Apollo, naked, stg. l., resting elbow on lyre placed on rock. *R.I.C.* 188 .. .. £30

20 E. R. CONCORDIA AVGG., Concordia stg. half-left, her cornucopiae double. *R.I.C.* 167 24

25 — R. — As last, but Concordia seated l. *R.I.C.* 168 (*Illus. on p.* 41) .. 24

25a As last, but with star in *rev.* field. *R.I.C.* 169 26

29 E. R. — Concordia seated l. before altar. *R.I.C.* 170 35

29a F(M). R. CONCOR . MIL., Concordia stg. l., holding two standards (Hy. ?; *rev. of Valerian I*). *R.I.C.* 213 (*Trau sale*) .. ..

30 E. R. DACIA, Dacia stg. l., holding standard (Hy.; *plated; rev. of Decius*). *R.I.C.* 198 .. ..

30a F(A). R. FELICITAS AVG., Felicitas stg. l., · in ex. *R.I.C.* 216 (*B.M.*) .. 28

30b As last, · · below bust and in ex. *R.I.C.* 216* (*B.M.*) 28

31 A. R. FELIC . PVBL., as **30a**. *R.I.C.* 135.. 100

32 F(M). R. FELICITAS PVBL., as last. *R.I.C.* 205 24

32a F(A). R. — As last. *R.I.C.* 217 26

32b As last, but · · each side. *R.I.C.* 217* 26

33a Quinarius. G. R. FELICITAS PVBLICA, as **30a**. *R.I.C.* 165 (*Trau sale*) 300

34 Antoninianus. E. R. — Felicitas stg. l., leaning against column. *R.I.C.* 188A (*A heavy coin; Cohen describes as* double ant., *and R.I.C. as just a* heavy ant.) 50

37a E. R. IOVI CONSERVAT., Jupiter stg. l. (Hy.; *rev. of Philip II*). *R.I.C.* 197 (*Trau sale*) 35

39 43

38 F(M). R. IVNO MARTIALIS, Juno seated l., holding ears of corn and sceptre. *R.I.C.* 209 30

38a F, · below bust (A). R. — As last, · in ex. *R.I.C.* 218* 30

38b As last, but · · · both sides. *R.I.C.* 218* 30

38c — but VII both sides. *R.I.C.* 218* 30

39 E. R. IVNONI MARTIALI, as **38,** but globe for sceptre. *R.I.C.* 177 .. 35

39a A. R. — As last. *R.I.C.* 132 (*Vienna*) 120

40a E. R. — Juno seated facing in round tetrastyle temple, peacock at her feet. *R.I.C.* 175 (*Dorchester hoard*) 85

40b As last, but star in *rev.* field. *R.I.C.* 176 85

43 As **40a,** but distyle temple, no peacock. *R.I.C.* 172 60

44 As last, but with peacock. *R.I.C.* 171 65

45 As **43,** but star in *rev.* field. *R.I.C.* 173 70

47 A. R. — As **44.** *R.I.C.* 131 120

48 E. R. — Juno seated between two children, in round distyle temple. *R.I.C.* 174 95

48a As last, with intermediate objects which may be more children. *R.I.C.* 174* (*B.M., ex Dorchester*) 95

49	**Antoninianus.** E. ℞. LIBERALITAS AVGG., Liberalitas stg. l. *R.I.C.* 178..	£45
52	C (*Cohen*) or H (*R.I.C.*) (A). ℞. LIBERTAS AVG., Libertas stg. l., holding pileus and cornucopiae. *R.I.C.* 226 (AVGG., *in error ?*)	45
55	E. ℞. LIBERTAS AVGG., Libertas stg. l., holding pileus and sceptre. *R.I.C.* 189	30
58	E. ℞. — As last, but she has her legs crossed and leans against column. *R.I.C.* 190	30
59	F(M). ℞. LIBERTAS PVBLICA, as **55.** *R.I.C.* 210	30
60	F(A). ℞. MARTEM PROPVGNATOREM, Mars walking r., holding spear and shield. *R.I.C.* 219	30
61	H(A). ℞. MARTI PACIFERO, Mars running l., holding laurel-branch and spear. *R.I.C.* 228	35
61a	As last, but VII below bust and in ex. *R.I.C.* 228*	35
61b	F(A). ℞. — As **61.** *R.I.C.* 220	32
63	**Medallion.** E. ℞. MONETA AVGG., the three Monetae stg. l. *R.I.C.* 164	
		Extremely rare
65	**Antoninianus.** E. ℞. PACI AVG., Pax stg. l., legs crossed, leaning against column (Hy.; *rev. of Aemilian*). *R.I.C.* 200	30
66	F(M). ℞. PAX AETERNA, Pax stg. l. *R.I.C.* 211	28
67	E. ℞. — As last. *R.I.C.* 195	28
68	H, ·· below bust (A). ℞. PAX AVG., as last. *R.I.C.* 229	30
70	E. ℞. PAX AVGG., as **66.** *R.I.C.* 179	24
71	As last, but star in *rev.* field. *R.I.C.* 180	26
72	F(M). ℞. — As **66.** *R.I.C.* 207	28
73	A. ℞. — As last. *R.I.C.* 133	100
77	E. ℞. PAX AVGVS., as last. *R.I.C.* 181	45
78	H(A). ℞. — As last, with ·· in ex. *R.I.C.* 230 (a)	28
78a	H, · below bust (A). ℞. — As **77.** *R.I.C.* 230 (a)*	28
78b	As last, but ···· below bust. *R.I.* 230 (a)*	28
78c	— · each side. *R.I.C.* 230 (a)*	28
78d	— ·· each side. *R.I.C.* 230 (a)*	28
78e	— ··· each side. *R.I.C.* 230 (a)*	28
78f	— ···· each side. *R.I.C.* 230 (a)*	28
78g	— ·· below bust; · in ex. *R.I.C.* 230 (a)*	30
79	I(A). ℞. — As **78.** *R.I.C.* 230 (b)	30
80	J(A). ℞. — As last, but with s c in field. *R.I.C.* 231 (a) (*mintmarks uncertain*)	50
80a	J(?), ···· below bust (A). ℞. — As last. *R.I.C.* 231 (a) (*Vienna*) ..	50
81	K(A). ℞. — As last. *R.I.C.* 231 (b) (*mintmarks uncertain*)	50
81a	H, ···· below bust (A). ℞. — As **80,** but reads AVGΛS. *R.I.C.* 231 (c) (*Budapest*)	50
85	E. ℞. PIETAS AVGG., Pietas, veiled, stg. l., raising both hands. *R.I.C.* 191	28
85a	As last, but with star in *rev.* field. *R.I.C.* 192 (*B.M., ex Dorchester*) ..	30
86	F(M). ℞. — As last. *R.I.C.* 212	30
88	E. ℞. — As **85,** but she stands before altar. *R.I.C.* 182	24
91	? ℞. P . M . TR . P . IIII COS . II, Felicitas stg.	
92	E. ℞. — Emperor stg. l., holding branch and short transverse sceptre. *R.I.C.* 140	26
94	E. ℞. — Emperor stg. l., sacrificing over lighted tripod and holding short sceptre. *R.I.C.* 141. *Illustrated at top of p.* 44	26
95	As last, but of heavy weight (5.5 gm.) *R.I.C.* 141	45

94   100

97a Antoninianus. E. ℞. PRINCIPI IVVENTVTIS, Apollo seated l., leaning against lyre (Hy.; *rev. of Her. Etr. or Hostilian*). *R.I.C.* 199 (*De Quelen sale*) £30

100 A. ℞. — Volusian stg. l., holding wand and reversed spear. *R.I.C.* 134   100

101 E. ℞. — As last. *R.I.C.* 183 40

106 E. ℞. PROVID . AVGG., Providentia (Hy. ?). *R.I.C.* 201 .. ..

107 E. ℞. PROVIDENT . AVG., Providentia stg. l., leaning on spear or sceptre and holding wand (Hy.). *R.I.C.* 202 28

108 E. ℞. PROVIDENTIA AVGG., Providentia stg. l., holding globe and sceptre. *R.I.C.* 193 30

109 E. ℞. — Providentia seated l., holding corn-ears (Hy.). *R.I.C.* 203

109a E. ℞. PVDICITIA AVG., Pudicitia r., raising veil (Hy.). *R.I.C.* 204

109b H(A). ℞. — As last, but Pudicitia seated l. *R.I.C.* 232 (*De Quelen sale*)

110 D, *but* C . M. (*sic*) *given by Cohen* (A). ℞. PVDICITIA AVGG., as last. *R.I.C.* 233 (b) (*gives* G . M.) 35

110a H, · below bust (A). ℞. — As last. *R.I.C.* 233 (a) 35

110b As last, but · · · below bust. *R.I.C.* 233 (a)* 35

110c — but · · · also in ex. *R.I.C.* 233 (a)* 35

111 A. ℞. ROMAE AETERNAE, Roma seated l. on shield, holding Victory and spear (Hy.; *rev. of Philip I*). *R.I.C.* 137 110

112 E. ℞. — As last (Hy.). *R.I.C.* 196 30

113 F(A). ℞. ROMAE AETERNAE AVG., as last. *R.I.C.* 221 28

113a As last, but · · each side. *R.I.C.* 221* 28

113b — · · · below bust and · · in ex. *R.I.C.* 221* 28

114 H, · · below bust (A). ℞. — As **113.** *R.I.C.* 234 (a) 30

114a As last, but VII below bust. 30

114b I, but ends VOLVSSIANVS IV (A). ℞. As **113,** but IV in ex. *R.I.C.* 234 (b) 30

114c C, · · below bust (A). ℞. — As last, but VI in ex. *R.I.C.* 234 (c).. .. 30

114d As last, but IV below bust and vi in ex. *R.I.C.* 234 (c)* 30

114e H, with · · below bust (A). ℞. SAECVLLVM NOVVM, as **115;** · · in ex. *R.I.C.* 236 (a) (*Vienna*) 40

114f I, with IV below bust. ℞. — As **115;** IV in ex. *R.I.C.* 236 (b) (*Lawrence*) 40

115 H(A). ℞. SAECVLVM NOVVM, statue of Roma (?) in centre of six-column temple. *R.I.C.* 235 35

115a As last, but · below bust. *R.I.C.* 235* 35

115b — · · below bust. *R.I.C.* 235* 35

115c — · · · below bust. *R.I.C.* 235* 35

115d — · · · · below bust. *R.I.C.* 235* 35

115e — VII below bust. *R.I.C.* 235* 35

115f — · both sides. *R.I.C.* 235* 35

115g — · · both sides. *R.I.C.* 235* 35

115h — · · · both sides. *R.I.C.* 235* 35

115i — VI both sides. *R.I.C.* 235* 35

115j — VII both sides. *R.I.C.* 235* 35

116 F(A). ℞. — As **115.** *R.I.C.* 222 35

118   135

118 **Antoninianus.** E. ℞. SALVS AVGG., Salus stg. r., feeding, out of patera,
     snake held in arms. *R.I.C.* 184   ..   ..   £26
118a F(M). ℞. — As last. *R.I.C.* 208 (*B.M.*, *ex Dorchester*)   30
119 **Quinarius.** G. ℞. — As last. *R.I.C.* 208B (top of p. 182) (*B.M.*) ..   300
119a **Antoninianus.** L. ℞. — As next. *R.I.C.* 185A (*Ratto sale*, 1928) ..   90
122 E. ℞. SALVS AVGVS., Salus stg. l., holding sceptre and feeding snake coiled
     around altar. *R.I.C.* 185   40
123 A (*Cohen has* VIB. *for* VIBIO, *in error ?*). ℞. SECVRITAS AVG., Securitas
     stg. r., legs crossed, leaning against column, r. hand to head. *R.I.C.* 136   100
125 H, · · · · below bust (A). ℞. VBERITAS AVG., Uberitas stg. l.; · · · · in ex.
     R.I.C. 237 (a)   30
125a As last, but VII both sides. *R.I.C.* 237 (a)   30
125b — but · both sides. *R.I.C.* 237 (a)*   30
125c — but · · both sides. *R.I.C.* 237 (a)*   30
125d — but · · · both sides. *R.I.C.* 237 (a)*   30
125e — but VI both sides. *R.I.C.* 237 (a)*   30
125f — but · · · below bust only. *R.I.C.* 237 (a)*   30
125g H or I, with IV both sides (A). *R.I.C.* 239 (b) (*Budapest*)..   32
125h I, but VOLVSSIANVS, and IV both sides (A). *R.I.C.* 237 (c) (*Budapest*) ..   32
126 H(A). ℞. VICTORIA AVG., Victory stg. r. on globe. *R.I.C.* 239 (a)   ..   32
126a As last, but VII in ex. *R.I.C.* 239 (a)*   32
126b As **126,** with · below bust. *R.I.C.* 239 (a)*   32
126c — with · · below bust. *R.I.C.* 239 (a)*   32
126d — with · · · · below bust. *R.I.C.* 239 (a)*..   32
126e I(A). As **126a,** · · · in ex. *R.I.C.* 239 (b)   34
127 H(A). ℞. — Victory advancing l. *R.I.C.* 238   30
127a As last, but · · in ex.   30
127b — but · · both sides. *R.I.C.* 238*   30
127c — but VI both sides. *R.I.C.* 238*   30
127d — but · below bust only. *R.I.C.* 238*   30
127e — but VII below bust only. *R.I.C.* 238*   30
128 E, but C . C. ℞. — Victory running r.   ..   ..
128a F, · · · · below bust (A). ℞ — As last, but running l., · · · · in ex. *R.I.C.*
     222A (*Budapest*)   32
129 F(A). ℞. VICTORIA AVGG., as last, but Victory advancing r. *R.I.C.* 223 ..   30
131 E. ℞. — As before, but Victory stg. l. *R.I.C.* 194   30
133 F(M). ℞. VIRTVS AVGG., Virtus stg. r., leaning on shield and holding
     spear. *R.I.C.* 206   24
133a **Quinarius.** F(M)?. ℞. — As last. *R.I.C.* 208A (top of p. 182) (*Trau*)   325
135 **Antoninianus.** E. ℞. — As before, but Virtus l. *R.I.C.* 186   ..   26
135a E. ℞. — As last, but star in field. *R.I.C.* 187   26
139 *Obv. ?* ℞. VOTIS DECENNALIBVS in laurel-wreath.   ..   ..   ..

AEMILIAN

A.D. 253

M. Aemilius Aemilianus, a native of Mauretania, born about 206, was governor of Pannonia and Moesia in the reign of Gallus. Having successfully repulsed a barbarian invasion of his province, he was proclaimed Augustus by his troops, and in a subsequent advance on Rome, he defeated Gallus. Aemilian was acknowledged emperor by the Senate, but after a short reign of three or four months he was murdered by his own soldiers, near Spoletum, when he had left Rome to defend his throne against Valerian who had invaded Italy.

Obverse legends and types.

A.   IMP . AEMILIANVS PIVS FEL . AVG.

B.   IMP . CAES . AEMILIANVS P . F . AVG.

C.   IMP . M . AEMIL . AEMILIANVS P . F . AVG.

Radiate bust draped and cuirassed right.   Most of his coins were struck at Rome.

(U)   Against a few pieces attributed by *R.I.C.* to an uncertain mint, probably in the Balkans.

2   10

2   **Antoninianus.** A. ℞. APOL . CONSERVAT., Apollo, naked, stg. half-left, holding branch and with l. hand on lyre set on ground or a rock.   *R.I.C.* 1   £130

5   B. ℞. APOLL . CONSERVAT., as last.   *R.I.C.* p. 196 (*genuine ?*) ..   ..

6   As **2**, but Apollo seated l.   *R.I.C.* 1* (*confirmation required*)

6a   As **5**, but Apollo seated l.   *R.I.C.* 1* (*Bachofen von Echt*) ..   ..   ..

6b   B. ℞. APOL . CONSERVAT, Diana stg. l., holding bow and arrow.   *R.I.C.* p. 196, no. 1 note (*Baranowsky sale*, 1931; *curious hybrid*) ..   ..   ..

6c   A. ℞. APOLL . SALVTARI, Apollo stg. l., resting elbow on lyre set on rock (Hy.; *rev. of Gallus*).   *R.I.C.* 27

8   B, but PIVS for P. ℞. CONCORDIA AVG., two r. hands clasped (Hy. ?). *R.I.C.* 28 (*unusual and uncertain*) ..   ..

10   A. ℞. DIANAE VICTRI., Diana as **6b**.   *R.I.C.* 2 (b)   140

11   B (*Cohen omits* P . F., *in error ?*). ℞. — As last.   *R.I.C.* p. 196, no. 2   140

11a   As **10**, but DIANE VICTRI.   *R.I.C.* 2 (b)* (*Berlin*)   140

13   A. ℞. ERCVL . VICTORI, Hercules stg. half-right, holding bow and resting r. hand on club; lion's skin over l. arm.   *R.I.C.* 3 (b)   130

13a   B. ℞. — As last.   *R.I.C.*, p. 196, no. 3 (*Vierordt sale*)   130

16   A. ℞. IOVI CONSERVAT, Jupiter, naked with hanging cloak, stg. l., but extending r. arm over Aemilian stg. beside him.   *R.I.C.* 4   130

17   B. ℞. — As last.   *R.I.C.* 14   130

19   ? ℞. — Jupiter presenting globe to emperor   ..   ..

22   A. ℞. MARTI PACIF., Mars walking l., holding branch, shield and spear. *R.I.C.* 5 (b)   120

23   B. ℞. — As last.   *R.I.C.* 15   120

23a   A. ℞. MARTI PACIL., as last.   (*Clive Dennett*)   120

24   Specimens of the last of heavy weight (5·4 and 5·7 gms.).   *R.I.C.* 15* ..   200

25   A. ℞. MARTI PROPVGT., Mars stg. l., leaning on shield and holding reversed spear.   *R.I.C.* 6   120

26 Antoninianus. A. ℞. PACI AVG., Pax stg. l., legs crossed and leaning on column. *R.I.C.* 8 .. .. £120
26a B. ℞. — As last. *R.I.C.* 19 (*B.M.*) 130
31 C(U). ℞. PAXS AVG., Pax running l. *R.I.C.* 23 250
32 A. ℞. P . M . TR . P . I P . P., Aemilian, in military dress, stg. l. sacrificing out of patera over tripod; on l., standard. *R.I.C.* 7 130
32a As last, but no tripod. *R.I.C.* 7A (*O.U.C.*).. 140
33 B. ℞. — As **32**. *R.I.C.* 16 140
33a B. ℞. — As last, but standard between the emperor and the tripod. *R.I.C.* 18 140
34 B. ℞. — As **32**, but without tripod. *R.I.C.* 17 140
35 A. ℞. P . M . TR . P . I P . P . C., as **33a**. *R.I.C.* 7* (*requires confirmation*)

32   41

41 A. ℞. ROMAE AETERN., Roma stg. l., holding phoenix on globe and spear; at her side, shield. *R.I.C.* 9 130
45 IMP . AEMILIANVS P . AVG. ℞. SALVS AVG., Salus stg. feeding snake, holding spear or sceptre (Hy. ?). *R.I.C.* 29 (*uncertain*) .. ..

47 A. ℞. SPES PVBLICA, Spes walking l. *R.I.C.* 10 120
48 B. ℞. — As last. *R.I.C.* 20 120
52 B. ℞. VICTORIA AVG., Victory advancing l. *R.I.C.* 21 120
53 A. ℞. — As last. *R.I.C.* 11 120
There is a Becker die as last but Victory stg. l.
57a C(U). ℞. — As last. *R.I.C.* 24 (*Budapest*) 250
58 C(U). ℞. — Nemesis, winged, stg. l., wheel at her feet. *R.I.C.* 25 .. 250

59 B. ℞. VIRTVS AVG., Virtus stg. l., foot on helmet, holding branch and spear. *R.I.C.* 22 120
60 A. ℞. — As last. *R.I.C.* 12 120
63 C(U). ℞. — Hercules stg. l., leaning on club, holding bow and lion's skin. *R.I.C.* 26 250
63a As last, but Hercules stg. r. (*British Museum*) 250
64 A. ℞. VOTIS DECENNALIBVS in laurel-wreath. *R.I.C.* 13 200

CORNELIA SUPERA

Completely unknown to history, but from the evidence of her coins she was probably the wife of Aemilian.

Obverse legends and type.

A.   C . CORNEL . SVPERA AVG.
B.   CORNEL . SVPERA AVG.
C.   COR . SVPERA AVG.
Diademed bust draped right on crescent.
Nos. in *R.I.C.* follow on from Aemilian.
(U)   Indicates uncertain mint, probably in the Balkans.

1   A.   R.   CONCORDIA AVGG., Concordia seated.   *R.I.C.* 32 *(confirmation required)*   ..   ..

1a   C.   R.   — Emperor and empress clasping r. hands.   *R.I.C.* 33 *(confirmation required)*   ..   ..

2   A.   R.   IVNO REGINA, Juno stg. l., peacock at her feet.   *R.I.C.* 34 *(Very doubtful. There is a Becker forgery)* ..   ..

3   5

3   C(U).   R.   IVNONI AVG., Juno seated l., holding flower and child in swaddling clothes.   *R.I.C.* 31 *(B.M.)* £3,500

4   B.   R.   VENVS VICTRIX, Venus stg. *(plated; anc. forgery).*   *R.I.C.* 35   ..

5   A.   R.   VESTA, Vesta stg. l.   *R.I.C.* 30   3,000

6   As last *(plated or Æ).*   *R.I.C.* 30*   ..   ..

7   A.   R.   — Vesta seated l., holding palladium and transverse sceptre. *R.I.C.* 31 *(confirmation required)*   ..   ..

VALUE OF THE COINS HEREAFTER

The values given here are for billon or silver-washed coins in average state. Really good silver pieces or silver-washed looking like silver coins are all worth more; whereas, all that are just Æ are worth very considerably less.

VALERIAN I or SENIOR

A.D. 253-260

P. Licinius Valerianus, descended from a good Roman family, held various offices in the service of the state until, in the reign of Trajan Decius, he was appointed Censor. Later he was sent by Trebonianus Gallus to put down the rebellion of Aemilian. Solely on account of his merits he was unanimously elected emperor on the death of Gallus and on the murder of Aemilian was left undisputed master of the empire. Almost at once on assuming the purple he associated with himself his son, Gallienus, with the title Augustus.

The reign of Valerian was marked by many frontier troubles, during which the Persians, under Sapor, invaded the Eastern provinces and entered Antioch. In 257 Valerian re-took Antioch and made it his base for further successes against the Persians. In 260, as he was advancing through Mesopotamia, his army was surrounded by the Persians and destroyed, and he was taken prisoner. He spent the remainder of his life in captivity in Persia.

Towards the end of their joint reign, the silver content of the antoninianus, already very low, was so drastically reduced, that the appearance of the coins was that of mere bronze. It was therefore necessary to coat them with a white metal to indicate that they represented silver. This wash was very thin and in most cases very soon disappeared.

Obverse legends.

A. IMP . CAES . P . LIC . VALERIANVS AVG.
B. IMP . C . P . LIC . VALERIANO AVG
C. IMP . C . P . LIC . VALERIANVS AVG.
D. IMP . C . P . LIC . VALERIANVS P . AVG.
E. IMP . C . P . LIC . VALERIANVS P . F . AVG.
F. IMP . C . VALERIANVS P . F . AVG.
G. IMP . P . LIC . VALERIANO AVG.
H. IMP . VALERIANVS AVG.
J. IMP . VALERIANVS P . AVG.
K. IMP . VALERIANVS P . F . AVG.
L. IMP . VALERIANVS PIVS AVG.
M. IMP . VALERIANVS PIVS FEL . AVG.
N. VALERIANVS P . F . AVG.

Obverse types.

a. Radiate bust draped right.
b. Laureate bust draped right.
c. Radiate bust draped and cuirassed right.
d. Laureate bust draped and cuirassed right.
e. Laureate bust cuirassed right.
f. Radiate bust cuirassed right.
g. Radiate bust cuirassed **left.**
h. Laureate head right.

Mints as attributed by *R.I.C.*

(L) Lugdunum (*R.I.C.* nos. 4-25).
(V) Moesia-Viminacum (*R.I.C.*, nos. 209-227).
(M) Mediolanum (*R.I.C.*, nos. 231-271).
(A) Asia-Antioch (*R.I.C.*, nos. 277-296).
Other pieces are attributed to Rome (*R.I.C.*, nos. 57-150).

1 **Medallion.** Ed. ℞. ADLOCVTIO AVGVSTORVM, Valerian, Gallienus and praetorian prefect stg. r. on platform, addressing four soldiers, carrying three standards and two shields. *R.I.C.* 57 (diam. 35 mm., wt. 25 gms.)
Great rarity

3 **Antoninianus.** Ca (V and A). ℞. AEQVITAS AVGG., Aequitas stg. l. *R.I.C.* 209 and 278 .. .. £12

3a Ea(A). ℞. — As last. *R.I.C.* 279 (*Voetter*) 16

5 **Medallion.** Ee. ℞. — The three Monetae stg. l.; at the feet of each, a pile of metal. *R.I.C.* 58 (*cannot now be found*) .. ..

5a Fe. ℞. — As last. *R.I.C.* 59 (*stolen from the Vatican in* 1797) .. ..

7 **Antoninianus.** Cf. ℞. AETERNITAS AVGG., Valerian, radiate, walking r., holding globe and raising r. hand. *R.I.C.* 66 18

8 Ca(V). ℞. AETERNITATI AVGG., Saturn, veiled, stg. r., holding scythe. *R.I.C.* 210 25

8a Ca. ℞. — As last, but holding sceptre. *R.I.C.* 67 (*Paris*) 22

9 Ea(V). ℞. — Sol stg. l., holding globe, raising r. hand. *R.I.C.* 211 .. 12

10 Ja(M). ℞. — As last. *R.I.C.* 232 12

13 Ea. ℞. ANNONA AVGG., Abundantia stg. l.; before, modius. *R.I.C.* 69 .. 12

14 Ca. ℞. — As last. *R.I.C.* 68 12

15 Ha. ℞. — As last. *R.I.C.* 70 12

13   25

17 Ea and/or c. ℞. APOLINI CONSERVA(T)., Apollo, naked, stg. l., leaning on lyre placed on rock. *R.I.C.* 72 12

18 Ca. ℞. — As last. *R.I.C.* 71 12

19 Fa. ℞. — As last .. ..

20 Ea and/or c. ℞. — As last, but without rock. *R.I.C.* 72 12

21 Fa. ℞. — As last .. ..

24 Ec. ℞. APOLLINI CONSERVA., as **17,** but Apollo clothed. *R.I.C.* 73 .. 12

25 Ca. ℞. APOLINI PROPVG., Apollo, half-naked, mantle flowing, stg. r., drawing bow. *R.I.C.* 74 14

25a Ce. ℞. — As last. *R.I.C.* 74 14

25b Ca and/or Ce and perhaps Ea. ℞. As before, but PROPVGN. *R.I.C.* 74/5 16

26 Ea. ℞. — As last. *R.I.C.* 75 14

28 Ea. ℞. APOLL. SALVTARI, as **17.** *R.I.C.* 76 15

29 Ca. ℞. BONAE FORTVNAE, Fortuna stg. l. *R.I.C.* 77 25

30 Ea. ℞. BONVS EVENT . AVG., Genius, naked, stg. by altar, holding corn-ears and patera. *R.I.C.* 78 25

31 Ca. ℞. CONCORDIA AVGG., Concordia stg. l., holding patera and double cornucopiae. *R.I.C.* 80 12

32 Ea. ℞. — As last, but Concordia seated l. *R.I.C.* 79 12

33 Ca(A). ℞. — Valerian and Gallienus stg. face to face, clasping hands. *R.I.C.* 280 30

34 Ea(A). ℞. — As last. *R.I.C.* 281 30

36 Antoninianus. Ja(M). ℞. CONCOR . EXERC., Concordia stg. l., sacrificing
at altar, holding cornucopiae. *R.I.C.* 233 .. .. £12

37 Ja(M). ℞. CONCORDIA EXERCIT., as last. *R.I.C.* 234 12

38 Ea. ℞. — As **31.** *R.I.C.* 82 12

39 Ca. ℞. — As last. *R.I.C.* 81 12

42 Ja(M). ℞. CONCORDIA EXERCITI, as **36.** *R.I.C.* 234 12

43 As last, but CONCORDIAE. *R.I.C.* 235 15

44 Ja(M). ℞. CONCOR . LEGG., as **32.** *R.I.C.* 236 20

45 Ja(M). ℞. CONCOR . MIL., Concordia stg. half-left, holding two military
ensigns. *R.I.C.* 237 (*has rev. type as* **31**) 14

46 Ja(M). ℞. CONCORDIA MILIT., as last. *R.I.C.* 239 14

47 Ca or perphaps c (M). ℞. — As last. *R.I.C.* 238 14

47a (Cohen, p. 541 note) Na(L). ℞. CONSACRATIO, eagle bearing emperor
to heaven. *R.I.C.* 4 35

48 Ha. ℞. CONSERVAT . AVGG., Apollo, naked, stg. l., holding laurel-branch
and leaning on lyre placed on a rock; Q in field or ex. *R.I.C.* 84 .. 14

48a As last, but CONSERVT. *R.I.C.* 84 14

49 Ea. ℞. As **48.** *R.I.C.* 83 14

49a Ea. ℞. As **48a.** *R.I.C.* 83 14

47   65

50 Ea. ℞. CONSERVAT . AVGG., Apollo as above; beside him, Diana stg. l.,
drawing arrow out of quiver and holding bow. *R.I.C.* 85 30

50a Ec. ℞. — As last. *R.I.C.* 85 30

50b Ea and/or c. ℞. — As last, with Q in ex. *R.I.C.* 85 30

50c (Cohen, Valerian Junior 2) Na(L). ℞. DEO VOLKANO, Vulcan stg. l. by
anvil in temple of four columns, holding hammer and pincers. *R.I.C.* 5 25

50d (Cohen, Valerian Junior 3) As last, but no anvil. *R.I.C.* 5 25

51 Ca(V). ℞. DIANA LVCIFERA, Diana stg. r., holding torch in both hands.
R.I.C. 212 25

53 Ea. ℞. FELICITAS AVGG., Felicitas stg. l. *R.I.C.* 87 12

54 Da. ℞. — As last. *R.I.C.* 88 12

55 Ca. ℞. — As last. *R.I.C.* 86 12

56 Ha and/or c (A). ℞. — As last. *R.I.C.* 283 12

57 Ka and/or c (A). ℞. — As last. *R.I.C.* 282 12

61 Ca(V). ℞. FELICITAS SAECVLI, Diana, crescent on head, stg. or walking r.,
scarf floating, holding torch in both hands. *R.I.C.* 213 16

65 Ca. ℞. FIDES MILITVM, Fides stg. front, looking l., holding two military
ensigns. *R.I.C.* 89 12

65a Ca(L). ℞. — As last. *R.I.C.* 6 16

66 As last, but of heavy weight (7·32 gms.; *classed by Cohen as* double
antoninianus). *R.I.C.* 6 35

68 Ea. ℞. — As **65.** *R.I.C.* 90 12

71 Antoninianus. Ja(M). R. FIDES MILITVM, Fides stg. r., holding standard and transverse ensign. *R.I.C.* 241 (stg. l., *in error ?*) £12
72 Ca. R. — As last .. ..
73 Ba(M). R. — As last. *R.I.C.* 240 15
74 Ga(M). R. — As last. *R.I.C.* 240 15
75 Ca(V). R. FORTVNA REDVX, Mercury stg. half-left, naked, holding purse and caduceus, mantle over arm. *R.I.C.* 214 30
76 Ha. R. — Fortuna stg. l. *R.I.C.* 91 12
76a As last, but with P, S or Q in field. *R.I.C.* 91 note 12
76b Ha(M). R. — As **76.** *R.I.C.* 242 12
77 La(L). R. GALLIENVS CVM EXERC . SVO, Jupiter, naked, stg. facing on a cippus on which IOVI VICTORI in three lines; he holds Victory and sceptre. *R.I.C.* 7 .. ..
78 Ha(L). R. — As last. *R.I.C.* 8 40
79 Ha(L). R. GERMANICVS MAX . TER., trophy between two seated captives. *R.I.C.* 9 40
79a Da(L). R. — As last. *R.I.C.* 9a (*Vienna*) 35
                                                                          35

92

93

81 Ha. R. IOVI CONSERVA., Jupiter stg. l. *R.I.C.* 94 12
83 Ca and/or c. R. — As last. *R.I.C.* 92 12
83a Ea. R. — As last. (*Dorchester*) 16
85 Ca and/or c. R. IOVI CONSERVAT., as last. *R.I.C.* 92 12
86 Ea and/or c. R. — As last, with Q or S in field 14
86a As last, but without the mintmarks. *R.I.C.* 93 14
87 Ka(A ?). R. — As **86** .. ..
88 Ha. R. IOVI CONSERVAT., as last 15
89 Ea. R. — As **86a** .. ..
90 **Quinarius.** Eb. R. IOVI CONSERVAT., as **81.** *R.I.C.* 146 125
92 **Denarius.** Cb. R. IOVI CONSERVATORI, as last. *R.I.C.* 143 150
93 **Quinarius.** As last. *R.I.C.* 147 125
94 **Antoninianus.** Ca and/or b. R. — As last. *R.I.C.* 92 12
99 Ea. R. IOVI STATORI, as last. *R.I.C.* 95 22
99a Ea. R. IVNO REGINA, Juno stg. l. (Hy. ?; *rev. of Salonina*). *R.I.C.* 96 16
101 Ca(V). R. LAETITIA AVGG., Laetitia stg. l. *R.I.C.* 215 12
101a Ca. R. — As last. *R.I.C.* 97 .. ..

102 Ea(V). R. — As last. *R.I.C.* 216 12
103 Ea(V). R. — Laetitia stg. r. *R.I.C.* 217 12

103a Antoninianus. Ea. ℞. LERIGIO AVGG., Diana stg. l., drawing arrow and
holding bow. *R.I.C.* 114 .. .. £35
105 (and **109**). Ca. ℞. LIBERALITAS AVGG., Liberalitas stg. l. *R.I.C.* 98 .. 12
106 Ja(M). ℞. — As last. *R.I.C.* 243 12
107 Da. ℞. — As last. *R.I.C.* 100 12
108 Ea. ℞. — As last. *R.I.C.* 99 12
109 Is a repeat of **105**
113 Ea. ℞. — Liberalitas seated l. *R.I.C.* 101 20
114 Ea. ℞. — As last, but Liberalitas (*Cohen*, Concordia) holding patera.
R.I.C. 101 20
115 Ea. ℞. — Valerian and Gallienus seated l. on curule chairs on platform;
behind them stands praefect. *R.I.C.* 102 35
116 Ea. ℞. LIBERALITAS AVGG . II, as **105**. *R.I.C.* 103 14
119 Ea. ℞. LIBERALITAS AVG. III, as last. *R.I.C.* 104 18
120 Ca. ℞. — As last .. ..
124a Ea and/or c. ℞. — As **115**. *R.I.C.* 105 35
125a Jb(?)(M). ℞. MARTI PACIFERO, Mars walking l., holding olive-branch
and spear. *R.I.C.* 244 (*Voetter*) (*obv. type* "b" *seems curious for an
antoninianus, perhaps an error for* "a" *or* "c") .. .. ..
126 Medallion. Ce. ℞. MONETA AVGG., the three Monetae stg. l.; at the
feet of each, a pile of metal (diam. 32 mm.). *R.I.C.* 60 .. .. *Very rare*
127 Cd. ℞. — As last (diam. 32 mm.). *R.I.C.* 60 .. .. .. *Very rare*
127a As last (diam. 27 mm.). *R.I.C.* 60 .. .. *Very rare*
128 Ed. ℞. — As last (diam 30 mm.). *R.I.C.* 61 .. .. *Very rare*
129 Ed. but bust to **left.** ℞. — As last (diam. 32 mm.) .. .. *Very rare*
130 Cd, but bust to **left.** ℞. — As last (diam. 30 mm.) .. .. *Very rare*
N.B.—*R.I.C.* 60 *gives sizes 36 to 30 mm., but does not indicate which are
obv. type* "d" *or* "e". *They have apparently not noticed that Cohen* 129 *and*
130 *is given with bust to left. R.I.C.* 61 *gives size 32 mm.; and R.I.C.* 63—
29 *and* 28 *mm.*
131 He. ℞. — As before (diam. 27 mm. or 28 mm.). *R.I.C.* 63 .. *Very rare*
131a Ed, but seen to waist and holding Victory on globe. ℞. — As last
(diam. 34 mm.). *R.I.C.* 62 (*Gnecchi*) .. .. .. *Extremely rare*
131b Ae. ℞. — As last (diam. 34 or 33 mm.). *R.I.C.* 64 (*Gnecchi*) .. *Extremely rare*
134 Denarius. Eb. ℞. ORIENS AVGG., Sol stg. l., holding whip and raising
r. hand. *R.I.C.* 144 150

119   135

135 Antoninianus. Ea. ℞. — As last. *R.I.C.* 106(?) 16
136 Quinarius. Cb. ℞. — As last. *R.I.C.* 148 125
140 Antoninianus. Ea. ℞. — Sol stg. facing, head l., holding globe and
raising r. hand. *R.I.C.* 106 14
140a As last, but *rev.* legend is retrograde 15
140b (Cohen, Valerian Junior 5) Na and/or c (L). ℞. — As last. *R.I.C.* 13
(walking l., *in error ?*) 16
141 Ha. ℞. — As **140**. *R.I.C.* 107 .. ..

142 **Antoninianus.** Ha. ℞. ORIENS AVGG, Sol walking l., mantle flowing, holding whip and raising r. hand. *R.I.C.* 107 .. .. £14
142a Ha(L). ℞. — As last. *R.I.C.* 11 14
143 Ja(L). ℞. — As last. *R.I.C.* 10 14
143a **(Cohen, Valerian Junior 6)** Na(L). ℞. — As last. *R.I.C.* 12 .. 15
144 Ea. ℞. — As last. *R.I.C.* 106 14
145 Ca(V). ℞. PACATORI ORBIS, Jupiter seated l., holding patera and sceptre; at his feet, eagle. *R.I.C.* 218 20
146 Ha. ℞. PAX AVGG., Pax stg. l. *R.I.C.* 110 12
146a As last, with T in field. *R.I.C* 110 (*Voetter*) 15
147 Ja and/or c (M). ℞. — As **146.** *R.I.C.* 245 12
149 Ea. ℞. — As last. *R.I.C.* 109 12
150 Ca. ℞. — As last. *R.I.C.* 108 12
150a As last, with T in field 15
150b **(Cohen, Valerian Junior 7)** Na(L). ℞. — As **146.** *R.I.C.* 14 .. 15
151 Ea. ℞. PAX AVGVSTI, as before. *R.I.C.* 111 12
152 Ea(A). ℞. PIETAS AVGG., Valerian and Gallienus stg. facing each other, sacrificing over altar between them, one holds eagle-topped sceptre, the other parazonium; sometimes, above in field, star or wreath. *R.I.C.* 285 15
153 Ca(A). ℞. — As last, but without mintmarks. *R.I.C.* 284 15
154 ? ℞ PIETAS AVGG., Salonina seated with three children around her (Hy.; *rev. of Salonina*) 22
154a Ka(M). ℞. — Sacrificial implements (Hy.?; *rev. of Saloninus*). *R.I.C.* 246 (*Budapest*) 22
155 Ca(V). ℞. PIETATI AVGG., Pietas stg. l., leaning against column, holding sceptre. *R.I.C.* 219 14
156 Ca. ℞. P . M . TR . P . II COS . II P . P., Jupiter, naked, but mantle on l. shoulder, stg. l. *R.I.C.* 141 12
157 Another, of heavy weight (5·60 gms.). *R.I.C.* 141 35
159 Ca. ℞. P . M . TR . P . II COS . P . P., Valerian, in toga, stg. r., sacrificing over altar and holding baton. *R.I.C.* 140 12
159a Ca(V). ℞. — As last, but Valerian stg. l. *R.I.C.* 208 14
N.B.—*Cohen dittos "laur." in error for nos.* 163-6.
163 Ea. ℞. P . M . TR . P . III COS . III P . P., Valerian seated l. on curule chair, holding globe and sceptre. *R.I.C.* 142ᵇ 25
164 Ea. ℞. P . M . TR . P . IIII COS . III P . P., Sol, radiate, stg. l., raising r. hand and holding whip. *R.I.C.* 142 (COS . II) 20
165 Ea. ℞. P . M . TR . P . V COS . III (*sic*) P . P., as last. *R.I.C.* 142ᵃ (COS . II) 20
165a Ka(M). ℞. P . M . TR . P . V COS . IIII P . P., Victory stg. l., captive at her feet. *R.I.C.* 231 (*Voetter*) 22

166 Ea and/or c. ℞. — Valerian seated, as **163.** *R.I.C.* 142ᶜ 20
169 Ha(A). ℞. — Valerian and Gallienus stg. face to face, each has a hand on shield which are pláced between them; in background, two spears. (This is a copy of the coin of Augustus, with Caius and Lucius Caesars on the *rev.*). *R.I.C.* 277 22
170 Another, of heavy weight (6·20 gms.). *R.I.C.* 277 35

173   **Antoninianus.** Ja and/or c (M).   ℞.   PROVID . AVGG., Providentia stg. l., holding ensign and pointing with baton to a globe at her feet.   *R.I.C.* 247   £12

174   Jc(M).   ℞. — As last, but cornucopiae in place of ensign.   *R.I.C.* 248   12

175   Ea.   ℞.   PROVIDENTIA AVGG., as last.   *R.I.C.* 113   12

176   Ca.   ℞. — As last. *R.I.C.* 112   12

176a   **(Cohen, Valerian Junior 8)** Na(L).   ℞.   PROVIDENTIA AVG. (*sic*), as 173, but holding sceptre in place of ensign.   *R.I.C.* 15   16

177   Hc.   ℞.   RELIGIO AVGG., Diana stg. l., drawing arrow from quiver and holding bow; Q in field. *R.I.C.* 115   25

177a   As last, but P in field. *R.I.C.* 115   25

178   Ea.   ℞. — As **177**, but nothing in field. *R.I.C.* 114   30

179   Ca(V).   ℞.   RESTITVT . GENER . HVMANI, Valerian, radiate and with cloak floating behind, stg. r., raising r. hand and holding globe.   *R.I.C.* 220 ..   22

179a   As last, but RESTITVTI.   *R.I.C.* 220   22

180   Ca.   ℞.   RESTITVTORI ORBIS, Jupiter (*R.I.C.* emperor) seated l., holding patera and sceptre; at his feet, eagle. *R.I.C.* 119   15

182   **Quinarius.** Eb.   ℞.   RESTITVTOR . ORBIS, Valerian, in military dress stg. l., holding spear and raising kneeling turreted female. *R.I.C.* 149 ..   150

183   **Antoninianus.** Ea.   ℞. — As last.   *R.I.C.* 117   16

184   Ca.   ℞. — As last. *R.I.C.* 116   16

185   Ha.   ℞. — As last. *R.I.C.* 118   16

187   Ea.   ℞. — As before, but Valerian stg. facing, looking r.   *R.I.C.* 117 ..   16

187a   Ea.   ℞.   RESTITVTORI ORBIS, as **182** or **187**.   *R.I.C.* 117 (*Voetter*)   ..   18

183   197

188   Ca(A).   ℞.   RESTITVT . ORIENTIS, turreted female, the Orient, stg. r., handing wreath to the emperor stg. l.   *R.I.C.* 286   18

189   Ea and/or c (A).   ℞. — As last.   *R.I.C.* 287   18

190   As last, with star or wreath in field above.   *R.I.C.* pl. I, 7   18

190a   As last, with two pellets beneath bust on *obv.*   (*David R. Sear*)..   ..   18

192   Ca.   ℞.   ROMAE AETERNAE, Roma seated l., holding Victory and spear. *R.I.C.* 120   12

192a   Ca(V).   ℞. — As last, Roma seated on shield.   *R.I.C.* 221   12

193a   **Medallion.** Nh.   ℞.   ROMAE AETERNE (*sic*), helmeted bust of Roma r. (diam. 22 mm.).   *R.I.C.* 65 (*Gnecchi*)   ..   .. *Extremely rare*

194   **Antoninianus.** Ja and/or c (M).   ℞.   SAECVLI FELICITAS, Felicitas stg. l. *R.I.C.* 249   12

195   As last, but SECVLI.   *R.I.C.* 249   14

196   Ja (L and M).   ℞.   SALVS AVGG., Salus stg. l., holding sceptre and feeding serpent arising from altar.   *R.I.C.* 16 and 254   12

197   Ca.   ℞. — As last. *R.I.C.* 121   12

200   Ja and/or c (M).   ℞.   SALVS AVG., Salus stg. r., feeding serpent held in her arms.   *R.I.C.* 251   12

201   Ka(M).   ℞. — As last. *R.I.C.* 250   14

202   E but AVC. a.   ℞. — As last   ..   ..

202a   Ka and/or c (M).   ℞.   SALVS AVGG., as last.   *R.I.C.* 252 (*Voetter*)   ..   18

202b   Ja and/or c (M).   ℞. — As last.   *R.I.C.* 253 (*Voetter*)   18

203   Ja(M).   ℞.   SALVS PVBLICA, as **196.**   *R.I.C.* 255   14

204   Antoninianus. Ha(M). ℞. SECVRIT . PERPET., Securitas stg. l., legs
crossed and leaning against column. *R.I.C.* 256 ..   ..   £12

205   Ja(L). ℞. — As last. *R.I.C.* 18 (PERP. in error ?)   14

206   La(L). ℞. — As last. *R.I.C.* 17 (PERP. in error ?)   14

207   Quinarius. Hb(L) — As last. *R.I.C.* 25..   125

207a Antoninianus (Cohen, Valerian Junior 9). Na and/or c (L). ℞. — As
last. *R.I.C.* 19. (PERP. in error ?)   16

208   Ja and/or c (M). ℞. SPES PVBLICA, Spes walking l. *R.I.C.* 257..   ..   12

209   Ka. ℞. — As last. *R.I.C.* 122 (*obv.* Ca.)..   12

210   Ma(?). ℞. — As last. *R.I.C.* 122a   12

210a Ma(M). ℞. — As last. *R.I.C.* 258   12

211   Ja(M). ℞. TEMPORVM FELICITAS, Felicitas stg. l. *R.I.C.* 259   ..   14

212   Ca(V). ℞. VENVS VICTRIX, Venus stg. l., leaning on shield and holding
helmet and transverse sceptre. *R.I.C.* 222   20

212a (Cohen, Valerian Junior 10) Na(L).   ℞. — As before, but she holds
palm and r. hand is raised. *R.I.C.* 20   20

214a (Cohen, Valerian Junior 11) Nc(L). ℞. VICT . AVGG., Victory stg. l.,
leaning on shield and holding palm, captive at her feet. *R.I.C.* 11..   ..   18

214b Ka(M). ℞. — As last, but no shield and she holds wreath and palm.
R.I.C. 260 (*Voetter*)   20

215   Ca. ℞. VICTORIA AVG., Victory walking l. *R.I.C.* 123   18

218   Ca. ℞. VICTORIA AVGG., as last. *R.I.C.* 124   15

218a Ca(V). ℞. — As last. *R.I.C.* 223   15

221   Ca. ℞. — Victory stg. l., resting on shield and holding palm. *R.I.C.* 127   12

222   As last, but heavy weight (5.20 gms.). *R.I.C.* 127   35

223   Ka(M). ℞. — As **221.** *R.I.C.* 261   12

224   Ea. ℞. — As last. *R.I.C.* 128   12

208   230

230   Ca and/or c. ℞. — Victory stg. l. *R.I.C.* 125   12

230a Ca(V). ℞. — As last. *R.I.C.* 224..   12

231   Ea. ℞. — As last. *R.I.C.* 126   12

231a Quinarius. Cb. ℞. — As last. *R.I.C.* 150 (*Voetter*)   150

236   Antoninianus. Ka(A). ℞. — As before, but Victory stands on globe.
R.I.C. 288   15

236a Ha(A). ℞. — As last. *R.I.C.* 289 (*Voetter*)   18

237   Ka(A). ℞. — As before, but seated captive before. *R.I.C.* 290   ..   18

240   Denarius. Cb. ℞. VICTORIAE AVGG., Victory in biga galloping r., she
holds whip. *R.I.C.* 145   150

241   Antoninianus. Ca(V). ℞. — Soldier stg. r., r. hand resting on shield,
holding spear. *R.I.C.* 225   25

242   Ea. ℞. VICTORIAE AVGG . IT . GERM., Victory stg. l., captive at feet.
R.I.C. 130   20

243   Ca. ℞. — As last. *R.I.C.* 129   20

244   Ca and/or c. ℞. VICTORIA EXERCIT., as before, but without captive.
R.I.C. 131   12

245 **Antoninianus.** Ea. ℞. VICTORIA GERM., as **221**. *R.I.C.* 132 (*wrong
  description*) £20
248 Ea. ℞. — As **242**; captive has hands tied behind back. *R.I.C.* 132 ..   20
251 Ba(M). ℞. VICTORIA GERMANICA, as last. *R.I.C.* 263   25
252 Ba(M). ℞. — Victory stg. l., leaning on shield and holding palm,
  captive at feet. *R.I.C.* 264   25
253 Ga(M). ℞. — As last. *R.I.C.* 264   25
254 Ja(M). ℞. — As last. *R.I.C.* 265   22
255 Ka(M). ℞. VICT . PART., as **248**. *R.I.C.* 262   ..   ..
255a Ja(M). ℞. — As last   ..   ..
255b **(Cohen, Valerian Junior 12)** Na(L). ℞. VICT . PARTICA, Victory walking
  r., treading down enemy. *R.I.C.* 22   30
255c **(Cohen, Valerian Junior 13)** Na(L). ℞. — Victory as last, but running
  l. *R.I.C.* 22   30
255d — — As last, but no enemy. *R.I.C.* 22   30
256 *Obv. ? (A)*. ℞. VICTORIA PARTHICA, Victory presenting wreath to emperor
  in military attire. *R.I.C.* 291
257 Ga and/or c (M). ℞. VIRTVS AVG., soldier (*Cohen*, Virtus or Roma) stg. l.,
  leaning on shield and holding Victory, spear rests against l. arm. *R.I.C.*
  266 (A very similar coin is given by *Cohen* under Valerian Junior 14, see
  below **278a**)   20
258 As last, but AVGG. *R.I.C.* 267   15
259 Ha. ℞. VIRTVS AVGG.,as last, but soldier stg.r. *R.I.C.* 134 (but incorrectly
  described)   15
263 Ca. ℞. — Soldier (*Cohen*, Mars) stg. l., leaning on shield and holding
  reversed spear. *R.I.C.* 133   12
263a Ca(V). ℞. — As last. *R.I.C.* 226   12
263b Ea(V). ℞. — As last. *R.I.C.* 227 (*Voetter*)   15
264 Ha. ℞. — As last. *R.I.C.* 134   12
265 Ja(M). ℞. — As last. *R.I.C.* 271   12
266 Ka(M). ℞. — As last. *R.I.C.* 270   12
267 Ea. ℞. — Soldier (*Cohen*, Mars) walking r., holding spear and trophy.
  R.I.C. 137   15
268 Ha. ℞. — Soldier (*Cohen*, Virtus) stg. r., leaning on shield and holding
  spear. *R.I.C.* 135   15
271 Ca. ℞. — As **257**. *R.I.C.* 136a (described without Victory)   ..   12
272 Ja(M). ℞. — As last. *R.I.C.* 268 (Roma described as seated on shield)   12
273 Ca. ℞. — Virtus stg. facing, holding two military ensigns. *R.I.C.* 136 ..   18
274 Ea. ℞. — As **267** (*Cohen*, Romulus). *R.I.C.* 137   15
275 Ha. ℞. — As last. *R.I.C.* 138   15
275a Ka(M). ℞. — As last. *R.I.C.* 269 (*Voetter*)   18
276 Ea and/or c (A). ℞. — Valerian and Gallienus stg. facing each other;
  one holds spear and globe, the other holds Victory and reversed spear.
  R.I.C. 293   14
277 Ca(A). ℞. — As last. *R.I.C.* 292   14
278a **(Cohen, Valerian Junior 14)** Gc(L or M). ℞. VIRTVS AVG., soldier
  (*Cohen*, Virtus) stg. l., holding Victory, spear and shield. *R.I.C.* 23   18
278b **(Cohen, Valerian Junior 15)** Na and/or c (L). ℞. VIRTVS AVGG., as last,
  but without shield. *R.I.C.* 24 (also without spear)   15
278c **(Cohen, Valerian Junior 16)** *Obv. ?* ℞. — Roma seated, holding
  Victory and spear (*This could be with obv.* Ja(M)). *R.I.C.* 268   ..   ..
279 Ea and/or c (A). ℞. VOTA ORBIS, two Victories fixing shield inscribed s · c
  on palm tree. *R.I.C.* 295   25
280 Ca(A). ℞. — As last. *R.I.C.* 294   25
281 Cg(A). ℞. — As last. *R.I.C.* 296   30

282 Antoninianus. Cc. ℞. VOTIS DECENNALIBVS in three lines in laurel-wreath. *R.I.C.* 139 .. .. £45

VALERIAN and GALLIENUS

9 Denarius. CONCORDIA AVGVSTORVM, laur., dr. and cuir. busts of the emperors face to face. ℞. LIBERALITAS AVGVSTORVM, Liberalitas stg. l. *R.I.C.* 3 .. .. *Extremely rare*

10 Medallion. PIETAS AVGVSTORVM, as last. ℞. MONETA AVGG., the three Monetae stg. l.; at the feet of each, a pile of metal. (Weight 30 gms.). *R.I.C.* 1 .. .. *Extremely rare*

11 FELICIBVS AVGG., as before. ℞. QVATERNIO in three lines. (Weight 90 gms.) *R.I.C.* 2 (in four lines. *This piece has not recently been verified*)

VALERIAN, SALONINUS (or VALERIAN JUNIOR), GALLIENUS and SALONINA

1 Medallion. PIETAS AVGVSTORVM, laur. dr. and cuir. bust l. of Valerian facing bare-headed dr. bust of a young prince r. ℞. CONCORDIA AVGVS-TORVM, diad. and dr. bust of Salonina r., facing laur., dr. and cuir. bust of Gallienus l. *R.I.C.* 1.. .. .. *A great rarity*

MARINIANA

Mariniana was the wife of Valerian. As all her coins are commemorative it would seem that she died before his accession or immediately after.

4   16

2 **Antoninianus.** DIVAE MARINIANAE, diad., veiled and dr. bust r., on crescent. ℞. CONSECRATIO, peacock stg. facing, hd. l., tail in splendour. *R.I.C.* 3 .. .. £90

3 — without diadem. ℞. — As last. *R.I.C.* 3 90

4 As 2. ℞. — As before, but looking r. *R.I.C.* 4 90

5 — without diadem. ℞. — As last, but v in field. *R.I.C.* 4 note .. 100

6 As last, but without v. *R.I.C.* 4 100

11 As 2. ℞. — As **2**, but peacock walking r. *R.I.C.* 5 100

14 As 3. ℞. — Peacock flying l., carrying empress to heaven. *R.I.C.* 6 .. 100

16 As last, but peacock flying r. *R.I.C.* 6 100

17 **Quinarius.** As last, but without crescent. *R.I.C.* 8 (*diademed*).. .. 450

18 **Antoninianus.** As. 2. ℞. — As **16** 100

19 — ℞. FELICIT . DEORVM, Felicitas stg. l. *R.I.C.* 7 250

GALLIENUS

Joint reign with Valerian 253-260 A.D.

Sole reign 260-268 A.D.

P. Licinius Egnatius Gallienus was the son of Valerian and was made co-emperor almost immediately after his father's accession. In 254 he was sent West and entrusted with the defence of the Rhine. He was fairly successful against the German tribes and when Valerian left for the East in 256, Gallienus was entrusted with the government of all the Western provinces. After Valerian was captured by the Persians, Gallienus found himself sole master of the empire and he had a very disturbed reign. There were fierce barbarian attacks on all the frontiers and many internal revolts as well as famine and plague. In the East Odenathus of Palmyra gained control, and in the West Postumus took over Gaul, Spain and Britain, and established an independent empire. After a succession of campaigns, Gallienus was eventually murdered at the siege of Milan in 268, when he was fifty years old. During his sole reign the antoniniani continued to decline in size and weight as well as in silver content.

Obverse legends.

A. IMP . CAES . GALLIENVS AVG.
B. IMP . C . P . LIC . GALLIENVS AVG.
C. IMP . C . P . LIC . GALLIENVS P . F . AVG.
D. IMP . GALLIENVS AVG.
E. IMP . GALLIENVS P . AVG.
F. IMP . GALLIENVS P . F . AVG.
G. IMP . GALLIENVS P . F . AVG . GERM.
H. IMP . GALLIENVS P . F . AVG . G . M.
J. IMP . GALLIENVS PIVS AVG.
K. GALLIENVS AVG.
L. GALLIENVS AVG . GERM . V.
M. GALLIENVS P . F . AVG.
N. GALLIENVS PIVS AVG.

Obverse types.

a. Radiate bust draped right.
b. Laureate bust draped right.
c. Radiate bust draped and cuirassed right.
d. Laureate bust draped and cuirassed right.
e. Laureate bust cuirassed right.
f. Radiate bust cuirassed right.
g. Radiate bust cuirassed left.
h. Radiate bust draped left.
k. Radiate head or bust right.
l. Radiate head or bust left.
m. Laureate head right.
n. Laureate head left.
p. Laureate bust right.
q. Laureate bust left.
r. Head left with crown of reeds.

Any of the above with one or more of the following added:
sc. Holding sceptre.
sc.ea. Holding sceptre surmounted by eagle.
sh. Holding shield.
sp. Holding spear.
w. Bust to waist.

Mints. *As attributed by R.I.C.*
(R) or nothing—Rome.
(L)   Lugdunum (*R.I.C.* nos. 5-64).
(V)   Moesia-Viminacium (*R.I.C.* nos. 287-301).
(M)   Mediolanum (*R.I.C.* nos. 306-415; sole reign 453-544).
(S)   Siscia (*R.I.C.* sole reign nos. 548-599).
(A)   Asia—Antioch and perhaps elsewhere (*R.I.C.* nos. 435-462; sole reign 600-678).

Other pieces are attributed to Rome (*R.I.C.* nos. 106-199; sole reign 135-380).

N.B.—S *before an R.I.C. number indicates that it is a coin of his sole reign.*

1 **Antoninianus.** Kk. R. ABVNDANT . AVG., Abundantia stg. r., emptying out corn (from cornucopiae ? *Possibly the same as* **5**)   ..   ..

2 **Denarius.** Km. R. — As last (*probably a misreading of next*)   ..

5   25

4 Dm. R. ABVNDANTIA AVG., Abundantia stg. r., emptying cornucopiae. *R.I.C.* S346   ..   ..   £100
5 **Antoninianus.** Kk. R. — As last.   10
5a As last, with B in field. *R.I.C.* S157   10
6 Ka. R. — As last. *R.I.C.* S157   10
7 Kl. R. — As last. *R.I.C.* S157   14
8 Ka(A). R. — Abundantia (*Cohen*, river-god) recumbent l., resting on urn and holding flower. *R.I.C.* S625   90
8a Kf(A). R. — As last. *R.I.C.* S625   90
9a **Medallion.** N, bare-headed bust dr. and cuir.r. R. ADLOCVTIO AVGG., two emperors on platform addressing three soldiers who hold ensigns; in background, praetorian prefect (diam. 37 mm.; wt. 37·28 gms.). *R.I.C.* 106 (*Gnecchi*)   ..   ..   *Extremely rare*
10 IMP . GALLIENVS PIVS FELIX AVG., laur. bust r., wearing low-necked robe, holding caduceus over l. shoulder. R. ADLOCVTIO AVGVSTI, as last (diam. 37 mm.). *R.I.C.* 107 ..   ..   *Extremely rare*
14 **Antoninianus.** Kl(M and S). R. ADVENTVS AVG., emperor, in military dress, riding l., holding spear and raising r. hand. *R.I.C.* S463 and S552   20
15 Kc(M and S). R. — As last. *R.I.C.* S463 and S552   20
15a Ka(M and S). R. — As last. *R.I.C.* S463 and S552   20
15b Kf(S). R. — As last. *R.I.C.* S552   20
16 Dl. R. — As last. *R.I.C.* S158   20
16a Da. R. — As last. *R.I.C.* S158   20
16b Kk(S). R. — Emperor riding r.; at foot, captive. *R.I.C.* S551 (*Voetter*)   22
20 Kk. R. AEQVIT . AVG., Aequitas stg. l. *R.I.C.* S159   9
20a Kk(S). R. — As last. *R.I.C.* S553   9
20b Kf(S). R. — As last. *R.I.C.* S553   10

23 **Denarius.** Km. ℞. AEQVITAS AVG., Aequitas stg. l. .. .. ..
23a Kd. ℞. — As last. *R.I.C.* S347 .. .. £100
24 **Antoninianus.** Kk. ℞. — As last. *R.I.C.* S159 8
24a As last, but s, z or Δ in field (*Cohen also has* P *and* VI, *possibly a misreading of one of the others*). *R.I.C.* S159 9
24b Kk(A). ℞. — As **24**, but star in field or ex. *R.I.C.* S627 9
25 Kc. ℞. — As **24**. *R.I.C.* S159 8
25a Kc. ℞. — As **24a**. *R.I.C.* S159 9
25b Kc(M). ℞. — As **24**, but s in field. *R.I.C.* S464 9
25c Kc(A). ℞. — As **24b**. *R.I.C.* S627 9
25d Ka(M). ℞. — As **25b**. *R.I.C.* S464 9
25e Ka(A). ℞. — As **24b**. *R.I.C.* S627 9
25f Kf(A). ℞. — As last. *R.I.C.* S627 9
25g K ?(A). ℞. — As **24**, but SPQR in ex. *R.I.C.* S627 14
26 (head) **27** (bust) Kl. ℞. — As **24**. *R.I.C.* S159 8
26a (head) **27a** (bust) Kl. ℞. — As **24a**. *R.I.C.* S159 10
26b (head) **27b** (bust) Kl(M). ℞. — As **25b**. *R.I.C.* S464 10
26c Kl(A). ℞. — As **24b**. *R.I.C.* S627 10
28 Mc(A). ℞. — As **23** .. ..
28a Mc(A). ℞. — As last, but star in field .. ..
28b Ma(A). ℞. — As last. *R.I.C.* S626 .. ..
28c Mf(A). ℞. — As last. *R.I.C.* S626 9
29 Bc. ℞. — As **23** (*probably a misreading*) .. .. ..
30 Kk(A). ℞. AEQVTAS AVG., as **24b**. *R.I.C.* S627 12
31 IMP . P . LIC . GALLIENVS AVG., k(A or V ?). ℞. AEQVITAS AVGG., Aequitas stg. l. .. ..
31a — f(A). ℞. — As last. *R.I.C.* 439.. 14
32a Ba(V). ℞. — As last. *R.I.C.* 288 (*Voetter*) 15
32b Bf(A). ℞. — As last. *R.I.C.* 436 (*Voetter*) 15
32c Df(A). ℞. — As last. *R.I.C.* 437 (*Voetter*) 15
32d IMP . LIC . GALLIENVS AVG., f. ℞. — As last. *R.I.C.* 438 (*Voetter*) .. 20
34 Kk(M). ℞. AET . AVG., Sol stg. l. .. ..
34a As last, but with MT in ex. *R.I.C.* S465a 13
35 Kk(M). ℞. AETERN . AVG., as last. *R.I.C.* S465a 8
35a As last, but nothing in ex. .. ..
36 Dh., with club on l. shoulder (M). ℞. — As **34a**. *R.I.C.* S465 18

28c   38b

38 Kk(M). ℞. AETERNITAS AVG., Sol stg. l. 10
38a As last, but with T in *rev.* field. *R.I.C.* S466 9
38b Kk. ℞. — As **38**, but with Γ in field. *R.I.C.* S160 9
39 Kf(M). ℞. — As **38a**. *R.I.C.* S466 9
39a Kf. ℞. — As **38b**. *R.I.C.* S160 9
40 Ka(M). ℞. — As **38a**. *R.I.C.* S466 9

40a Antoninianus. Ka. ℞. — As **38b**. *R.I.C.* S160 .. .. .. £9
41 As **40,** but of heavy weight (8.05 gms.; *Cohen*, double antoninianus).
R.I.C. S466 30
41a As **40a,** but of heavy weight (as last). *R.I.C.* S160 (*Probably only one of
the last two exist*) .. ..
42 Denarius. Dm. ℞. — As **38**. *R.I.C.* S348 100
44 Antoninianus. Kc(A ?). ℞. — Saturn stg. r., holding scythe, ᴘxᴠ in
ex. (*this stands for* ᴛʀ . ᴘ . xᴠ) (*Possibly one of the next two*) .. .. ..
44a Ka(A). ℞. — As last, but holding sceptre. *R.I.C.* S606 15
44b Kf(A). ℞. — As last. *R.I.C.* S606 15
44c Ka(S). ℞. — Saturn stg. holding sceptre; ᴘ and star in field. *R.I.C.*
S554 12
44d Kc(S). ℞. — As last. *R.I.C.* S554 12
44e Kf(S). ℞. — As last. *R.I.C.* S554 12
44f Kh, sc. ea. (S). ℞. — As last. *R.I.C.* S554 25
44g Kl(S). ℞. — As last. *R.I.C.* S554 18
45 Bc. ℞. — As **44**. (*Possibly a mistake for* **53**) .. .. ..
46 Kc(A). ℞. — She-wolf r., suckling Romulus and Remus .. ..
46a Kc(A). ℞. — As last, with palm or ꜱ ᴘ ǫ ʀ in ex. .. ..
46b Ka(A). ℞. — As last. *R.I.C.* S628 15
46c Kf(A). ℞. — As last. *R.I.C.* S628 15
47 Kl(A). ℞. — As **46** and/or **46a** .. ..
47a Kh, sc. ea. (A). ℞. — As **46a**. *R.I.C.* S628 25
48 Denarius. K, laur. bust dr. and cuir. l. (A). ℞. — As **46**. *R.I.C.* S677 125
48a Kd. ℞. — As last. *R.I.C.* S349 (*perhaps an error*) 125
50 Antoninianus. Mf(A). ℞. ᴀᴇᴛᴇʀɴɪᴛᴀᴛɪ ᴀᴠɢ., Sol, half-naked, stg. l.,
holding globe .. ..
50a Mf(A). ℞. — As last, but with star in field. *R.I.C.* S629 10
51 Kf(S). ℞. — As **50**. *R.I.C.* S555 9
51a Kf(S). ℞. — As **50a**. *R.I.C.* S555.. 10
51b Kf(A). ℞. — As **50,** but with star in field or ex. *R.I.C.* S630 .. 10
51c Ka(S). ℞. — As **50** and/or **50a**. *R.I.C.* S555 10
52 Kk. ℞. ᴀᴇᴛᴇʀɴɪᴛᴀᴛɪ ᴀᴠɢ., two joined hands .. ..
53 Ba(V). ℞. ᴀᴇᴛᴇʀɴɪᴛᴀᴛɪ ᴀᴠɢɢ., Saturn, veiled, stg. r., holding sceptre
(*Cohen*, scythe). *R.I.C.* 289 20
53a Df(M). ℞. — Sol stg. l. *R.I.C.* 373 (*Voetter*) 15
55 Ka. ℞. ᴀɴɴoɴᴀ ᴀᴠɢ., Abundantia stg. r., l. foot on prow, holding
rudder (*Cohen*, on globe) and corn-ears. *R.I.C.* S161 8
55a Ka. ℞. — As last, ᴠ in field. *R.I.C.* S161 9
55b Ka. ℞. — As last, ǫ in ex. *R.I.C.* S161 10
55c Kf. ℞. — As one or all of the last three. *R.I.C.* S161 10
55d Kk. ℞. — As **55**. *R.I.C.* S161 8
55e Kk. ℞. — As **55a** and/or **55b**. *R.I.C.* S161 9
55f Kl. ℞. — As **55c**. *R.I.C.* S161 12
55g Kh, with club over l. shoulder. ℞. — As **55c**. *R.I.C.* S161 20
55h Ka(S). ℞. — As **55,** but sceptre in place of rudder. *R.I.C.* S556
(Annona) 10
55i Kk(S). ℞. — As last. *R.I.C.* S556 10

N.B.—S *before an R.I.C. number indicates that it is a coin of his sole reign.*

56 **Antoninianus.** Kk. ℞. ANNONA AVG., Abundantia stg. half-left before
modius, holding corn-ears and anchor £9
56a Kk. ℞. — As last, but with Q in field or in ex. *R.I.C.* S162 9
57 Kf. ℞. — As last. *R.I.C.* S162 9

57a Kf. ℞. — As **56** 9
58 Ka. ℞. — As **56,** but cornucopiae in place of anchor 9
58a Ka. ℞. — As last, but with Q in field or in ex. *R.I.C.* S162 9
59 Kh. ℞. — As **58** 10
59a Kh. ℞. — As **58a.** *R.I.C.* S162 10
60 Kk(S). ℞. — As **58.** *R.I.C.* S557 (Annona) 8
60a Kk. ℞. — As **58a.** *R.I.C.* S162 9
60b Kf(S). ℞. — As **60.** *R.I.C.* S557 9
60c Kk. ℞. ANNONA AVGG., as **58** (Hy.). *R.I.C.* S336 (Annona) 10
63 Fk. ℞. APOLINI CONSERVA., Apollo, naked, stg. l., holding lanrel-branch
and lyre placed on rock .. ..
63a Fa(M). ℞. — As last. *R.I.C.* 374 12
64 Gc. ℞. — As last. *R.I.C.* 126 15
65 Cf. ℞. — As last. *R.I.C.* 125 (*obv.* C) 12
66 Ca. ℞. — As last. *R.I.C.* 125 12
71 Ba and/or f. ℞. APOLINI PROPVG., Apollo, naked, but with floating cloak,
stg. r., drawing bow. *R.I.C.* 128 14
71a Kf(S). ℞. APOLL . CONSERVAT., Apollo stg. l., holding laurel-branch and
cornucopiae. *R.I.C.* S559 (*Voetter*) 15
72 Kk. ℞. APOLLINI CONS . AVG., Centaur walking r., drawing bow; in ex., z
or H (*Cohen,* z backwards). *R.I.C.* S163 12
73 Kk. ℞. — Centaur walking l., holding globe and trophy (*Cohen,* arrows);
in ex., H, I, N (*Cohen,* M) or z. *R.I.C.* S164 12
74 Kh. ℞. — As last. *R.I.C.* S164 12

74a   77

74a Ka. ℞. — As last. *R.I.C.* S164 12
74b Kk, sh. ℞. — As last. *R.I.C.* S164 12
74c Kk(S). ℞. — (or CON). Centaur galloping l., shooting arrow r. *R.I.C.*
S558 15
74d Kk(S). ℞. — As last, but s in field, or sI in ex. *R.I.C.* S558 .. 15
74e Kh(S). ℞. — — As **74c** and/or **74d.** *R.I.C.* S558 15
75 Kk. ℞. APOLLINI CONS . AVG., griffin walking r., Δ in ex. *R.I.C.* S166.. 12
76 Kk. ℞. — Griffin walking l., Δ in ex. *R.I.C.* S166 12
77 Dk. ℞. — As last. *R.I.C.* S165 15

N.B.—*In nos. 78, 79 and 80 Cohen has dittoed obv. D instead of* K.

78 **Antoninianus.** Kk. ℞.. — As last, but griffin seated l. *R.I.C.* S166 £12

79 Kk. ℞.— As **75,** but griffin stg. r. 12

79a Kk. ℞. — As **75,** but griffin seated r. *R.I.C.* S166 12

80 Kk. ℞. — Pegasus stg. r. *R.I.C.* S167 12

81 Cf. ℞. APOLLINI CONSERVA., Apollo stg. l., as **63.** *R.I.C.* 127 (*? wrong description*) 12

81a Cf. ℞. — Apollo stg. r., as **71.** *R.I.C.* 127 (*this is either a mistake for type* 81 *or wrong reference no.*). .. ..

86 Kk(A). ℞. APOLLI . PAL., Apollo, in long robe, stg. l., holding patera (or globe) and cross-headed sceptre; SPQR in ex. *R.I.C.* S631 40

87 Ka(A). ℞. APOLLINI PAL., Apollo as last. but wearing short dress. *R.I.C.* S631 40

87a Kf(A). ℞. — As last. *R.I.C.* S631 40

88 Kh(A). ℞. — As last. *R.I.C.* S631 40

N.B.—*Referring to the last four,* R.I.C. *says,* sometimes to r., tripod.

89 Kk(M). ℞. APOLLO CONSER., Apollo, naked, stg. l., holding olive-branch and mantle. *R.I.C.* S468 8

89a Ka. ℞. — As last, but only holds olive-branch; Λ in ex. *R.I.C.* S168 10

89b Kk. ℞. — As last. *R.I.C.* S168 10

89c Kk. ℞. — As **89,** but holds olive-branch and lyre. *R.I.C.* S169 .. 14

91 Kk(M). ℞. — Apollo, naked, stg. facing, hd. r., placing r. hand on head and l. on lyre placed on ornate altar (*R.I.C.,* rock). *R.I.C.* S467 8

92 Kk(M). ℞. APOLLO CONSERV., as last. *R.I.C.* S467 8

92a Ka and/or Kk. ℞. — As **89a.** *R.I.C.* S168 10

93

98

93 Kk(M). ℞. APOLLO CONSERVA., as **91.** *R.I.C.* S467 8

93a Ka and/or Kk. ℞. — As **89a.** *R.I.C.* S168 10

94 Gk. ℞. — Apollo stg. l., holding laurel-branch and leaning on shield. *R.I.C.* 129 (*obv.,* a) 14

96 Kk(M). ℞. BONAE FORTVNAE, Fortuna stg. l., holding rudder, usually on globe, and cornucopiae. *R.I.C.* S469 9

96a Kf(S). ℞. — As before, but no globe. *R.I.C.* S561 10

97 **Denarius.** Fp with aegis (M ?). ℞. — As **96** 120

97a Ep(M). ℞. — As **96a.** *R.I.C.* 412 120

97b Eb(M). ℞. — As last. *R.I.C.* 412ᵃ (*Probably the same coin as* 97, *but one description incorrect*) 120

98 **Antoninianus.** Kk(M). ℞. BON . EVEN . (or EVENT.) AVG., Genius, naked, stg. l. before lighted altar, holding patera and corn-ears; MT in ex. *R.I.C.* S470 9

99 Kf(M). ℞. — As last, but nothing in ex. *R.I.C.* S470 9

99a Kf(S). ℞. BON . EVEN . AVG., Genius stg. l., holding patera. *R.I.C.* S560 (*Voetter*) 14

100 Kk(M). ℞. BONVS EVENTVS AVG., as **98.** *R.I.C.* S470 9

102　Antoninianus. Kk. ℞. CLEMENTIA TEMP., Clementia stg. l., leaning
against column, holding sceptre. *R.I.C.* S170 (*obv.*, a) £1

104 Ka(M). ℞. COHH . PRAET . VI P . VI F., lion, rad., walking r. *R.I.C.* 370　5

105 Kf(M). ℞. — As last. *R.I.C.* 370.. 5

106 K, his bust seen from the back with rad. helmet, sp. and sh. (M). ℞. —
As last. *R.I.C.* 370 (rad., cuir. bust l., sp. and sh., ? *in error*) 7

107 Kl(M). ℞. — As last. *R.I.C.* 370 6

108 Kg, sc. (M). ℞. — As last. *R.I.C.* 370 7

109 Kg, sc. on shoulder, sh. (M). ℞. — As last. *R.I.C.* 370 7

110 Kl(M). ℞. COHH . PRAET . VII P . VII F., as last. *R.I.C.* 372 6

111 Ka(M). ℞. — As last. *R.I.C.* 372 5

112 Kf(M). ℞. — As last. *R.I.C.* 372.. 5

113 Kf(M). ℞. As before, but P . VI F. *R.I.C.* 371 .. .. ..
R.I.C. says that the reading of 113, 114 *can hardly be correct.*

114 Kl, bust with bare neck (M). ℞. As last. *R.I.C.* 371 .. .. ..

109　　　　　　　　　　　　　131a

116 Kk(M). ℞. CONCOR . AVG., Concordia seated l.; MT in ex. *R.I.C.* S471

116a Kk(A). ℞. — As last, but II in ex. *R.I.C.* S562.. .. .. ..

116b As last, but nothing in ex. *R.I.C.* S562 .. ..

117 Ea(M). ℞. CONCOR . AVGG., as before, but double cornucopiae. *R.I.C.* 375

117a Ea(M). ℞. CONCOR . EXERC., Concordia stg. l., sacrificing out of patera
over altar and holding cornucopiae. (*Dorchester*) 1

117b Ea(M). ℞. CONCOR . LEGG., as **117.** *R.I.C.* 376 (*Voetter*) 2

118 Ea(M). ℞. CONCOR . MIL., Concordia stg. l. *R.I.C.* 377 1

119 Kk(M). ℞. CONCORD . EQVIT., Concordia stg. l., holding patera and rudder
on globe. *R.I.C.* S472 2

122 Kk(S). ℞. CONCORDIA AVG., as last, but holding patera and double cornucopiae. *R.I.C.* S563 (*obv.*, f).. 1

123 Ba. ℞. CONCORDIA AVGG., as last, but single cornucopiae. *R.I.C.* 130 ..

125 Bc or a. ℞. — Two joined hands. *R.I.C.* 131 1

129 Bc. ℞. CONCORDIA EXERC., as **122.** *R.I.C.* 132 1

131 Ba. ℞. CONCORDIA EXERCIT., as last. *R.I.C.* 132 1

131a Bf. ℞. — As last. *R.I.C.* 132 1

134 Bc(M). ℞. CONCORDIA MILIT., as last. *R.I.C.* 378 1

134a Bf(M). ℞. — As last. *R.I.C.* 378 1

136 Ba. ℞. CONCORDIAE AVG., as **122** .. ..

136a Ba. ℞. CONCORDIAE AVGG., as **123.** *R.I.C.* 130 1

137 Ea(M). ℞. CONCORDIAE MILITVM, as last. *R.I.C.* 379 1

138 Da(L). ℞. CONSECRATIO, lighted altar. (Hy.; *rev. of Valerian* II). *R.I.C.*
9 and S337 2

138a Da(L). ℞. — Eagle. (Hy.; *rev. of Valerian* II). *R.I.C.* S337 (*Voetter*) .. 3

138b Antoninianus. Kk. ℞. CONSERVAT . AVGG., Diana stg. l., drawing
arrow from quiver and holding bow; Q in field (Hy.). *R.I.C.* S339 .. £16

139 Kk(?). ℞. CONSERVATOR AVG., head of Bacchus wearing ivy-wreath.
(*Possibly a mistake for* 141) 150

140 Kf(A) ℞. — Aesculapius stg. l., leaning on staff around which is en-
twined a serpent. *R.I.C.* S632 12

140a Kf. ℞. — As last; in ex., XII. *R.I.C.* S172 12

140b Ka and/or f (A). ℞. — As last, but SPQR in ex. *R.I.C.* S632 (*Voetter*) 14

141 Kk. ℞. CONSERVATOR EXERC., female head r., wearing ivy-wreath (*Cohen*),
or wreath of reeds (*R.I.C.*). *R.I.C.* S173 150

142 Kk. ℞. CONSERVAT . AVGG., Apollo, naked, stg. l., leaning on lyre. (Hy.;
rev. of Valerian I?). *R.I.C.* S338 16

143 Ka. ℞. CONSERVT AVGG., as last. (Hy.; *rev. of Valerian* I) 16

144 Kk. ℞. CONSERVAT . PIETAT., emperor, in military dress, stg. l., holding
sceptre, extending hand (? holding patera) to kneeling figure (? female);
XII in field or ex. *R.I.C.* S171a 25

145 As last, but PETAT. *R I C* S171a 25

145a Ak. ℞. — As **144.** *R.I.C.* S171 30

146 Kk. ℞. COS . IIII P . P., emperor in quadriga, holding reins and branch.
R.I.C. S150 75

147 Kk. ℞. DACIA, Dacia stg. l., holding staff surmounted by ass's head
(*barbarous*) .. ..

149 Ma(L). ℞. DEO MARTI, Mars leaning on shield in temple of four columns.
R.I.C. 10 18

149a Mc(L). ℞. — As last. *R.I.C.* 10 18

149b Mf(L). ℞. — As last. *R.I.C.* 10 18

150 Ml or g, w. sp. sh. (L). ℞. — As last. *R.I.C.* 10 20

151 Another, as last, of heavy weight and thick flan. *R.I.C.* 10 note.. .. 30

152 Kk(A). ℞. DEO VOLCANO, Vulcan in temple of four columns, holding
hammer and pincers, anvil at feet. *R.I.C.* S633 (*obv.*, a) 40

153 Dk. ℞. DIANAE CONS . AVG., doe walking r., looking back; Є in ex. *R.I.C.*
S176 10

153a As last, but large pellet or globe in ex. *R.I.C.* S176 10

153b Df. ℞. — As **153** and/or **153a.** *R.I.C.* S176 10

140   154

154 Kk. ℞. — As **153.** *R.I.C.* S177 10

155 Dk. ℞ — Doe walking l., looking r.; Є in ex. *R.I.C.* S176 10

155a As last, but large pellet or globe in ex. *R.I.C.* S176 10

153b Df. ℞. — As **155** and/or **155a.** *R.I.C.* S176 10

156 Kk. ℞. — As **155.** *R.I.C.* S177 10

157 Kk. ℞. — Stag walking r.; in ex., X, XI, XII or I. *R.I.C.* S179 .. 10

158 Kk. ℞. — As last, but stag walking l. *R.I.C.* S179 10

159 Dk. ℞. — As last, but nothing in ex. *R.I.C.* S178 10

159a Dk. ℞. — As **157,** but nothing in ex. *R.I.C.* S178 10

R.I.C. indicates that one or all of **157, 158** *and* **160,** *also has obv. type a.*

160 Kk. ℞. — As **158** with the stag looking backwards. *R.I.C.* S179 .. 10

N.B.—S *before an R.I.C. number indicates that it is a coin of his sole reign.*

161 Antoninianus. Kk. ℞. DIANAE CONS . AVG., Goat stg. r.; in ex., *s*.
R.I.C. S182 .. .. £10
162 Kk. ℞. — Antelope walking r.; in ex., *s*, XI or XII. *R.I.C.* S181 .. 10
163 Dk. ℞. — As last, but also with Γ or nothing in ex. *R.I.C.* S180 .. 10
164 Df. ℞. — As last. *R.I.C.* S180 10
165 Kk. ℞. — Antelope walking l.; in ex., Γ, X, XI or XII. *R.I.C.* S181 .. 10
166 Kg. ℞. — As last. *R.I.C.* S181 10

167 Kf. ℞. — As last. *R.I.C.* S181 10
167a Ka. ℞. — As last or **162**. *R.I.C.* S181 (*Voetter*) 10
167b Ka, sh. ℞. — As last. *R.I.C.* S181 (*Voetter*) 18
167c Kk. ℞. — Boar walking r.; in ex., H. *R.I.C.* S183 (*Voetter*) 22
169 Dc. ℞. DIANA FELIX, Diana walking r., drawing arrow out of quiver and
holding bow, accompanied by hound r. *R.I.C.* S174 18
169a Df(M). ℞. — As last. *R.I.C.* 380 18
170 Dl (R and M). ℞. — As last. *R.I.C.* S174 and 380 18
170a Dg. sp. sh. (M). ℞. — As last. *R.I.C.* 380 (*Voetter*) 22
171 Ml. ℞. — As last. *R.I.C.* S175 20
173 Kk(M). ℞. — Diana stg. r., holding spear and bow, hound before her.
R.I.C. S473 18
174 Kl(M). ℞. — As last. *R.I.C.* S473 20
175 Kk. ℞. — As last .. ..
177 Ba(V). ℞. DIANA LVCIFERA, Diana stg. r., holding torch in both hands.
R.I.C. 290 15
178 Ka(A). ℞. DONA AVG., Mercury, half-naked, stg. l., dog at feet. *R.I.C.*
S634 30
179 Kk. ℞. FECVNDITAS AVG., Fecunditas stg. l., holding cornucopiae and
extending hand to child. *R.I.C.* S184 14
179a Kl. sh. sp. (S). ℞. FELICI. or FELICIT. AET., Felicitas stg. l., leaning on
column, holding caduceus. *R.I.C.* S564 (*Voetter*) 20
179b Kf(S). ℞. — As last. *R.I.C.* S185 14
180 Kk. ℞. FELICIT. AET., as last. *R.I.C.* S185 15
181 Kk. (R and S). ℞. FELICI. AVG., Felicitas stg. l. *R.I.C.* S187 and S565 8
181a Kf. ℞. — As last. *R.I.C.* S187 8
183 Kk. ℞. FELICIT. AVG., Felicitas stg. r., holding caduceus and globe;
T in field. *R.I.C.* S188 9
184 Kf. ℞. — As last. *R.I.C.* S188 9
184a Kf. and/or k (S). ℞. — As **181**. *R.I.C.* S565 8
185 Kk. ℞. — Felicitas stg. r., holding sceptre and globe .. .. ..

185a Kk. ℞. — As last; P, S, T or Γ in field. *R.I.C.* S189 9

186 **Antoninianus.** Kk. (R and M). ℞. FELICIT . AVG., Felicitas stg. l., holding caduceus and sceptre; P, S or T in field or ex. *R.I.C.* S191 and S474 .. .. £9

187 Fk. ℞. — As last (*Cohen*). *R.I.C.* S190 (but without mintmarks) .. 8

188 **Denarius.** K (*Cohen carries forward obv.* F *in error*) e. ℞. — As last without mintmarks. *R.I.C.* S350 100

189 **Quinarius.** K, laur. bust cuir. l., sp. sh. (M). ℞. — As last. *R.I.C.* S542 150

189a **Denarius.** Kq, sp. sh. ℞. — As last. *R.I.C.* S350 120

190 **Antoninianus.** Dk. ℞. — As last, but holding caduceus and cornucopiae; in field, P. *R.I.C.* S186 9

190a Df. ℞. — As last, but nothing in field. *R.I.C.* S186 9

191 Bc. ℞. FELICIT . DEORVM, Felicitas stg. l., holding caduceus and sceptre. *R.I.C.* 133 14

192 Kk. ℞. FELICIT . PVBL., Felicitas seated l.; T in ex. *R.I.C.* S192 .. 9

193 Kf. ℞. — As last. *R.I.C.* S192 9

193a Kf(S). ℞. FELICITAS AVG., Felicitas stg. r., holding sceptre and globe. *R.I.C.* S566 (*Voetter*) 14

195 Cf. ℞. FELICITAS AVGG., as **192,** but stg. l. *R.I.C.* 135 12

196 Bf. ℞. — As last. *R.I.C.* 134 12

197 GALLIENVS P . F . AVG . GERM., a. ℞. — As last. *R.I.C.* 136a .. 15

198 Gf. ℞. — As last. *R.I.C.* 136 12

199 Hf. ℞. — As last. *R.I.C.* 136 12

200 Kf(S). ℞. — As last. *R.I.C.* S565 (AVG., *which is probably correct*) .. 8

206 Bc. ℞. FELICITAS SAECVLI, Diana walking r., holding torch in both hands. (*Perhaps the same as next*). .. ..

206a Ba(V). ℞. — As last. *R.I.C.* 291 20

209 Kk(M). ℞. FID . MILITVM, Fides (*R.I.C.* Felicitas *in error*) stg. l., holding two ensigns. *R.I.C.* S475 8

210 Kk(M). ℞. FID . PRAET . . . ., Genius, half-naked, stg. l., holding patera and cornucopiae; to r., ensign .. ..

210a Kl(M). ℞. FID . PRAET., as last. *R.I.C.* S476 16

213 Kk (M and S). ℞. FIDEI LEG., three trophies. *R.I.C.* S477 and S567 40

216 Kk(S). ℞. FIDEI PRAET., legionary eagle between two ensigns. *R.I.C.* S568 15

217 Kf(S). ℞. — As last. *R.I.C.* S568 15

218a Kf(S). ℞. FIDEI PRAET . VOTA X . Genius as **210,** but globe for patera. *R.I.C.* S569 (*Voetter*) 22

219 Kk(A). ℞. FIDES AVG., Mercury, naked but mantle on l. arm, stg. l.; in ex., PXV .. ..

219a Ka(A). ℞. — As last. *R.I.C.* S607 12

219b Kf(A). ℞. — As last. *R.I.C.* S607 12

220 Kk(M). ℞. FIDES EXERC. VIII., Fides stg. l., holding legionary eagle and ensign; usually, if not always, in field, P. *R.I.C.* S478 12

221 Ka(M). ℞. — As last. *R.I.C.* S478 12

222 Kl(M). ℞. — As last. *R.I.C.* S478 12

223 K, bust to waist l., wearing rad. helmet, sh. sp. (M). ℞. — As last. .. 30

223a Kc, w. (M.). ℞. — As last. *R.I.C.* 478 (*in error for last ?*) ..

224 **Medallion.** D, laur. bust, cuir. l., sp. sh. (the shield ornamentation includes the emperor riding l., soldier in front and behind). ℞. FIDES EXERCITVS, emperor in military dress, stg. l., crowned by Victory stg. behind him; he offers his hand to Roma stg. r. before him; below, two rivers, Rhine and Main reclining, facing each other (38-36 mm.; 36.00-39.35 gms.). *R.I.C.* 108 .. .. *Extremely rare*

225 **Antoninianus.** Ka(M). ℞. FIDES LEG., emperor stg. facing, hd. l., holding ensign and transverse sceptre; behind, ensign. *R.I.C.* S479 .. £22
225a Ka(A). ℞. — Emperor stg. l., holding two ensigns. *R.I.C.* S635 .. 25
227 Df(M). ℞. FIDES MIL., Fides stg. l., holding two ensigns. *R.I.C.* 381 12
227a Kk(M). ℞. — As last. *R.I.C.* S480 10
229 Kk(M). ℞. FIDES MILIT., Fides stg. l., holding ensign and transverse sceptre; in ex., MP. *R.I.C.* S481 10
236 Bf. ℞. FIDES MILITVM, as **227,** but stg. facing, hd. l. *R.I.C.* 137 .. 12
237 Bc. ℞. — As last. *R.I.C.* 137 12
237a Cf. ℞. — As last (*Dorchester*) 12
237b Gf. ℞. — As last. *R.I.C.* 138 (*Voetter*) 15
238 Kf(M). ℞. — As last. 12
238a Kk(M). ℞. — As last. *R.I.C.* S480 12
244 **Quinarius.** Mm. ℞. — As **229,** but sceptre vertical and nothing in ex. *R.I.C.* S367 100
245 Dm. ℞. — As last. *R.I.C.* S366 100

236   257

246 **Antoninianus.** Kk. ℞. — As last, N in field. *R.I.C.* S192a .. 8
247 Kf. ℞. — As last. *R.I.C.* S192a 8
247a Kf(S). ℞. — Fides stg. between ensign and sceptre or two ensigns. *R.I.C.* S571 10
247b Kk(S). ℞. — As last. *R.I.C.* S571 10
249 Df(L). ℞. — Eagle, holding in its beak a wreath, looking r. and stg. on a globe between two ensigns. *R.I.C.* 13 18
250 Mc or f(L). ℞. — As last. *R.I.C.* 14 18
251 Mg, sp. sh. (L). ℞. — As last. *R.I.C.* 15 20
252 Lg, w. sp. sh. (L). ℞. — As last. *R.I.C.* 16 20
253 Jc or f(L). ℞. — As last. *R.I.C.* 11 18
253a Ef(L). ℞. — As last. *R.I.C.* 12 (*Paris*) 20
257 Kc or f(S). ℞. FIDES MILITVM within laurel-wreath. *R.I.C.* S570 .. 25
259 Ka(A). ℞. FORTVNA AVG., Fortuna stg. l., by altar, holding cornucopiae; in ex., SPQR. *R.I.C.* S636 12
260 **Denarius.** Km. ℞. FORT . REDVX, as last, but in ex., S. *R.I.C.* 351 .. 100
261 **Antoninianus.** Dk(M). ℞. — Fortuna seated l., in ex.; MS. *R.I.C.* S483 9
262 Ea(M). ℞. — As last. *R.I.C.* S482 9

263 Gf. ℞. — As last, but no mintmark. *R.I.C.* 140 15
264 Gk. ℞. — As last. .. ..

5 **Antoninianus.** Kk(S). ℞. FORTVNA RED. (or REDVX), Fortuna stg. l., holding rudder (or wreath) and cornucopiae; no mintmark; or star, B, S, SI or II in field (*Cohen only gives* SI). *R.I.C.* S572 .. .. £9

6 Ka(S). ℞. — As last. *R.I.C.* S572 9

7 Kc(S). ℞. — As last. *R.I.C.* S572 9

9 Ka. ℞. FORTVNA REDVX, Fortuna stg. l.; sometimes with S in ex. (*Cohen*, in field). *R.I.C.* S193.. 8

0 Kc and/or f. ℞. — As last. *R.I.C.* S193 8

1 K, rad. helmeted bust r., w. sp. sh. ℞. — As last. *R.I.C.* S193 .. 12

2 Kl. ℞. — As last. *R.I.C.* S193 10

6 **Denarius.** E (*R.I.C.* 'K' *in error ?*) m. ℞. — As before, but rudder on globe, no mintmark. *R.I.C.* S352 100

7 **Antoninianus.** Kf(A). ℞. — Fortuna stg. l., holding caduceus and cornucopiae; in ex., VIIC (*this stands for* COS . VII). *R.I.C.* S613 .. 10

7a Ka(A). ℞. — As last, but SPQR in ex. *R.I.C.* S637 10

7b Kf(A). ℞. — As last. *R.I.C.* S637 10

9 Kk(M). ℞. — Fortuna seated l.; S or MS in ex. *R.I.C.* S484 9

9a Kk. ℞. — As last, but S in ex. *R.I.C.* S194a 9

0 Kf(M). ℞. — As **279**. *R.I.C.* S484 9

0a Kf. ℞. — As **279a**. *R.I.C.* S194a 9

1 Dk(M). ℞. — As **279** (*Cohen gives*, or SM). *R.I.C.* S483 9

1a Dk. ℞. — As **279a**. *R.I.C.* S194 9

2 Da(M). ℞. — As **281**. *R.I.C.* S483 9

2a Da. ℞. — As **279a**. *R.I.C.* S194 9

2b Df(M). ℞. — As **279**. *R.I.C.* S483 9

3 F, rad. bust l., w. with imperial mantle, sc. ea. ℞. — As **279**, but without mintmark. *R.I.C.* 139 25

4 Bc. ℞. — Mercury stg. l., mantle on l. arm .. .. ..

4a Ba(V). ℞. — As last. *R.I.C.* 292 22

6 Kk. ℞. FORTVNAE REDVCI, as **279** but without mintmark ..

6a Kk. ℞. — As **284**, but S in ex. *R.I.C.* S195 (*an error for last ?*) ..

7 Kk. ℞. GALLIENVS AVG., Mars stg. r., holding branch. *R.I.C.* S196 .. 30

8 Kk. ℞. — Emperor stg. r., holding patera (*barbarous Gallic fabric*). *R.I.C.* S196 30

9 Kc. ℞. GENIO AVG., Genius, modius on hd., stg. l. before altar. *R.I.C.* S197 9

0 Kh(A). ℞. — As last. *R.I.C.* S638 9

1 Kk. ℞. GENIV . AVG., as last, but no altar and ensign to r. *R.I.C.* S197 .. 9

1a Kk. ℞. — As last, Q or VI in field. *R.I.C.* S197.. 9

1b Kk(A). ℞. — As last, palm in ex. *R.I.C.* S638 9

2 Kf. ℞. — As **291**. *R.I.C.* S197 9

2a Kf. ℞. — As **291a**. *R.I.C.* S197 9

3 Kf. ℞. — As **291**, but Genius turreted, V in field. *R.I.C.* S197 9

N.B.—*With nos* **291a** *to* **299**, *in a few cases, the mintmark could be in the exergue.*

N.B.—S *before an R.I.C. number indicates that it is a coin from his sole reign.*

294 Antoninianus. Kc. ℞. GENIVS AVG., Genius stg. l. *R.I.C.* S197 .. £9
295 Kl. ℞. — As **289.** *R.I.C.* S197 10
295a Kl(A). ℞. — As **289** or **291b** or **294.** *R.I.C.* S638 10
296 Kf. ℞. — As **291.** *R.I.C.* S197 9
296a Kf. ℞. — As **291a.** *R.I.C.* S197 9
297 Kk. ℞. — As **291.** *R.I.C.* S197 9
297a Kk. ℞. — As **291a.** *R.I.C.* S197 9
298 Kk. ℞. — As **293.** *R.I.C.* S197 9
299 Kl, seen from back, sp. sh. ℞. — As **291a.** *R.I.C.* S197 18

N.B.—*From* **294** *to* **299,** *in a few cases, the mintmark may be in the exergue.*

300 Dk. ℞. — As **291.** *R.I.C.* S198 9
300a Dk. ℞. — As **291a** 9
301 Da. ℞. — As **291.** *R.I.C.* S198 9
301a Da. ℞. — As **291a** 9
304 Kk. ℞. GENIVS EXE . . . ., Genius stg. l. *R.I.C.* S199 (*obv.*, f) 20

296a 305a

305 Kf. ℞. GERMAN . MAX . TR . P., trophy; at base, two seated captives, hands behind their backs. *R.I.C.* S200 18
305a Df. ℞. GERMAN . MAX . TER., as last 20
306 Fc(M). ℞. GERMANICVS MAXIMVS, as last. *R.I.C.* 382 15
306a Ff(M). ℞. — As last. *R.I.C.* 382 15
306b IMP . GALLIENVS P . F . AVGG. (*sic.*), a(M). ℞. — As last. *R.I.C.* 383 .. 20
306c Bf. ℞. — As last. *R.I.C.* 142 (*Paris*) 20
307 IMP . P . LIC . GALLIENVS P . F . AVG., rad. hd. ℞. GERMANICVS MAX . TER., as last (*obv. is perhaps misdescription of next*) .. ..
307a Cf. ℞. — As last. *R.I.C.* 141 20
308 Mc(L). ℞. GERMANICVS MAX . V., as last. *R.I.C.* 18 15
309 As last, but heavy flan (5.4 gms.). *R.I.C.* 18 30
310 Mg, sc. or sp. sh. (L). ℞. — As last. *R.I.C.* 18.. 18
311 As last, but heavy flan (5.8 gms.). *R.I.C.* 18 30
312 Ef(L). ℞. — As last. *R.I.C.* 17 15
313 As last, but GERMACVS (*Cohen*), GERMANCVS (*R.I.C.*) MAX. V. *R.I.C.* 17 note 18
314 Lg, sc. or sp. sh. (L). ℞. — As **308.** *R.I.C.* 19 18

316

315 Quinarius. Me(L). ℞. — As last. *R.I.C.* 60   ..   ..   ..   £150

316 Antoninianus. Kk. ℞. HERCVLI CONS . AVG., lion walking l.; A in ex.
R.I.C. S201 *Illustrated at bottom of page 72*   25

317 Kk. ℞. — Wild boar walking (or running) r.; Є in ex. *R.I.C.* S202 ..   18

318 As last, but HERCVLO CONS . AVG. (*Cohen says* C in ex.). *R.I.C.* S202   ..   18

322 Kk. ℞. INDVLG . AVG., Spes walking l.; Δ in ex. *R.I.C.* S204   12

322a Kk(M). ℞. — As last, but P or S in ex. *R.I.C.* S485   12

322b Kf. ℞. — As **322.** *R.I.C.* S204   12

323 Da. ℞. — As last. *R.I.C.* S203   12

326

325 Quinarius. Km. ℞. INDVLGENT . AVG., Indulgentia seated l., holding
branch and sceptre. *R.I.C.* S368   125

326 Antoninianus. Kk. ℞. — As last, but P in ex. *R.I.C.* S205 (*the* P
sometimes appears as D)   10

327 Kf. ℞. — As last. *R.I.C.* S205   10

330 Quinarius. Km. ℞. INDVLGENTIA AVG., as **325.** *R.I.C.* S368   ..   125

331 Antoninianus. Kk. ℞. — Indulgentia or Providentia, legs crossed,
leaning on column, holding baton and cornucopiae; at feet, wheel; XI in
field. *R.I.C.* S206   12

332 Kf. ℞. — As last. *R.I.C.* S206   12

336 Kc(A). ℞. INVICTO AVG., Sol, rad., stg. l., raising r. hand and holding
whip; SPQR in ex. *R.I.C.* S640   25

337 Kk(A). ℞. INVICTVS, Sol as before, but running l.; star in field   ..   25

337a Kc(A). ℞. — As last. *R.I.C.* S639   25

338 *Obv. ?* ℞. — Sol passing by (?), holding whip; star in field   ..   ..

338a Kc(A). ℞. INVICTVS AVG., as **336.** *R.I.C.* S640   25

339 Kk(S). ℞. IO . CANTAB., Jupiter, in military attire, stg. l. *R.I.C.* S573   40

340 Kf, sometimes highly ornamented (S). ℞. — As last. *R.I.C.* S573 ..   45

341 Kf. ℞. IOVI CONS . AVG., goat walking l.; in ex., S. *R.I.C.* S207   ..   10

242 Kk. ℞. — As last. *R.I.C.* S207   10

343 Kl. ℞. — As last. *R.I.C.* S207   10

344 Kk. ℞. — Goat walking r.; in ex., S. *R.I.C.* S207   10

345 Kf. ℞. — As last. *R.I.C.* S207   10

346 Kc (*R.I.C.; but Cohen says* 'to left'). ℞. — As last. *R.I.C.* S207   ..   10

347 Kh, seen from back, sp. and sh. on which hd. of Medusa. ℞. — As last,
R.I.C. S207   20

348 Kh, seen from back. ℞. — As last. *R.I.C.* S207   15

351　　　　　　　　　　　　　358

351　Antoninianus. Bc. ℞. IOVI CONSERVA., Jupiter, naked, but cloak on
l. shoulder, stg. l. *R.I.C.* 143　　..　　..　　..　　..　　..　　..　£12

353　Kk. ℞. — As last. *R.I.C.* S208 (? with *s* in field or ex.)　　..　　..　9

354　Kl. ℞. — As last. *R.I.C.* S208 (as last) ..　　..　　..　　..　　..　10

356　Kg, with helmet, sp. sh. (M). ℞. — As before, but with eagle at feet;
s in field. *R.I.C.* S486　　..　　..　　..　　..　　..　　..　　..　15

356a As last, but mint of Rome, with s in field or ex. *R.I.C.* S208　　..　15

357　Kl(M). ℞. — As **356**. *R.I.C.* S486　　..　　..　　..　　..　　..　10

357a Kl. ℞. — As **356a**. *R.I.C.* S208　　..　　..　　..　　..　　..　10

357b Kk(M). ℞. — As **356**. *R.I.C.* S486　　..　　..　　..　　..　　..　8

357c Kk. ℞. — As **356a**. *R.I.C.* S208 ..　　..　　..　　..　　..　　8

358　Kg(M). ℞. — As **356**　　..　　..　　..　　..　　..　　..　10

359　Kc(M). ℞. — As last. *R.I.C.* S486　　..　　..　　..　　..　　..　8

359a Kc and/or f. ℞. — As **356a**. *R.I.C.* S208　　..　　..　　..　　..

359b Ak. ℞. — As **356a**. *R.I.C.* S209 (*Voetter*)　　..　　..　　..　12

N.B.—*R.I.C. S486 gives one or more of these without mintmarks.*
　　　R.I.C. S208/9 gives one or more of these with N in field.

360　Kc(M). ℞. — Jupiter seated l., holding Victory and sceptre; P in field.
R.I.C. S487　　..　　..　　..　　..　　..　　..　　..　　..　10

360a Kk(M). ℞. As last, or as **367**. *R.I.C.* S487　　..　　..　　..　10

361　Kk. ℞. IOVI CONSERVAT., as **351**, but with N (or II or III) or V in field.
R.I.C. S210　　..　　..　　..　　..　　..　　..　　..　　..　9

361a Kf. ℞. — As last. *R.I.C.* S210　　..　　..　　..　　..　　..　9

362　Kf(A). ℞. — As last, but nothing in field, PXV in ex. *R.I.C.* S608
(globe for thunderbolt)　　..　　..　　..　　..　　..　　..　12

363　Bf. ℞. — As last, but nothing in field or ex. *R.I.C.* 143　　..　12

365　Dg w., sc. ea. ℞. — Jupiter, clothed, stg. r.; in ex., S (*Cohen*) or *s*
(*R.I.C.*) *R.I.C.* S211　　..　　..　　..　　..　　..　　..　25

366　Kk(A). ℞. — Jupiter, naked but cloak floating behind him, stg. l.,
holding globe and sceptre. *R.I.C.* S641 (*obv. l, possibly in error*) ..　　..　12

367　Kf(M). ℞. — Jupiter seated, as **360**, but the P in ex. *R.I.C.* S487　　..　18

N.B.—*For this with Kk obv. see* **360a**.

367a Ka. ℞. — (or CONSERVATORI), Jupiter stg. l., holding globe and spear.
R.I.C. S212　　..　　..　　..　　..　　..　　..　　..　　..　20

367b Kl(A). ℞. — — As **365**. *R.I.C.* S641　　..　　..　　..　　..　10

370　Bc. ℞. IOVI CONSERVATORI, Jupiter, naked, but cloak on l. shoulder,
stg. l. *R.I.C.* 143　　..　　..　　..　　..　　..　　..　　..　12

371　Quinarius. Bb. ℞. — As last. *R.I.C.* 189　　..　　..　　..　125

375　Antoninianus. Ka or f (or c) (A). ℞. — As **366**. *R.I.C.* S641　　..　8

376　Ka and/or f (A). ℞. — As last, but P . XV in ex. *R.I.C.* S608　　..　10

376a Ka and/or f (A). ℞. — As last, but VII C in ex. *R.I.C.* S614　　..　10

377　Bc. ℞. — Jupiter, naked but cloak floating behind him, stg. l.; at his feet,
small figure of emperor. *R.I.C.* 143..　　..　　..　　..　　..　14

378 **Antoninianus.** Cc(A). ℞. IOVI CONSERVATORI, Gallienus, in military dress, stg. r., holding reversed spear and receiving globe from Jupiter stg. l., naked except for mantle over arm and behind him, and holding sceptre; in field above, wreath. *R.I.C.* 440.. .. .. £14

378a As last, but nothing in field. *R.I.C.* 440 note 14

379 Cc(A). ℞. — As **378,** but Gallienus holds sceptre. *R.I.C.* 440 .. 14

379a As last, but nothing in field. *R.I.C.* 440 note 14

380 Jc and/or f (L). ℞. IOVI CRESCENTI, Jupiter as a child seated on goat r. *R.I.C.* 20 30

381 Ka(A). ℞. IOVI PATRI, Jupiter stg. r., head l.; in ex., palm-branch. *R.I.C.* S642 15

381a Ka(A). ℞. IOVI PROPVG., Jupiter walking l. *R.I.C.* S643 (*Voetter*) .. 20

382 Kk. ℞. IOVI PROPVGNAT., Jupiter naked, but with flowing cloak, walking l., looking back, holding thunderbolt 8

382a As last, with IX, X or XI in field. *R.I.C.* S214 (XI only) 9

383 Dk. ℞. — As **382.** *R.I.C.* S213 8

383a Dk. ℞. — As **382a.** *R.I.C.* S213 9

384 Ka, sp. sh. ℞. — As **382a.** *R.I.C.* S214 10

384a Ak. ℞. — (or PROPVGNATORI). As before, N or XI in field. *R.I.C.* S215 (*Voetter*) 12

386 Kf. ℞. IOVI PROPVGNATORI, Jupiter stg., holding thunderbolt and eagle 12

386a Kk (or as **384**). ℞. — As **382a.** *R.I.C.* S214 12

388 Kk. ℞. IOVIS STATOR, Jupiter naked, stg. facing, hd. r. *R.I.C.* S216 .. 8

388a Kk. ℞. — As last, but *s* in field. *R.I.C.* S216 9

389 Kf. ℞. — As **388** and/or **388a.** *R.I.C.* S216 9

389a Kf seen from the back. ℞. — As last. *R.I.C.* S216 10

390 IMP . GALLIENVS PIVS FEL . AVG., h, w. ℞. — As last, *R.I.C.* S218 .. 14

390a Ak. ℞. — As last. *R.I.C.* S217 (*Voetter*) 12

394 Ka(A). ℞. IOVI STATORI, as before; star in field or ex. 10

394a Ka. ℞ — As before, C (or *s* ?) in field 10

394b Ka and/or f (A). ℞. — Jupiter stg., holding spear; nothing, or star in field. *R.I.C.* S645 9

395 Kk. ℞. — As **394** or last; *s* in field (heavy flan). *R.I.C.* S219 note .. 20

395a As last, or nothing in field (ordinary flan). *R.I.C.* S219 12

396 Ma(A). ℞. — As **394b;** nothing or star in field or ex. *R.I.C.* S644 .. 9

396a Mf(M). ℞. — Jupiter stg. l., holding Victory and sceptre. *R.I.C.* S488 14

397 Dc and/or f (L). ℞. IOVI VICTORI, Jupiter, naked, holding Victory and sceptre (or spear), stg. facing on cippus, inscribed IMP . C . E . S (*imperator cum exercitu suo*). *R.I.C.* 22 18

398 Ec and/or f (L). ℞. — As last. *R.I.C.* 21 18

399 Mc and/or f (L). ℞. — As last. *R.I.C.* 23 18

400 Mg, sp. sh. (L). ℞. — As last. *R.I.C.* 23 20

N.B.—S *before an R.I.C. number indicates that it is a coin from his sole reign.*

402 Antoninianus. Kk. ℞. IOVI VLTORI, Jupiter, naked, walking l., looking back, holding thunderbolt, cloak on arm; s in field. *R.I.C.* S221 .. £8

403 Kf. ℞. — As last. *R.I.C.* S221 8

404 Dc. ℞. — As last. *R.I.C.* S220 8

405 Dg, sp. sh. ℞. — As last. *R.I.C.* S220 15

408 Kf. ℞. — As before, but Jupiter stg. facing, hd. r.; in field, v or s. *R.I.C.* S221 10

408a Kk. ℞. — As last. *R.I.C.* S221 10

409 Dk. ℞. — As last. *R.I.C.* S220 9

409a Kc. ℞. — As **402** or **408.** *R.I.C.* S221 9

409b Kl. ℞. — As last. *R.I.C.* S221 12

409c Kl, sp. sh. ℞. — As last. *R.I.C.* S221 15

409d Kg with helmet, sp. sh. ℞. — As last. *R.I.C.* S221 18

415 Kc or a (A). ℞. IVBENTVS AVG., emperor, in military dress, stg. l., holding Victory and spear; in ex., VIIC. *R.I.C.* S615 15

416 Kk. ℞. IVNO CONSERVAT., Juno stg. l., peacock at feet (Hy.; *rev. of Salonina*). *R.I.C.* S222 14

417 Kk. ℞. IVNO REGINA, as last .. ..

417a Kk. ℞. — As last; Q in field. *R.I.C.* S223 14

418 Kk. ℞. — Juno stg. l., but without peacock .. .. ..

418a Kk. ℞. — As last; Q in field. *R.I.C.* S223 14

419 Kk. ℞. IVNONI CONS . AVG., goat walking l.; Δ in ex. *R.I.C.* S224 .. 14

421 Ec(L and M). ℞. LAETIT . TEMP., Jupiter as a child, seated on goat walking l. *R.I.C.* 24 and 384 22

421a Ef(M). ℞. — As last. *R.I.C.* 384 22

423 Kk. ℞. LAETITIA AVG., Laetitia stg. l.; in field, IV, V or VI, or in ex., P (or B), S or V. *R.I.C.* S226 9

423a Kk(M). ℞. — As last, s in field or P or s in ex. *R.I.C.* S489 10

424 Ka or f and/or c. ℞. — As **423.** *R.I.C.* S226 10

425 Kf(A). ℞. — As before, but VIIC in ex. *R.I.C.* S616 10

425a Kf(M). ℞. — As **423a.** *R.I C.* S489 10

425b Ka(A). ℞. — As **425.** *R.I.C.* S616 10

426 Kl. ℞. — As before, but nothing in ex. *R.I.C.* S226 (*only given with mintmark, as* **423**) 12

427 Kl., sc. ℞. — As last or **423.** *R.I.C.* S226 (club or sc.) 15

427a Kg with helmet, sp. sh. ℞. — As **423.** *R.I.C.* S226 15

427b Kh with imperial mantle, sc. ea. ℞. — As last. *R.I.C.* S226 15

427c Kk. ℞. — As last. *R.I.C.* 226 (*perhaps a mistake for next*) .. ..

428 Mk. ℞. — As before, P in ex. 10

428a GALLIENVS P . AVG., f (M). ℞. — As before, but nothing in ex. *R.I.C.* S490 10

429 Dh with imperial mantle, sc. ea. ℞. — As last. *R.I.C.* S225 15

430 Bf. ℞. — As last. (Hy.? *or misreading of* **437**) .. ..

435	**Antoninianus.** Cf. ℞. LAETITIA AVGG., Laetitia stg. l. *R.I.C.* 145		£15
436	Another, similar, on heavy flan (5.23 gms.). *R.I.C.* 145 note		25
437	Bc (*Cohen has laur., in error ?*). ℞. — As last. *R.I.C.* 144		15
437a	Bf. ℞. — As last. *R I.C.* 144		15
437b	Ba(V). ℞. — As last. *R.I.C.* 293		15
438	Gf. ℞. — As last. *R.I.C.* 146		15
439	Kf. ℞. — As last. (Hy. ? *or misreading of* **424/5**)		
440	Ff(A). ℞. — As last. *R.I.C.* 441		12
441	Dc(A). ℞. — As last. *R.I.C.* 442		12
441a	Df(A). ℞. — As last. *R.I.C.* 442 (*Voetter*)		15
442	Kk. ℞. LAETITIA FVND., as last. (Hy.; *rev. type of Tacitus and Florianus*)		18

441a   447

443	Kk or f (M). ℞. LEG . I ADI . V P . V F. (*Legio prima Adjutrix, quintum pia, quintum fidelis*), Capricorn r. *R.I.C.* 314		90
444	As last, but heavy (5.25 grms.). *R.I.C.* 314 (*note gives this to* **450**)		90
445	Kl. ℞. — As last. *R.I.C.* 314		90
446	Kk(M). ℞. LEG . I ADI . VI P . VI F., as last. *R.I.C.* 315		50
447	Kf(M). ℞. — As last. *R.I.C.* 315		50
448	Kg, sp. sh. (M). ℞. — *R.I.C.* 315		60
449	Kf, lance on shoulder (M). ℞. — *R.I.C.* 315 (bust to l.)		60
449a	Kl(M). ℞. — *R.I.C.* 315		60
450	Kl(M). ℞. As before, but E for F. *R.I.C.* 316		60
451	Kf(M). ℞. Legend as **446**, pegasus flying r. (Hy.) *R.I.C.* 317		60
452	Kg with helmet, sp. sh. (M). ℞. LEG . I ADI . VII P . VII F., Capricorn r. *R.I.C.* 318		60
453	Kf(M). ℞. — As last. *R.I.C.* 318		50
454	K rad. hd. (M). ℞. LEG . I (*sic.*) AVG . VI P . VI F., Mars stg., holding spear and shield. (Hy.; *or possibly a mis-description of a* **459** *or a blundered specimen of same*). *R.I.C.* 319		
455	Kf(M). ℞. LEG . I ITAL. (Italica) VI P . VI F., boar running r. *R.I.C.* 320		50
456	Kc(M). ℞. — As last. *R.I.C.* 320		50
457	Kg or l, sp. sh. (M). ℞. — As last. *R.I.C.* 320		60
458	Kf(M). ℞. LEG . I ITAL . VII P . VII F., hippocamp r. *R.I.C.* 321		60
458a	Kl(M). ℞. — As last. *R.I.C.* 321 (*Paris*)		80
459	Ka(M). ℞. LEG . I MIN . (*Minervia*) VI P . VI F., Minerva stg. l., holding palladium (or Victory) and leaning on shield; spear rests against l. arm. *R.I.C.* 322		90
459a	Kf(M). ℞. — As last. *R.I.C.* 322		90
460	Kl, sp. on shoulder, sh. (M). ℞. — As last. *R.I.C.* 322		100
461	Kl(M). ℞. — As last. *R.I.C.* 322		90
462	Kg seen from back, sp. sh. (M). ℞. — As last. *R I.C.* 322		100
463	Ka(M). ℞. LEG . I MIN . VII P . VII F., as last. *R.I.C.* 323		110
464	Kl(M). ℞. — As last. *R.I .C.* 323		110

465 **Antoninianus.** Kf(M). ℞. LEG . II ADI . VI P . VI F., pegasus flying r.
R.I.C. 324 .. .. £50
466 Kc, sp. on l. shoulder (M). ℞. — As last. R.I.C. 324 (obv. l., sp.) .. 60
467 Kl, sp. forward, sh. (M). ℞. — As last. R.I.C. 324 60
468 Kl(M). ℞. — Wild boar. R.I.C. 325 80
469 Kl(M). ℞. LEG . II AD . VII P . VII F., pegasus flying r. R.I.C. 326 .. 75
470 Kl(M). ℞. LEG . II CL . ADI. (Claudia Adjutrix) VI P . VI F., capricorn r.
R.I.C. 327 75
470a Kf(M). ℞. — As last. R.I.C. 327 60
471 Kf(M). ℞. LEG . II ITAL . VI P . VI F., as last. R.I.C. 328 50

465 472

472 Kf(M). ℞. — She-wolf to l., suckling Romulus and Remus. R.I.C. 329 75
473 Ml(M). ℞. — As last. R.I.C. 329 75
473a Mk(M). ℞. — As last. R.I.C. 329 75
474 Kf, sp. forward (M). ℞. — As last. R.I.C. 329.. 75
474a Kf, sp. over shoulder (M). ℞. — As last. R.I.C. 329 75
475 Kf, sp. or sc. over l. shoulder (M). ℞. LEG . I ITAL . VII P . VII F., as last.
R.I.C. 330 (should read LEG . II) 75
476 Kf(M). ℞. — As last. R.I.C. 330 60
477 K bust with rad. helmet, w seen from the back, sp. sh. (M). ℞. LEG .
IT ITAL . VII P . VII F., ibis or stork walking r. R.I.C. 331 (should read
LEG . III) 85
478 Kl, sp. sh. (M). ℞. LEG . II PART. (Parthica) V P . V F., centaur, holding
globe, running l. R.I.C. 332.. 60
479 Kf(M). ℞. — Centaur walking l., holding globe and club. R.I.C. 333 55
480 Kf(M). ℞. LEG . II PART . VI P . VI F., as last. R.I.C. 334 .. 50
481 Kf(M). ℞. — As last, but without club. R.I.C. 335 50
482 Kl, sp. sh. (M). ℞. — As last. R.I.C. 335 55
483 Kf(M). ℞. — Centaur running r., holding club. R.I.C. 336 50
484 Kl, sp. sh. (M). ℞. — As last. R.I.C. 336 55
485 Kf(M). ℞. — Centaur running l., holding club. R.I.C. 337 55
486 Kl(M). ℞. LEG . II PART . VII P . VII F. As last. R.I.C. 338 60

483 490

487 Kf(M). ℞. LEG . III ITAL . VI P . VI F., stork walking r. R.I.C. 339 .. 60
488, 493 Kl(M). ℞. — As last. R.I.C. 339 70

489 **Antoninianus.** Kl, sp. sh. (M). ℞. LEG . III ITAL . VI P . VI F., stork
    walking r. *R.I.C.* 339..   ..   ..   £75
490 Ka(M). ℞. — As last. *R.I.C.* 339. *Illustrated on p.* 78..   ..   60
491, 494 Kf, sc. (M). ℞. — As last. *R.I.C.* 339   70
492 Kl with helmet, seen from the back, sp. sh. (M). ℞. — As last. *R.I.C.*
    339   80
495 Kk (*R.I.C.* a and f) (M). ℞. — Bull r. *R.I.C.* 340 (*misreading*)   ..   60
496 Kc(M). ℞. LEG . III ITAL . VII P . VII F., stork walking r. *R.I.C.* 341 ..   70
497 Kl(M). ℞. — As last. *R.I.C.* 341..   60
498 Kg with helmet, seen from the back, sp. sh. (M). ℞. — As last. *R.I.C.*
    341   60
499 Kf(M). ℞. LEG . IIII FL . (*Flavia*) VI P . VI F., rad. lion walking r. *R.I.C.*
    342   75
500 Kf(M). ℞. — Lion running r. *R.I.C.* 343   50
501 Kk(M). ℞. — As last. *R.I.C.* 343   50
502 Kl(M). ℞. LEG . IIII FL . VII P . VII F., as last. *R.I.C.* 344   ..   50
503 Kk or f(M). ℞. — As last. *R.I.C.* 344   50

510   504

504 Kf(M). ℞. LEG . V MAC . (*Macedonica*) VI P . VI F., Victory stg. r.; at her
    feet, eagle. *R.I.C.* 345   75
505 Kg, sp. sh. (M). ℞. — As last. *R.I.C.* 345   75
505a As one of the last two. ℞. — As last, but Victory stg. l. *R.I.C.* 345 ..   75
506 Kc or f (M). ℞. LEG . V MAC . VII P . VII F., as **504**. *R.I.C.* 345 (a)   70
507 Kl(M). ℞. — As last. *R.I.C.* 345 (a)   70
508 Kg. sp. sh. (M). ℞. LEG . VI CL . (*Claudia*) VI P . VI F., bull walking r.
    R.I.C. 346 (*should read* LEG . VII)   75
509 Kg(M). ℞. LEG . VI MAC . VII P . VII F., as **504**. *R.I.C.* 347 (*should read*
    LEG . V)   90
510 Kc(M). ℞. LEG . VII CL . VI P . VI F., bull walking r. *R.I.C.* 348   ..   50
511 Kf, sp. or sc. (M). ℞. — As last. *R.I.C.* 348   60
512 Kl seen from back, sh. sp. (M). ℞. — As last. *R.I.C.* 348   ..   70
513 Kl(M). ℞. — As last. *R.I.C.* 348..   60
514 Kf(M). ℞. — As before, but CLA. *R.I.C.* 349   70
515 Kf(M). ℞. LEG . VII CL . VII P . VII F., as before. *R.I.C.* 350 ..   50
516 Kl(M). ℞. — As last. *R.I.C.* 350..   60
517 K, bust l. with rad. helmet, sp. sh. (M). ℞. — As last. *R.I.C.* 350 ..   60
518 Ka(M). ℞. — As last. *R.I.C.* 350   50
519 Kf(M). ℞. — Lion running r. (*R.I.C.* r. or l. with or without radiation).
    R.I.C. 351   80
520 Kl(M). ℞. — As last. *R.I.C.* 351   80
521 Kf(M). ℞. LEG . VIII AVG . V P . V F., bull walking r. *R.I.C.* 352   ..   65
521a Kl(M). ℞. — As last. *R.I.C.* 352   70
522 Kf(M). ℞. LEG . VIII AVG . VI P . VI F., as last. *R.I.C.* 353   ..   50
523 Kl(M). ℞. — As last. *R.I.C.* 353..   50

N.B.—S *before an R.I.C. number indicates that it is a coin from his sole reign.*

524 **Antoninianus.** Kf(M). ℞. LEG . VIII AVG . VII P . VII F., bull walking r. *R.I.C.* 354 .. .. £80
525 Kl(M). ℞. — As last. *R.I.C.* 354.. 80
526 K, bust l., seen from the back with rad. helmet, sp. sh. (M). ℞. — As last. *R.I.C.* 354 80
527 Kf or g, w. (M). ℞. LEG . VIIII AVG . VI P . VI F., lion to r. *R.I.C.* 355 (*there was no such legion*) 100
528 K ? (*R.I.C.* l.) (M). ℞. LEG . VIIII VI P . VI F., as **504** (*the rev. is either a die-sinker's error or misreading of the* **504** *rev.*). *R.I.C.* 356 75
529 Kf(M). ℞. LEG . X GEM . (*Gemina*) VI P . VI F., bull to r. *R.I.C.* 357 .. 50
529a Kk(M). ℞. — As last. *R.I.C.* 357 50
530 Kf, sp. (M). ℞. — As last. *R.I.C.* 357 55
531 Kg, sp. sh. (M). ℞. — As last. *R.I.C.* 357 60
532 Kk(M). ℞. — As before, but VII P . VII F. 50
532a Ka(M). ℞. — As last. *R.I.C.* 358 50
532b Kc(M). ℞. — As last. *R.I.C.* 358 50
532c Kk(M). ℞. — As last. *R.I.C.* 358.. 50
533 Kk with bare shoulders (M). ℞. LEG . XI CL . VI P . VI F., Neptune stg. r. *R.I.C.* 359 80
534 Kl(M). ℞. — As last. *R.I.C.* 359 80
534a Kl, sh. (M). ℞. — As last. (*John J. Hergenhan*) 80
535 Kf(M). ℞. — As last. *R.I.C.* 359.. 80
535a Kc(M). ℞. — As last. *R.I.C.* 359 80
536 K as **526** (M). ℞. — As last. *R.I.C.* 359 (*omits* rad. helmet *and not always* seen from the back) 80

535a   537

537 Kf(M). ℞. LEG . XIII GEM . VI P . VI F., Victory walking r., holding wreath and palm, meeting lion walking l. *R.I.C.* 360 75
538 Kl(M). ℞. — As last. *R.I.C.* 360.. 75
539 Kg, sp. pointing forward (M). ℞. — As last. *R.I.C.* 360 80
540 Kf(M). ℞. LEG . XIIII GEM . VI P . VI F., capricorn r. *R.I.C.* 361 .. 50
541 Kl, sp. sh. (M). ℞. — As last. *R.I.C.* 361 55

542a

542 Kc(M). ℞. LEG . IIXX (*should be* XXII) VI P . VI F., as last. *R.I.C.* 362 .. 60
542a Kf(M). ℞. — As last. *R.I.C.* 362.. 60
543 Kg, w. sp. sh. (M). ℞. — As last. *R.I.C.* 362 70

544 **Antoninianus.** Kl(M). ℞. LEG . IIXX VII P . VII F., as last. *R.I.C.* 363 .. £60
545 Ka(M). ℞. — As last. *R.I.C.* 363 60
546 Kb. ℞. — As last. *R.I.C.* 363 60
547 Kf, sc. on l. shoulder (M). ℞. — As last. *R.I.C.* 363 75
548 *Obv.* ? (M). ℞. LEG . XX VI P . VI F., as last. *R.I.C.* 364 (*probably* **551** *misread*).. .. ..
549 Kf(M). ℞. LEG . XXI (*probably* XIII *misread*) GEM . VI P . VI F., as **537**. *R.I.C.* 365 60
550 K, rad. bust dr. and cuir. l., seen from behind, sp. sh. (M). ℞. LEG . XXII VI P . VI F., capricorn running r. *R.I.C.* 366 55
551 Kf(M). ℞. — As last. *R.I.C.* 366.. 50
552 *Obv.* ? (M). ℞. LEG . XXX VLP . (*Ulpia*) VI P . VI F., as last. *R.I.C.* 367 (*blundered or misread*) .. ..
553 Kf(M). ℞. LEG . XXX VLP . VI P . VI F., Neptune stg. r. *R.I.C.* 368 .. 85
554 Kc(M). ℞. — As last. *R.I.C.* 368 85
554a Kl(M). ℞. — As last. *R.I.C.* 368.. 85
555 Kf(M). ℞. LEG . XXX VLP . VII P . VII F., as last. *R.I.C.* 369 100
556 Ka(M). ℞. — As last. *R.I.C.* 369 100
557 Kl(M). ℞. — As last. *R.I.C.* 369.. 100

563a

558 Kk. ℞. LIB . AVG., Liberalitas stg. l., S in ex. *R.I.C.* S227 10
562 Kk. ℞. LIBERAL . AVG., as last, but nothing in ex., S, P or T in field. *R.I.C.* S227 9
563 Ka. ℞. — As last. *R.I.C.* S227 9
563a Kf. ℞. — As last. *R.I.C.* S227 9

N.B.—*R.I.C. also gives* Q *in field for one or all of last three.*

564 **Quinarius.** Kd. ℞. — As before, without mintmark. *R.I.C.* S369 .. 125
565 **Antoninianus.** Kk. ℞. LIBERALIT . AVG., as last. *R.I.C.* S228 .. 9
566 Ec(M). ℞. LIBERALITAS AVGG., as last. *R.I.C.* 385 9
566a Ea(M). ℞. — As last. *R.I.C.* 385.. 9
567 Ff(A). ℞. — As last. *R.I.C.* 443 9
568 Df(A). ℞. — As last. *R.I.C.* 444 9
569 Dc(A). ℞. — As last. *R.I.C.* 444 9
570 Bf. ℞. — As last. *R.I.C.* 147 9
571 Cf. ℞. — As last. *R.I.C.* 148 9
571a Bc. ℞. — Similar, but Liberalitas seated. *R.I.C.* 149 (*Voetter*) .. 12
571b Cf. ℞. — Valerian and Gallienus seated on two curule chairs; behind them stands Liberalitas. *R.I.C.* 150 (*Vienna*) 30
579 Cf. ℞. LIBERALITAS AVGG . III, as **558**. 15
579a Cc. ℞. — As last. *R.I.C.* 151 15
579b Ea(M). ℞. — As last. *R.I.C.* 386 (*Voetter*) 15
584 Cc. ℞. — As **571b**, but citizen stands between them; no Liberalitas .. 30

585 Antoninianus. Kk. ℞. LIBERITAS (*sic*) AVG., Libertas stg. l., holding cap in r. hand, l. hand hanging £12

586 Kk. ℞. LIBERO P . CONS . AVG., panther walking l.; B (*R.I.C.* or A) in ex. *R.I.C.* S230 12

586a Kk(S). ℞. — As last; B (*R.I.C.* or nothing) in ex. *R.I.C.* S574 .. 12

587 Kc. ℞. — As **586.** *R.I.C.* S230 12

588 Kh. ℞. — As last. *R.I.C.* S230 (and/or Kg) 12

589 Kl. ℞. — As last. *R.I.C.* S230 12

589a Kl(S). ℞. — As **586a.** *R.I.C.* S574 12

590 Dk. ℞. — As **586.** *R.I.C.* S229 12

590a Kf. ℞. — As **586** or **591.** *R.I.C.* S230 12

590b Kf., sh. ℞. — As last. *R.I.C.* S230 14

591 Kk. ℞. — Panther walking r.; B (*R.I.C.* or A) in ex. *R.I.C.* S230 .. 12

591a Kk(S). ℞. — As last; B (*R.I.C.* or nothing) in ex. *R.I.C.* S574 .. 12

N.B.—*R.I.C. indicate that some of* **586a, 589a, 592a** *and* **591a** *may be without* AVG. *at end of rev. legend.*

592 Kl. ℞. — As **591.** *R.I.C.* S230 12

592a Kl(S). ℞. — As **591a.** *R.I.C.* S574 12

586   593

593 Kk. ℞. LIBERT . AVG., Libertas stg. l., legs crossed and leaning on column; S in field. *R.I.C.* S232 9

594 Ka. ℞. — As last. *R.I.C.* S232 9

594a Kf. ℞. — As last. *R.I.C.* S232 9

594b Df. ℞. — As last. *R.I.C.* S231 (*Voetter*) 9

595 Kk. ℞. LIBERTAS, Libertas stg. l.; XI in field. *R.I.C.* S233 10

596 Kk. ℞. LIBERTAS AVG., as last. *R.I.C.* S233 .. .. ..· 9

596a Ak. ℞. — As last. *R.I.C.* S234 (*Voetter*) 14

598 Ka(A). ℞. LVBENTVS AVG., Gallienus, in military dress, stg. l., holding Victory and spear; VIIC in ex. *R.I.C.* S615 18

599 Kf(A). ℞. LVNA LVCIF., Diana, crescent on hd., stg. or walking r., scarf floating, holding torch in both hands; P . XV in ex. *R.I.C.* S609 12

600 Kc(A). ℞. — As last. *R.I.C.* S609 12

600a Ka(A). ℞. — As last. *R.I.C.* S609 12

600b Kc. ℞. — As last, but nothing in ex. *R.I.C.* S235 14

600c Kf. ℞. As last or next. *R.I.C.* S235 14

601 Kk. ℞. LVNA LVCIFERA, as **600b.** *R.I.C.* S235 12

601a Kk(A). ℞. — As last. *R.I.C.* S646 9

602 Kl(A). ℞. — As last. *R.I.C.* S646 10

602a Kc and/or f. ℞. — As last. *R.I.C.* S646 9

604 Ka(A). ℞. MARS AVG., Mars stg. r., leaning on shield and holding spear; SPQR in ex. *R.I.C.* S647 12

604a Ka(A). ℞. MARS RED . AVG., as last. *R.I.C.* S648 (*Voetter*) 14

605 Kf(A). ℞. MARS VICTOR, Mars, naked with floating cloak, walking r., holding spear and shield; in ex., branch. *R.I.C.* S649 9

606 **Antoninianus.** Kc(A). R. MARS VICTOR, Mars walking r. in fighting attitude, holding spear and shield. *R.I.C.* S469 .. .. £9
606a Kc(A). R. — As last; in ex., palm or branch. *R.I.C.* S649 10
607 Kk(A). R. — As **606.** *R.I.C.* S649 9
607a Kl(A). R. — As one of the last four. *R.I.C.* S649 10
607b Kk(A). R. MARS VLTOR, as **605** or **606a.** *R.I.C.* S650 14
608 Kk(M). R. MARTI CONSER., Mars walking l., holding branch, shield and spear; in field, P. *R.I.C.* S491 14
609 Kk(M). R. MARTI PACIF., as last, but nothing in field. *R.I.C.* S492 .. 8
609a Ka or f? R. — As last. *R.I.C.* S236 .. ..
611 Kf(M). R. MARTI PACIFE., as last. *R.I.C.* S492 9
612 Kg, with rad. helmet, w. sp. sh. (M). R. — As last. *R.I.C.* S492 .. 15
613 Ka and/or f (M). R. MARTI PACIFER., as last. *R.I.C.* S492 10

617a

614 Kf (R and M). R. MARTI PACIFERO, as **609.** *R.I.C.* S236 and S492 .. 10
617 Kk. R. — As last, but Mars stg. l. *R.I.C.* S236 8
617a Kk. R. — As last, but A, H or X in field. *R.I.C.* S236 8
618 Ka. R. — As **617.** *R.I.C.* S236 8
618a Ka. R. — As **617a.** *R.I.C.* S236 8
618b Kf. R. — As **617.** *R.I.C.* S236 8
618c Kf. R. — **617a.** *R.I.C.* S236 8
619 **Denarius.** Dp. R. — As **617.** *R.I.C.* S353 100
620 **Quinarius.** Dm. R. — As last. *R.I.C.* S370 125
622 **Antoninianus.** Kf. (R and M). R. — As **609.** *R.I.C.* S236 and S492 .. 10
622a Df(L). R. MARTI PROPVG., Mars stg. r., holding spear and trophy. *R.I.C.* 25 (*Voetter*) 15
622b Bf. R. MARTI PROPVGN. or PROPVGT., Mars stg. l., leaning on shield, holding spear. *R.I.C.* 152 (*Voetter*) 15
622c Cf. R. — As last. *R.I.C.* 153 (*Voetter*) 12
622d Df. R. MARTI PROPVGN., Mars stg. r., holding spear and shield. *R.I.C.* S237 10
625 Kg, with rad. helmet, seen from the back, sp. sh. (R and M). R. MARTI PROPVGNAT., Mars walking r., holding shield and spearing enemy on ground. *R.I.C.* S238 and S493 20
625a Kh, w. wearing imperial mantle, sc. ea. R. — As last. *R.I.C.* S238 .. 22
626 Kk (R and M). R. — As last. *R.I.C.* S238 and S493 18
626a Kf. R. — As last. *R.I.C.* 238 18

N.B.—*R.I.C. gives one or all of the last four of Rome, also with* x *in field, and possibly reading* PROPVGNA.

626b Ak. R. — As before, with x in field. *R.I.C.* S239 (*Voetter*) 18

N.B.—S *before an R.I.C. number indicates that it is a coin from his sole reign.*

628 Antoninianus. Kk. R. MARTI PROPVGNATORI, Mars walking r., holding spear and shield. *R.I.C.* S240 (*gives obv.* 1 *with* x *in field*) £12

629 Kf. R. — As last. *R.I.C.* S240 (*with* x *in field*) 12

630 Kk. R. MARTI VICTORI AVG., Mars stg. l., holding patera and spear. *R.I.C.* S241 10

631 Kk. R. MERCVRIO CONS . AVG., hippocamp r.; in field, H or N. *R.I.C.* S242 20

632 Kf(A). R. MINERVA AVG., Minerva stg. r., holding spear and shield; in ex., branch or SPQR. *R.I.C.* S651 10

633 Kc(A). R. — As last. *R.I.C.* S651 10

634 Kc(A). R. — Minerva stg. l., leaning on shield and holding spear; in ex., VIIC. *R.I.C.* S617 (*obv.* a or f) 10

634a Kc(A). R. — As last, but branch or SPQR in ex. *R.I.C.* S651 10

634b Kk(A). R. — As last. *R.I.C.* S651 10

635 Kl(A). R. — As last, with nothing in ex. 10

635a Kl(A). R. — As **634a.** *R.I.C.* S651 10

636 Kk. R. MONETA AVG., Moneta stg. r. *R.I.C.* S243 10

638 Medallion. Dm. R. MONETA AVG., the three Monetae stg. half-left; at their feet, piles of metal (diam. 29 mm.). *R.I.C.* S137 .. .. *Very rare*

639 Fm. R. — As last. (Diam. 29 mm.; weight 21.50 gms.). *R.I.C.* S136 *Very rare*

639a Fd. R. — As last. (30 mm.; 29.29 gms.). *R.I.C.* S136 (*Gnecchi*) *Very rare*

640 IMP . GALLIENVS PIVS F . AVG., m. R. — As last. (30 mm.; 20 gms.). *R.I.C.* S140 .. .. *Very rare*

640a As last, but obv. legend ends GERM. *R.I.C.* S140 .. .. *Very rare*

641 IMP . GALLIENVS PIVS FEL . AVG., d. R. — As last. (34 mm.; 28 gms.). *R.I.C.* S139 .. .. *Very rare*

641a — — q, w. sp. sh. R. — As last. *R.I.C.* S139 (*Gnecchi*) .. *Very rare*

641b Cq, w. sp. sh. R. — As last. (34 mm.; 22.50 gms.). *R.I.C.* S138, *Gnecchi*) .. .. *Very rare*

642 IMP . GALLIENVS PIVS FELIX AVG., d. R. — As last. (38 mm.; 46 gms.). *R.I.C.* S141 .. .. *Extremely rare*

642a GALLIENVS PIVS F . AVG., n. R. — As last. (28 *mm.*; 21.55 gms.). *R.I.C.* S142 (*Gnecchi*) .. .. *Very rare*

655 Fd, but to left, w., sp. over r. shoulder, sh. on which hd. of Medusa. R. — As last. (36 mm.; 38.00 gms.). *R.I.C.* 110 .. .. .. *Extremely rare*

655a As last. (35 mm.; 25.00 gms.). *R.I.C.* 110 .. .. .. *Extremely rare*

656 Ge. R. MONETA AVGG., as before. (28 mm.; 28.00 gms.). *R.I.C.* 112 *Very rare*

657 Gd. R. — As last. (32 mm.; 30.50 gms.). *R.I.C.* 112 .. .. *Very rare*

658 B but CAES. for C., d. R. — As last. (34-32 mm.; 27.59-24.08 gms.). *R.I.C.* 113 .. .. *Very rare*

659 Fe. R. — As last. (30-28 mm.; 24.50-18.50 gms). *R.I.C.* 111 *Very rare*

659a Fd. R. — As last. (32 mm.; 26.55 gms.). *R.I.C.* 111 (*Gnecchi*) *Very rare*

660 Fd, but to left, w., holding globe surmounted by Victory. R. — As last. (32 mm.; 27.00 gms.). *R.I.C.* 110 .. .. *Very rare*

661 Cd, but to left. R. — As last. (35-31 mm.; 27.50-20.10 gms.). *R.I.C.* 109 .. .. *Very rare*

N.B.—*Of many of these medallions other sizes and weights are known.*

668

667 Antoninianus. Kk. ℞. NEPTVNO CONS . AVG., hippocamp r.; N or s (or
A or Δ) in ex. *R.I.C.* S245 .. .. £15
668 Kf. ℞. — As last. *R.I.C.* S245 15
669 Dk. ℞. — As last. *R.I.C.* S244 15
669a Kk. ℞. — Hippocamp l., no marks. *R.I.C.* S246 15
670 Kk. ℞. — Capricorn r.; s in ex. (or N, A or Δ ?). *R.I.C.* S245 15
672 Medallion. GALLIENVM AVG . P . R., laur. bust dr. l., seen from the back,
sp. sh. ℞. OB CONSERVATIONEM PATRIAE, Salus stg. r. (*R.I.C.* 1.),
feeding serpent held in her arms. *R.I.C.* S143 .. .. .. *Extremely rare*
673 — — ℞. OB CONSERVATIONEM SALVTIS, as before (diam. 26-22 mm.;
weight, 12.80-8.85 gms.). *R.I.C.* S144 .. .. .. *Extremely rare*
678 GALLIENVM AVG . SENATVS, as before. ℞. OB LIBERTATEM RECEPTAM,
Libertas stg. l. (27-25 mm.; 12.00-11.00 gms.). *R.I.C.* S145 .. *Extremely rare*
680 GALLIENVM AVG . P . R., as before. ℞. OB REDDIT . LIBERT., as last (28-27
mm.; 10.78-14.10 gms.). *R.I.C.* S146 .. .. *Extremely rare*
681 Antoninianus. Kk. ℞. — As last. *R.I.C.* S247 40
685 Kk(M). ℞. ORIENS AVG., Sol, rad., half-naked, stg. l., holding whip and
raising r. hand. *R.I.C.* S494 8
685a Kk(M). ℞. — As last, but P or s in ex. *R.I.C.* S494 8
686 As either of last two, but rad. hd. instead of rad. bust. *R.I.C.* S494 .. 8
687 Kf(M). ℞. — As **685** and/or **685a**. *R.I.C.* S494 8
689 Ga. ℞. — As **685,** but globe for whip. *R.I.C.* 154 8

690 Kk(M). ℞. — As last. *R.I.C.* S495 8
690a Kk(M). ℞. — As last, but P or s in ex. *R.I.C.* S495 8
691 Ka(M). ℞. — As **689.** *R.I.C.* S495 8
691a Ka(M). ℞. — As **690a.** *R.I.C.* S495 8
692 Kl(M). ℞. — As **689.** *R.I.C.* S495 9
692a Kl(M). ℞. — As **690a.** *R.I.C.* S495 9
692b GALLIENVS P . AVG., k(M). ℞. — As **689.** *R.I.C.* S496 10
693 Mk. ℞. — As last. *R.I.C.* S251 10
694 Fk, sp. (M). ℞. — As last. *R.I.C.* 387 15
694a El(M). ℞. — As last. *R.I.C.* 388 18
695 Fl, seen from behind, sp. (M). ℞. — As last. *R.I.C.* 387 15
695a IMP GALLIENVS AVG . GER., l, r. hand raised. ℞. — As last. *R.I.C.* S496a
(*Voetter*) 20

698　Denarius.　Km.　Ŗ.　ORIENS AVG., Sol, rad., walking l., raising r. hand and holding whip.　*R.I.C.* S354　..　　..　　..　　..　　..　　..　　£100

699　Antoninianus.　Kk.　Ŗ.　— As last.　*R.I.C.* S249　..　　..　　..　　8

699a　Kk.　Ŗ.　— As last, but z or ⩽ in field.　*R.I.C.* S249　　..　　..　　9

700　Kf.　Ŗ.　— As **698**.　*R.I.C.* S249　..　　..　　..　　..　　..　　8

700a　Kf.　Ŗ.　— As **699a**.　*R.I.C.* S249　　..　　..　　..　　..　　8

700b　Kl.　Ŗ.　— As **698** and/or **699a**.　*R.I.C.* S249　..

700c　Ak.　Ŗ.　— As before, z in ex.　*R.I.C.* S250 (*Voetter*)　..　　..　　12

701　Dk.　Ŗ.　— As **698**.　*R.I.C.* S248　　..　　..　　..　　..　　10

701a　Dk.　Ŗ.　— As **700c**.　*R.I.C.* S248　　..　　..　　..　　..　　10

702　Fa(M ?).　Ŗ.　— As **698** or **700c**　..　　..　　..　　..　　..

704　Ek(M).　Ŗ.　— (the AVG. in ex.), Sol, rad., holding whip, in galloping quadriga l.　*R.I.C.* S497　　..　　..　　..　　..　　..　　..　　50

704a　As last, but without IMP. at beginning of *obv.* (M).　*R.I.C.* S498 (*Voetter*)　　50

705a　　　　　　　　　　716a

705　Cc(A).　Ŗ.　— Turreted female (the Orient) stg. r., presenting wreath to Gallienus stg. l. in military dress and holding spear.　*R.I.C.* 445　..　　..　　22

705a　As last, with a wreath also in field　..　　..　　..　　..　　..　　22

708　Gk.　Ŗ.　ORIENS AVGG., Sol, rad., half-naked, stg. or walking l.　..　　..　　12

708a　Ga and/or f.　Ŗ.　— As last.　*R.I.C.* 154　..　　..　　..　　..　　12

710　Ga.　Ŗ.　— As last, but holding whip instead of globe.　*R.I.C.* 154　..　　12

714　Ba(V).　Ŗ.　PACATORI ORBIS, Jupiter seated l., holding patera and sceptre; at feet, eagle.　*R.I.C.* 294 (*Cohen has obv.* C., *and omits* sceptre)　..　　..　　18

715　Ak.　Ŗ.　PAX AETERNA, Pax stg. l.　..　　..　　..　　..　　..　　9

715a　Ak.　Ŗ.　— As last, T, Δ or N in field.　*R.I.C.* S254　　..　　..　　9

716　Dk.　Ŗ.　— As **715**　..　　..　　..　　..　　..　　..　　..　　9

716a　Dk.　Ŗ.　— As **715a**.　*R.I.C.* S252　　..　　..　　..　　..　　8

717　Kk.　Ŗ.　— As **715a** (*Cohen says* O or N).　*R.I.C.* S253　..　　..　　9

718　Kk.　Ŗ. PAX AETERNA AVG., as before, Δ in field.　*R.I.C.* S253　　..　　8

719　Dk.　Ŗ.　— As last or **715a**.　*R.I.C.* S252　　..　　..　　..　　8

720　Ak.　Ŗ.　— As last.　*R.I.C.* S254　..　　..　　..　　..　　..　　8

721　Fk of l.　Ŗ.　— As **718**　..　　..　　..　　..　　..　　..

727　Kk.　Ŗ.　PAX AVG., Pax l. as **715**; in field, T, V or Δ.　*R.I.C.* S256　..　　8

727a　Kk(S).　Ŗ.　— As last; in field, nothing, ZI or SI.　*R.I.C.* S575　..　　9

728　Kf.　Ŗ.　— As **727**.　*R.I.C.* S256　..　　..　　..　　..　　..　　8

728a　Kf(S).　Ŗ.　— As **727a**.　*R.I.C.* S575　..　　..　　..　　..　　9

729　Kg, sp. over shoulder (S).　Ŗ.　— As **727a**.　*R.I.C.* S575 (sp. and sh.)　12

729a　Ka(S).　Ŗ.　— As last.　*R.I.C.* S575　..　　..　　..　　..　　9

729b　Kc(S).　Ŗ.　— As last.　*R.I.C.* S575　　..　　..　　..　　..　　9

730　Da.　Ŗ.　— As **727**, Δ or V in field.　*R.I.C.* S255　..　　..　　9

731　Df.　Ŗ.　— As last.　*R.I.C.* S255　..　　..　　..　　..　　..　　9

739 **Antoninianus.** Kk(R and M). ℞. PAX AVG., Pax stg. l., holding olive-branch in the air and l. hand resting on sceptre. *R.I.C.* S256 and S499 .. £10

N.B.—*According to R.I.C. the Rome specimens of* **739, 741** *and* **742** *should have* T *or* V *or* Δ *in field.*

741 Kk(R, M and S). ℞. — Pax walking l. *R.I.C.* S256, S501 and S576 10
741a Kk(M). ℞. — As last, with s in ex. *R.I.C.* S501 10
741b Kf(M). ℞. — As **741** or last. *R.I.C.* S501 10
741c Kl(M). ℞. — As last. *R.I.C.* S501 10
742 Kg seen from behind sp. and sh. (R and S). ℞. — As **741.** *R.I.C.* S256 (h *instead of* g) and S576 15
742a Ka(S). ℞. — As last. *R.I.C.* S576 10
742b Kf(S). ℞. — As last. *R.I.C.* S576 10
742c Kl (S). ℞. — As last. *R.I.C.* S576 (*Voetter*) 10
743 Ba. ℞. — As last. *R.I.C.* 155 10
744 Da(M). ℞. — As last 10
744a Dk(M). ℞. — As last. *R.I.C.* S500 10
744b Dk(M). ℞. — Similar, but with s in ex. *R.I.C.* S500 10
744c GALLIENVM PRINC. P . R., f. ℞. — Pax stg. or walking as before; T, V or Δ in ex. *R.I.C.* S257 25
745 **Medallion.** Fm. ℞. — Pax seated l. (diam. 32 mm.; wt. 21.44 gms.). *R.I.C.* S147 .. .. *Extremely rare*
746 **Antoninianus.** Kk(R and S). ℞. — Pax seated l. *R.I.C.* S258 and S577 8
747 Kf(R and S). ℞. — As last. *R.I.C.* S258 and S577 8
747a Kc(S). ℞. — As last. *R.I.C.* S577 8
748 Ng, w., holding trophy and sh. (S). ℞. — As last. *R.I.C.* S577 (*with obv. legend* K, *in error ?*) 25

754

750 Ec(M). ℞. PAX AVGG., Pax stg. l. *R.I.C.* 391 12
750a Ef(M). ℞. — As last. *R.I.C.* 391 12
751 Fc(M). ℞. — As last. *R.I.C.* 390 12
752 Dc(M). ℞. — As last. *R.I.C.* 392 12
752a Df. ℞. — As last, or with T or V in field (Hy.). *R.I.C.* S341 10
753 Kk. ℞. — As **752a** (Hy.). *R.I.C.* S341ᵃ 10
753a Kf. ℞. — As last (Hy.). *R.I.C.* S341ᵃ (*Voetter*).. 10
754 Ba. ℞. — As **750.** *R.I.C.* 155 12
754a Bf(M). ℞. — As last. *R.I.C.* 389 12
755 **Quinarius.** Bb. ℞. — As last. *R.I.C.* 190 125

N.B.—S *before an R.I.C. number indicates that it is a coin from his sole reign.*

756 Antoninianus. Hf. ℞. PAX AVGG., Pax stg. l., T or V in field. *R.I.C.* 156 (*obv.* Fc) 12
756a Fc. ℞. — As last, without mintmarks. *R.I.C.* 156 12
757 IMP . GALLIENVS AVG . G . M., C. ℞. — As **756** 15
764 Dc. ℞. —Pax walking l.; in field, V. 15
765 Hf. ℞. — As last, or without mintmark. *R.I.C.* 157 12
765a Hc. ℞. — As last. *R.I.C.* 157 12
766 Kf(M). ℞. PAX AVGVSTI, as **764,** but ϛ in field. *R.I.C.* S502 9
766a Kf. ℞. — As last, but ϛ in field. *R.I.C.* S259 9
767 Kg, with helmet, seen from the back, sp. sh. ℞. — As last. *R.I.C.* S259 15
767a Kg, with helmet, sp. sh. (M). ℞. — As **766.** *R.I.C.* S502 15
768 Kf(M). ℞. — Pax stg. l., holding transverse spear and shield. *R.I.C.* S503 12
769 Ka(A). ℞. PAX FVNDATA (sometimes retrograde), trophy between two (Parthian) captives, in attitude of sadness. *R.I.C.* S652 10
769a Ka(A). ℞. — As last, palm in ex. *R.I.C.* S652 10
770 Kl(A). ℞. — As **769.** *R.I.C.* S652 12
770a Kl(A). ℞. — As **769a.** *R.I.C.* S652.. 12
771 Kc(A). ℞. — As **769.** *R.I.C.* S652 10
771a Kc(A). ℞. — As **769a.** *R.I.C.* S652 10

769a 774a

773 Kk. ℞. PAX PVBLICA, Pax seated l. 10
773a Kk. ℞. — As last; V in ex. *R.I.C.* S260 10
774 Kf. ℞. — As **773** 10
744a Kf. ℞. — As **773a.** *R.I.C.* S260 10
777 Kf(M). ℞. PERPETVITATI AVG., Securitas stg. facing, hd. l., leaning against column, holding globe and sceptre. *R.I.C.* S504 10
777a Kf(M). ℞. — As last; P in field. *R.I.C.* S504 10
778 Kk(M). ℞. — As **777.** *R.I.C.* S504 10
778a Kk(M). ℞. — As **777a.** *R.I.C.* S504 10
779 Kl(M). ℞. — As **777.** *R.I.C.* S504 10
779a Kl(M). ℞. — As **777a.** *R.I.C.* S504 10
780 Bc(M ?). ℞. — As last 10
781 Ef(M). ℞. PIET . SAECVLI, goat (of Amalthea) to r., suckling the infant Jupiter. *R.I.C.* 394 25
781a Ec(M). ℞. — Infant Jupiter riding l. on goat. *R.I.C.* 393 25
783 Da(M). ℞. PIETAS AVG., Pietas stg. l. before altar, both hands raised and outspread; in ex., P (or ϛ). *R.I.C.* S506 10
783a Dk(M). ℞. — As last; in ex., P or ϛ. *R.I.C.* S506 10
783b Dl, sp. sh. (M). ℞. — As last. *R.I.C.* S506 (*Voetter*) 12
784 Fh, with imperial mantle, sc. ea. (M). ℞. — As last. *R.I.C.* S505 .. 14
785 Fk(M). ℞. — As last. *R.I.C.* S505 9
785a Kl, sp. square sh., (M). ℞. — As last. *R.I.C.* S505 (*Voetter*) .. 15
786 Kk(M). ℞. — As before; P or ϛ in field; in ex., P, or MP. *R.I.C.* S507 10
786a Kk (M). ℞. — As before, but nothing in field or in ex. (*John J. Hergenhan*) 10

786b Antoninianus. Kf(S). R. PIETAS AVG., Pietas sacrificing l. *R.I.C.* S578 £14
786c Kf(S). R. — Pietas stg. l., holding patera; in field, P II. *R.I.C.* S579 14
787 Kk. R. — Pietas (*Cohen*, Nemesis ?) stg. l., holding sceptre and cornucopiae; at her feet, wheel. *R.I.C.* S262 14
787a Kf. R. — Pietas stg. l., holding patera and transverse sceptre; in field,
XI. (*John J. Hergenhan*) 14
788 Kf(A). R. — Gallienus, veiled, stg. l., sacrificing over lighted tripod,
holding transverse sceptre; in ex., VIIC. *R.I.C.* S618 (spear or sceptre) 10
788a Fa(A). R. — As last. *R.I.C.* S618 10
789 Kk. R. — Sacrificial implements. *R.I.C.* S261 50
790 Quinarius. Kb. R. PIETAS AVGG., Pietas seated l., extending hand to
two or three children, and holding sceptre. *R.I.C.* 191 125
791 Antoninianus. Kk. R. — Pietas stg., hd. l., legs crossed, leaning on
column and pointing baton at wheel at her feet; x in field. *R.I.C.* S263.. 12
791a As last, without mintmark (Hy.). *R.I.C.* S342 12
791b Ak. R. — As **791**. *R.I.C.* S264 (*Voetter*) 12
792 Ca(A). R. — Valerian and Gallienus, face to face, sacrificing at altar;
one holds eagle-tipped sceptre, the other a parazonium. *R.I.C.* 447 .. 15
792a As last, but above them, wreath or star. *R.I.C.* 447 15
792b Cc(A). R. — As **792**. *R.I.C.* 447 15
792c Cc(A). R. — As **792a**. *R.I.C.* 447 15
793 Ba(A). R. — As **792**. *R.I.C.* 446 15
794 *Obv.* ? R. PIETAS SAECVLI, as last. .. ..

788   806

795 Ba (*C.*, c) (V). R. PIETATI AVGG., Pietas stg. l., leaning on column,
holding sceptre. *R.I.C.* 295 12
795a Ka(S). R. P . M . TR . P . COS . II (*should be* III), emperor walking r.,
holding spear and globe. *R.I.C.* S548 (*Voetter*) 16
797 Bc. R. P . M . TR . P . II COS . P . P., Virtus (*Cohen*) or soldier (*R.I.C.*)
stg. l., leaning on shield and holding reversed spear. *R.I.C.* 115 .. 14
797a Ba. R. — As last. *R.I.C.* 115 (*Voetter*) 14
797b Bf. R. — As last. *R.I.C.* 115 (*Voetter*) 14
798 Df. R. — Gallienus, veiled, stg. l., sacrificing at altar 14
798a Ba(V). R. — As last. *R.I.C.* 287 14
799 Ef. R. — As last. 14
800 Bc. R. P . M . TR . P . II COS . II (*sic.*) P . P., Jupiter, naked, stg. l.
R.I.C. 116 14
800a Ba. R. — As last. *R.I.C.* 116 14
800b Bf. R. — As last. *R.I.C.* 116 14
802 Cf. R. P . M . TR . P . III COS . III P . P., Sol, rad. and half-naked, walking
l., holding whip and raising r. hand. *R.I.C.* 117 14
803 Bf. ' R. P . M . TR . P . IIII COS . II (*sic.*), as **798**. *R.I.C.* 118 .. 16
804 IMP . GALLIENVS AVG . GERM., f (*Cohen*, c). R. P . M . TR . P . IIII COS . III
P . P., as **802**. *R.I.C.* 120 12
805 Gk. R. — As last .. ..
805a Gf. R. — As last. *R.I.C.* 119ᵈ 12
806 Cf. R. — As last. *R.I.C.* 119 12

807 **Antoninianus.** Mf(L). ℞. P . M . TR . P . V COS . III, Mars walking r., holding spear and trophy. *R.I.C.* 5 .. .. £20

808 Gf. ℞. P . M . TR . P . V COS . III P . P., as **802.** *R.I.C.* 121 20

812 Mf(L). ℞. P . M . TR . P . V COS . IIII P . P., as last. *R.I.C.* 6 (Apollo, *in error ?*) 20

813 Ma. ℞. — Gallienus, laur., seated l. on curule chair, holding globe and sceptre. *R.I.C.* 122 15

814 Kk. ℞. — Gallienus in quadriga l., holding eagle-tipped sceptre. *R.I.C.* S154 note (*possibly misreading for* TR . P . X, *see* **837**) .. ..

815 Df(A). ℞. — Valerian and Gallienus stg. facing each other, each leaning on shield; behind them, two spears. *R.I.C.* 435 15

816 Dg, with aegis, sp. (M). ℞. P . M . TR . P . VI COS., Roma seated l., holding Victory and spear; at her side, shield; in ex., s. *R.I.C.* S453 (TR . P . VII) 15

817 Dk(M). ℞. — As last. *R.I.C.* S453 (TR . P . VII) 12

818 Kk(M). ℞. P . M . TR . P . VII COS., emperor stg. l., sacrificing at lighted tripod or altar, holding short sceptre; MP in ex. *R.I.C.* 309 12

818a Kk(M). ℞. — As last, but without letters in ex. *R.I.C.* 309 12

819 Dk(M). ℞. — As **818** or **818a.** *R.I.C.* 308 12

819a Ek(M). ℞. — As last. *R.I.C.* 307 12

819b Ek(M). ℞. — As before, but emperor also holds patera; P in ex. *R.I.C.* S459 12

819c Dk(M). ℞. — As last; P or MP in ex. *R.I.C.* S460 12

820 Fk(M). ℞. — As **818.** *R.I.C.* 306 12

820a Fk(M). ℞. — As **818a.** *R.I.C.* 306 12

820b Fk(M). ℞. — As **819b.** *R.I.C.* S458 12

820c Fk(M). ℞. — As last, but without letter in ex. *R.I.C.* S458 12

821 Fl(M). ℞. — As **818.** *R.I.C.* 306 14

821a Fl(M). ℞. — As **818a.** *R.I.C.* 306 14

821b Fl(M). ℞. — As **819b** or **820c.** *R.I.C.* S458 14

822 Gk. ℞. — As **818a.** *R.I.C.* 123 12

822a Gc. ℞. — As last. *R.I.C.* 123 12

822b Gf. ℞. — As last. *R.I.C.* 123 12

822c Gk(M). ℞. — As **820c.** *R.I.C.* S461 12

823 IMP . GALLIENVS P . AVG . GERM., k. ℞. — As **818.** *R.I.C.* 124 (as **818a**) 15

823a — — (M). ℞. — As **819b.** *R.I.C.* S459 15

824 Dk(M). ℞. — Gallienus, veiled, seated l. on curule chair, holding globe and sceptre; MS in ex. *R.I.C.* 312 12

824a Dk(M). ℞. — As last, but s in ex. *R.I.C.* S457 12

824b Dk(M). ℞. — As last two, but nothing in ex. *R.I.C.* 312 and S457 .. 12

825 Ek(M). ℞. — As **824.** *R.I.C.* 311 ? 12

825a Ek(M). ℞. — As **824a.** *R.I.C.* S456 12

825b Ek(M). ℞. — As **824b.** *R.I.C.* 311 12

826 Fk(M). ℞. — As **824b.** *R.I.C.* 310 and S455 12

827 Ek(M). ℞. — Gallienus stg. in quadriga proceeding l., holding branch and being crowned by Victory, who stands behind him and holds palm. *R.I.C.* 313 and S454 (*on the latter the* COS *is in ex.*) 35

829 Kk(S). ℞. P . M . TR . P . VII COS . P . P., Gallienus, in military dress, holding spear and parazonium, stag. facing between two river-gods (Rhine and Maine), crouching face to face, each holding reed. *R.I.C.* S549 .. 45

830 Ml, sp. sh. ℞. P . M . TR . P . VII COS . III P . P., Mars, naked with mantle floating, walking r., holding spear and trophy. *R.I.C.* S151 15

831 Mf(L and R). ℞. P . M . TR . P . VII COS . IIII P . P., as last. *R.I.C.* 8 and S152 12

832 Ml, sp. sh. ℞. — As last. *R.I.C.* S152 15

N.B.—*R.I.C.* 7 *has this legend with rev. type as* **831** *and* **812** *with obv. as* **832,** *giving them these numbers.*

835 **Antoninianus.** Kf. ℞. P . M . TR . P . VIIII COS . IIII P . P., emperor stg. l., sacrificing, as **818a.** *R.I.F.* S153 .. .. £12

835 Kf. ℞. P . M . TR . P . VIIII COS . IIII P . P., emperor stg. l., sacrificing, as **818a.** *R.I.C.* S153 12

835a Kf(M). ℞. — Similar, but as **820c.** *R.I.C.* S462 12

837 Kl, sp. sh. ℞. P . M . TR . P . X COS . IIII P . P., emperor in quadriga l., holding sceptre. *R.I.C.* S154 (helmeted and cuir. ?) 50

N.B.—*The rev. legends of some of the coins from the Asia mint* (A) *from* **839** *to* **849a** *finish up in the exergue.*

839 Mf(A). ℞. P . M . TR . P . XI COS . V P . P., Serapis, with modius head-dress, stg. l., raising r. hand and holding sceptre. *R.I.C.* S600 12

840 *Obv.* ? ℞. P . M . TR . P . XII COS VI P . P., emperor on horseback ..

835a   844

842 Kg(A). ℞. — Lion, rad., walking l.; in ex., palm-branch to r. *R.I.C.* 601 (*has* C *for* COS) 22

842a As last, but the palm branch to l. *R.I.C.* 601 note 22

843 Kf(A). ℞. P . M . TR . P . XIII C . VI P . P., as **842.** *R.I.C.* 602.. .. 14

844 Kc or a and/or f (A). ℞. — As **842a,** but with bull's hd. between paws. *R.I.C.* 602 14

845 Kg(A). ℞. — As last. *R.I.C.* 602 (dr. and cuir.) 15

845a K, dr. and cuir. l., sc. on shoulder. *R.I.C.* 602 15

846 Kh, sc. on shoulder (A). ℞. — As last. *R.I.C.* 602 (imperial mantle, sc. ea.) 15

847 Kl(A). ℞. — As last. *R.I.C.* 602 15

848 Kf(A). ℞. P . M . TR . P . XV P . P., Neptune, half-naked, stg. l., foot on prow, holding trident; VIIC in ex. (*R.I.C. gives this as continuing the obv. legend*). *R.I.C.* S603 12

849 Kc(A). ℞. — As last. *R.I.C.* S603 12

849a Ka(A). ℞. — As last. *R.I.C.* S603 12

850 Kk. ℞. P . M . TR . P . XV COS . VII, Gallienus, in military dress, stg. l., holding globe and sceptre or spear. *R.I.C.* S155 12

850a Ka(A). ℞. P . M . TR . P . XVI, lion with bull's hd. between paws; SPQR in ex. *R.I.C.* S604 (*Voetter*) 18

850b Kf(A). ℞. — As last. *R.I.C.* S604 (*Voetter*) 18

851 Kk(S). ℞. P . M . TR . P . XVI COS . VII, as **850.** P or star in field. *R.I.C.* S550 12

851a Kk. ℞. — As last, without letter in field. *R.I.C.* S156 12

852 Kc(S). ℞. — As last. *R.I.C.* S550 12

852a Kf. ℞. — As last. *R.I.C.* S156 12

852b Ka(S). ℞. — As **851** or **852.** *R.I.C.* S550 12

852c Kf(S). ℞. — As last. *R.I.C.* S550 12

852d Kl(S). ℞. — As last. *R.I.C.* S550 (*Voetter*) 14

852e Kh(S). ℞. — As last. *R.I.C.* S550 (*Voetter*) 14

852f Ka(A). ℞. P . M . TR . P . XVII, AS **850a.** *R.I.C.* S605 (*Voetter*).. .. 16

852g Kf(A). ℞. — As last. *R.I.C.* S605 (*Voetter*) 16

N.B.—S *before an R.I.C. number indicates that it is a coin from his sole reign.*

852h Antoninianus. Kk. ℞. PRINC . IVVENT., prince stg. l., holding globe and sceptre; at foot, captive; P in ex. (Hy.; *rev. of Valerian II*). *R.I.C.* S265 .. .. £18

853 Ek. ℞. PRINCIPI IVVENT., as **850** 15

853a Ea(L). ℞. PRINCIPI IVVENTVT., as last, but emperor stg. r. *R.I.C.* 26 .. 18

854 Kk(S). ℞. PROVI . AVG., Providentia stg. l., holding cornucopiae and pointing baton to globe at feet. *R.I.C.* S580 8

854a Kk. ℞. — As last; v, x or M in field (*R.I.C.* P, v, N or x). *R.I.C.* S267.. 9

854b Kk(S). ℞. — As last; II or P II in field. *R.I.C.* S580 9

855 Kf(S). ℞. — As **854**. *R.I.C.* S580 8

855a Kf(S). ℞. — As **854b**. (*British Museum*) 9

855b Kf. ℞. — As **854a**. *R.I.C.* S267 9

855c Kf(M). ℞. — As **854,** but MT in ex. *R.I.C.* S509ᵇ (sceptre for cornu-copiae) 9

856 Dk. ℞. — As **854**. *R.I.C.* S266 9

856a Dk(M). ℞. — As **855c**. *R.I.C.* S509ᵃ (sceptre for cornucopiae) .. 9

857 IMP . GALLIENVS AVG . GERM., k. ℞. — As **854,** but x in field. *R.I.C.* S269 14

854b   860a

859 Kk(R and M). ℞. PROVID   G., Providentia stg. l., holding globe and transverse sceptre; P in field. *R.I.C.* S270 and S508ᵃ 8

859a Kk(M). ℞. — As last, but nothing in field, MP in ex. *R.I.C.* 508ᵃ 8

860 Kf. ℞. — As **859**. *R.I.C.* S270 8

860a Kf. ℞. — As before, but nothing in field or ex. 9

860b Dk. ℞. — As **859a,** but P or MP in ex. *R.I.C.* S508 (*Voetter*) .. 10

861 GALLIENVS P . AVG., k. (M). ℞. — As **859** and **859a**. *R.I.C.* 508ᵇ .. 10

862 Kk. ℞. — As **854**. .. ..

862a Kk. ℞. — As last, but v or x in field (*R.I.C.* P, v, N or x). *R.I.C.* S267 8

863 Ka. ℞. — As last. *R.I.C.* S267 8

864 Kk(S ?). ℞. — Providentia stg. l., as **854** but sceptre for cornucopiae. *R.I.C.* S580 8

864a Kk(S). ℞. — As last, P II in field. *R.I.C.* S580 (as **854**) 8

865 Quinarius. Km. ℞. — As **864**. *R.I.C.* S371 125

866/7 Antoninianus. Dk. ℞. — As last. .. ..

866a Dk. ℞. — As **854**. *R.I.C.* S266 8

866b Dk(M). ℞. — As **864,** but MT in ex. *R.I.C.* S509ᵃ 8

868 Ec(M ?). ℞. — As **864** or **864a** 8

868a Ec(M). ℞. — As **866b**. *R.I.C.* S509 8

869 Kk. ℞. — As **854,** but leans against column and x in field. *R.I.C.* S267 8

870 Ef(M). ℞. PROVID . AVGG., Providentia stg. l., pointing baton at globe at her feet and holding military ensign. *R.I.C.* 395 (holding cornucopiae) 14

872 Kk(S). ℞. PROVIDEN . AVG., as **854**. *R.I.C.* S580 8

872a Kk. ℞. — As **854a**. *R.I.C.* S267 8

873 K, helmeted bust dr. r. (S). ℞. — As **864** or **864a**. *R.I.C.* S580 (holding cornucopiae) 15

874 Kk. ℞. PROVIDENT . AVG., Providentia stg. l., holding transverse sceptre and globe 10

874a Kk. ℞. — As last, P in field. *R.I.C.* S270 10

874b Antoninianus. Ka ?(A). ℞. PROVIDENT . AVG., Mercury, naked, cloak on l. arm, stg. l.; SPQR in ex. *R.I.C.* S653 (*Voetter*) £12

875 Ka(A). ℞. PROVIDENTIA AVG., as last, but nothing in ex. .. ..

875a Ka(A). ℞. — As **874b.** *R.I.C.* S653 10

876 Kc(A). ℞. — As **875** 10

876a Kc(A). ℞. — As **874b.** *R.I.C.* S653 10

876b Kf(A). ℞. — As last. *R.I.C.* S653 10

876c Kf(A). ℞. — As **875.** (*A. D. Merson*) 10

877 Kf(A). ℞. — As before, but VIIC in ex. 12

878 Kl(A). ℞. — As **875** or last 12

878a Kl(A). ℞. — As **874b.** *R.I.C.* S653 12

879a Kf(A). ℞. — Providentia stg. l., as **854,** but VIIC in ex. *R.I.C.* S619 .. 10

879b Kh, sc. ea. (A). ℞. — As last. *R.I.C.* S619 12

879c Kf. ℞. — As last, but XXIA in ex. (Hy.; *rev. of Probus*). *R.I.C.* S343 .. 15

880 Kf(M). ℞. — As before, but Providentia leaning on column (as **885**); s in field. *R.I.C.* S510 10

N.B.—880 *and* **881** *are possibly also of Rome with another mintmark—see R.I.C. S267*

881 Kl(M). ℞. — As last. *R.I.C.* S510 12

882 IMP . GALLIENVS AVG . G . M., c with aegis. ℞. — As last, x in field. *R.I.C.* S269 15

882a Ak. ℞. — (?) as last or **854.** *R.I.C.* S268 (*Voetter*) 12

889b

885 Hk. ℞. PROVIDENTIA AVGG., Providentia stg. l., leaning against column, holding cornucopiae and pointing with baton to a globe at her feet. *R.I.C.* 163 14

886 G, but GERS for GERM., a. ℞. — As last 14

887 Bf. ℞. — As last. *R.I.C.* 161 14

887a Cf. ℞. — As last. *R.I.C.* 162 (*possibly an error*).. .. ..

888 Cf. ℞. — As **885,** but no column. *R.I.C.* 159 12

889 Bk. ℞. — As last .. ..

889a Ba. ℞. — As last. *R.I.C.* 158 12

889b Bf. ℞. — As last. *R.I.C.* 158 12

890 Denarius. Bp. ℞. — As last. 125

890a Bf(? ?). ℞. — As **885.** *R.I.C.* 188 (*wrongly described ?, perhaps as last*) 125

891 Ce(A). ℞. — As **888.** *R.I.C.* 461 (*omits globe*) 125

892 Antoninianus. Gk. ℞. — As last. *R.I.C.* 160 12

892a Kk. ℞. PROVIND . AVG., Providentia stg. l., holding globe and sceptre (Hy. ?). *R.I.C.* S271 14

893 Kk. ℞. PVDICITIA, Pudicitia, veiled, stg. l.; Q in field (Hy.; *rev. of Salonina*). *R.I.C.* S272 12

893a Kk. ℞. — As last, but nothing in ex. (Hy.). *R.I.C.* S272 12

894 Fl. ℞. — As last .. ..

895   Antoninianus. Mc(L). R. RESTIT . GALLIAR., Gallienus, in military
      dress, stg. l., holding spear (*C.*) or sceptre (*R.I.C.*) and raising kneeling
      turreted female (Gaul), who holds cornucopiae. *R.I.C.* 29   ..   ..   £18

896   Ml, sp. sh. (L). R. — As last. *R.I.C.* 29   18
897   Dc and/or f (L). R. — As last. *R.I.C.* 28   18
898   Ec(L). R. — As last. *R.I.C.* 27   18
898a Ef(L). R. — As last. *R.I.C.* 27   18
900   Ec(L). R. RESTITVT . GALLIAR., as before. *R.I.C.* 30   18
900a Ef(L). R. — As last. *R.I.C.* 30   18
901   Ba (*Cohen,* c *in error*) (V). R. RESTITVT . GENER . HVMANI, Gallienus,
      wearing toga, walking r. and raising both hands, one holds globe.
      R.I.C. 296   18
902   Bc and/or a (A). R. RESTITVT . ORIENTIS, woman (*the Orient*) stg. r.,
      presenting wreath to Gallienus stg. l., holding spear or sceptre   15
902a As last, but · · in ex. *R.I.C.* 448   15
902b As last, but · in ex. *R.I.C.* 448   15
903   Cc and/or a (A). R. — As one or more of the last three   15
904   L (without the v), g, sp. sh. (L). R. RESTITVTOR GALLIAR., as **895.**
      R.I.C. 34   20
905   Lg, sp. sh. (L). R. — As last. *R.I.C.* 34..   20
906   Df(L). R. — As last. *R.I.C.* 31   18
907   Mg, sp. sh. (L). R. — As last. *R.I.C.* 33   20
907a Mf(L). R. — As last. *R.I.C.* 33 (*perhaps in error?*)   ..   ..
908   Jf(L). R. — As last. *R.I.C.* 32   18
909   Mc(L). R. RESTITVTOR GALLIARVM, as before. *R.I.C.* 35   22
911   Gk and/or Hk. R. RESTITVTOR ORBIS, Gallienus stg. l., holding spear and
      raising turreted figure who kneels before him   15
911a Gf and/or Hf. R. — As last, but holds sceptre. *R.I.C.* 165   15
911b Cf. R. — As last. *R.I.C.* 164 (*Voetter*)   15
912   Kk. R. — As **911** (Hy.?)   15
918   Ba (*C.*, c) (V). R. ROMAE AETERNAE, Roma seated l., holding Victory and
      spear; at her side, shield (or seated on shield). *R.I.C.* 297   12

919   Kc(A). R. — As last, but star in field or ex. *R.I.C.* S655   9
919a Ka(A). R. — As **918,** or last, or with SPQR in ex. *R.I.C.* S655   ..   9
919b Kf(A). R. — As last. *R.I.C.* S655   9
919c Kh(A). R. — As last. *R.I.C.* S655   9
920   Mf(A). R. — As **919**; star in field. *R.I.C.* S654   9
920a Mf(L and A). R. — As last, but no mintmark. *R.I.C.* 36 and S654 ..   9

921	**Antoninianus.** Ca(A). R. ROMAE AETERNAE, Roma seated l. on shield, holding spear and presenting Victory to Gallienus stg. r.; in field above, wreath or star. *R.I.C.* 449 ..	£14
921a	Cc(A). R. — As last. *R.I.C.* 449	14
922	Kl(A). R. SAECVLARES AVG., stag r.; branch in ex.	16
922a	Kh, sc. ea. (A). R. — As last, or nothing in ex. *R.I.C.* S656..	16
923	Kf(A). R. — As last. *R.I.C.* S656	14
924	Kc(A). R. — As last. *R.I.C.* S656	14
925	Dc. R. — Antelope or gazelle l. ..	16
925a	Dc. R. — As last; x in ex. *R.I.C.* S273	16
925b	As **922**, but SAECVLARHS AVG. *Cohen* 922 note (*Paris*)	16
926	Ec and/or a (M). R. SAECVLI FELICITAS, Felicitas stg l. *R.I.C.* 396 ..	12
927	Ka(A). R. SALVS AVG., Apollo, naked, stg. l.; to r., tripod; PXV in ex. *R.I.C.* S610	12
927a	Kf(A). — As last. *R.I.C.* S610	12
928	Dk(M). R. — Aesculapius stg. l., holding serpent-entwined staff; MP or P in ex. *R.I.C.* S511^b (MP *only*)	12
929	Df(M). R. — As last. *R.I.C.* S511^b (MP *only*) ..	12
930	Ek(M). R. — As last. *R.I.C.* S511^a (MP *only*) ..	12
931	Fk(M). R. — As last, but MP in field, or P in ex. *R.I.C.* S511	12
932	Kk. R. — Salus stg. r., feeding serpent held in her arms. *R.I.C.* S274^a	8
932a	Kf. R. — As last. *R.I.C.* S274^a	8
932b	Kk. R. — As last, but T or XII in field. *R.I.C.* S274^a ..	8
932c	Kf. R. — As last. *R.I.C.* S274^a ..	8
932d	Kk(M). R. — As **932**, but MS in ex. *R.I.C.* S512^a	8
932e	Kf(A). R. — As last, but SPQR in ex. *R.I.C.* S657	10
932f	Ka(A). R. — As last. *R.I.C.* S657	8
932g	Kc(A). R. — As last. *R.I.C.* S657	8
932h	Df. R. — As **932** and **932b**. *R.I.C.* S274 (*Voetter*)	10
933	Ek(M). R. — As **932**, but T in field, or MS in ex. *R.I.C.* S512	8
934	Kk(S). R. — Salus stg. l., holding sceptre and feeding serpent rising from altar; in field, SI. *R.I.C.* S581	8
934a	Kk(S). R. — As last; in field, nothing, star, P, star and P, or I. *R.I.C.* S581	8
934b	Kf(S). R. — As **934** and/or **934a**. *R.I.C.* S581	8
934c	Kl(S). R. — As last. *R.I.C.* S581	10
934d	Kh(S). R. — As last. *R.I.C.* S581	10
935	Kk. R. — Salus seated l., feeding serpent rising from altar; P in field. *R.I.C.* S275	10
935a	**Quinarius.** Kp. R. — As last, but without P. *R.I.C.* S542^a (*B.M.*)	100
936	**Antoninianus.** Ea(M). R. SALVS AVGG., Salus stg. r., feeding serpent held in her arms. *R.I.C.* 399	12
937	Ef(M). R. — As last. *R.I.C.* 399	12
938	Fa(M). R. — As last. *R.I.C.* 398	12
939	Ha and/or f. R. — As last. *R.I.C.* 167 ..	12
940	Ea(M). R. — As **934**, but nothing in field. *R.I.C.* 397	12
940a	Ec(M). R. — As last. *R.I.C.* 397 (*Illustrated at top of next page*)	12
941	Ef(M). R. — As last. *R.I.C.* 397	12
941a	Fl(M). R. — As last (*Dorchester*) ..	12
942	Ba. R. — As last. *R.I.C.* 166 ..	12
942a	Kk. R. SALVS AVGVSTI, as **935a**. *R.I.C.* S276 (*Voetter*)	10

940a   953

943 Antoninianus. Df(M). ℞. SALVS ITAL., Salus (?), rad., stg. r., offering
fruits to Gallienus stg. l., holding spear and with r. hand raised. *R.I.C.* 400   £50

944 Ec(M). ℞. SALVS PVBLICA, as **940.** *R.I.C.* 401 12

948a Ea and/or c (M). ℞. SECVLI FELICITAS, Felicitas stg. l. *R.I.C.* 396 (*Cohen*
926 note; *Paris*) 14

949 Kk(M). ℞. SECVR . TEMPO., Securitas stg. l., legs crossed, leaning on
column, holding sceptre; MS in ex. *R.I.C.* S513 10

950 Kk(M). ℞. — As last, but no sceptre. *R.I.C.* S513 10

951 Kk. ℞. SECVRIT . or SECVRT . AVG., as last, but VI in field. *R.I.C.* S277 9

951a Kk. ℞. — As last, but nothing in field. *R.I.C.* S277 9

951b Kk(M). ℞. SECVRIT . AVG., as last, but MS in ex. *R.I.C.* S514 10

951c Ba. ℞. SECVRIT . AVGG., Securitas leaning on column holding sceptre.
R.I.C. 168 12

953 Kk. ℞. SECVRIT . ORBIS, Securitas seated l., holding sceptre and hand to
hd.; T or VI in ex. *R.I.C.* S278 8

954 Kf. ℞. — As last. *R.I.C.* S278 8

956 Kf. ℞. — Securitas seated l., holding caduceus and cornucopiae,
T in ex. *R.I.C.* S279 8

957 Kk. ℞. — As last. *R.I.C.* S279 8

960 Quinarius. Km(R and M). ℞. SECVRIT . PERPET., as **949,** but nothing
in ex. *R.I.C.* S372 and S543 100

961 Antoninianus. Kk(M). ℞. — As last. *R.I.C.* S516 10

961a Kk. ℞ — As last, but H in field *R.I.C.* S280 10

962 Kf(M). ℞. — As **961.** *R.I.C.* S516 10

962a Kf. ℞. — As **961a.** *R.I.C.* S280 10

963 Ka, w. (M). ℞. — As **961.** *R.I.C.* S516 10

964 Denarius. Dm. ℞. — As **961.** *R.I.C.* S355 100

964a Kq. ℞. — As **961a.** *R.I.C.* S356 100

964b Antoninianus. Dk. ℞. — As **961.** *R.I.C.* S515 12

965 Dl, w. (M). ℞. — As last. *R.I.C.* S515 15

965a Kl. ℞. — As **961a.** *R.I.C.* S280 12

973a Kk(M). ℞. SECVRITAS PVB., as **953,** but MS in ex. *R.I.C.* S517 12

974 Kk. ℞. SECVRITAS PVBL., as last, but VI or T in ex. *R.I.C.* S281 .. 10

974a Kk. ℞. SECVRIT . PVBL., as last. *R.I.C.* S281 (*Voetter*) 10

976 Kf(S). ℞. SISCIA AVG., Siscia, both hands raised, sitting l. on bank of
river Savus, in which a river nymph is swimming. *R.I.C.* S582 .. 150

977 Kk(S). ℞. — As last. *R.I.C.* S582 150

977a Ka(S). ℞. — As last. *R.I.C.* S582 150

977b Ka, seen from behind (S). ℞. — As last. *R.I.C.* S582 150

N.B.—S *before an R.I.C. number indicates that it is a coin from his sole reign.*

978 **Antoninianus.** Kk(S). ℞. SOLI COMTI AVG., pegasus r., springing heavenwards. *R.I.C.* S583 .. .. £14
978a Kk. ℞. — As last or next. *R.I.C.* S283 12
979 Kk. ℞. SOLI CONS . AVG., as last; A, H, N or VI in ex. *R.I.C.* S283 .. 12
979a Kf. ℞. — As last. *R.I.C.* S283 12
980 Dk. ℞. — As last, but only A or N in ex. *R.I.C.* S282 12
981 Kk. ℞. — Pegasus springing l.; H or N in ex. *R.I.C.* S284 12
982 **Denarius.** Km. ℞. — Pegasus flying l. *R.I.C.* S357 110
983 **Antoninianus.** Kk. ℞. — Bull stg. r.; XI in ex. *R.I.C.* S285 .. 14
984 Kl. ℞. — As last. *R.I.C.* S285 15
985 Kg. ℞. — As last. *R.I.C.* S285 15

979   1010b

987 Kc(A). ℞. SOLI INVICTO, Sol, rad. and half-naked, stg. l., holding whip. *R.I.C.* S658 10
987a Kl(A). ℞. — As last. *R.I.C.* S658 (*?in error for next*) .. ..
988 **Denarius.** Kq. ℞. — As last (*?in error for next*) .. ..
988a **Antoninianus.** Kl. ℞. — Sol walking r., holding whip and raising r. hand. *R.I.C.* S286 14
989 Kc(A). ℞. — Sol, in long robe, stg. facing, hd. l.; PXV or VIIC in ex. .. 12
989a Ka(A). ℞. — As last. *R.I.C.* S611 and S620 12
989b Kf(A). ℞. — As last. *R.I.C.* S611 and S620 12
989b Ka(s). ℞. SPES PVB., Spes walking r. *R.I.C.* S584 (*Voetter*) 12
990 Ek(M). ℞. SPES PVBLICA, Spes walking l. *R.I.C.* 403 14
991 Ef(M). ℞ — As last. *R.I.C.* 403 14
992 Ec(M). ℞. — As last. *R.I.C.* 403 14
993 **Quinarius.** Ed(M). ℞. — As last. *R.I.C.* 414 125
993a Ek(M). ℞. — As last. *R.I.C.* S544 (*wrong obv. type ?*).. 125
993b **Denarius.** E, laur. bust dr. and cuir. l. (M). ℞. — As last. *R.I.C.* 413 140
994 **Antoninianus.** Fc(M). ℞. — As last. *R.I.C.* 402 14
994a Ff(M). ℞. — As last. *R.I.C.* 402 14
995 Kf(S). ℞. — As last. *R.I.C.* S584 10
996 Kk(S). ℞. — As last. *R.I.C.* S584 10
998 Mf(L and A). ℞. S . P . Q . R . OPTIMO PRINCIPI in laurel-wreath. *R.I.C.* 37 and S659 22
1005 **Denarius.** Mn. ℞. TRIB . POT . VIII COS . III, Mars, naked but for helmet, holding transverse spear and shield, walking r.; before him, reclining and sleeping Rhea Silvia l. *R.I.C.* S345 250
1008 **Antoninianus.** Kk(S). ℞. VBERITAS AVG., Uberitas stg. l., holding bunch of grapes and cornucopiae. *R.I.C.* S585 8
1009 Kf(S). ℞. — As last. *R.I.C.* S585 8
1010a Dk. ℞. — As last, but purse for grapes. *R.I.C.* S287 10
1010b Kf. ℞. — As last. 10
1010c Kk. ℞. — As last, but ϵ in field. (*John G. Hergenhan*) 10

1011 Medallion. IMP . GALLIENVS AVG . COS . V, m. R. VBERITAS AVG.,
       Uberitas stg. l., as last (35 mm.; 20 gms.). *R.I.C.* S135 (as **1008**)   *Extremely rare*

1012 Antoninianus. Dk. R. VBERTAS AVG., as last. *R.I.C.* S287 ..   ..   £10

1013 Denarius. Dm. R. — As last or **1008**. *R.I.C.* S358   100

1014 Antoninianus. Kk. R. — As **1008**. *R.I.C.* S585   10

1016 Denarius. GALLIENAE AVGVSTAE, r. R. VBIQVE PAX, Victory in biga
       galloping r., holding whip. *R.I.C.* S359   350

1019 Mr. R. — As last. *R.I.C.* S360   300

1020 Antoninianus. Kc(A). R. VENER . VICTRIX, Venus stg. l., holding
       helmet, spear and shield (or leaning on shield); SPQR in ex. *R.I.C.* S660 ..   10

1021 Kc(A). R. VENERI VICTRICI, as last, but without SPQR. *R.I.C.* S660 ..   10

1021a Ka(A). R. — As **1020** or **1021**. *R.I.C.* S660   10

1021b Kf(A). R. — As last. *R.I.C.* S660   10

1021c Ka(A). R. — As **1021**, but VIIC in ex. *R.I.C.* S621 (*Voetter*)..   12

1021d Kf(A). R. — As last. *R.I.C.* S621 (*Voetter*)   12

1021e Kc(?) (A). R. VENRI VICTRICI, as **1021a**. *R.I.C.* S660   ..   12

1022 Denarius. Kb(A). R. VENVS AVG., as **1020** (*?error for next*) ..   ..

1022a Antoninianus. Ka(A). R. — As last. *R.I.C.* S661 (*?error for last*)

1023 Kk. R. VENVS FELIX, Venus stg. l., holding apple and sceptre; Δ in ex.
       R.I.C. S288   10

1024 Kk. R. VENVS VICTRIX, as **1020**, but N in field, nothing in ex. *R.I.C.*
       S289   9

1025 Ba (*Cohen*, c) (V). R. — As last. *R.I.C.* 298   9

1026 Kk. R. VESTA, Vesta seated l., holding wreath (or simpulum, *R.I.C.*)
       and sceptre; Q (or P, *R.I.C.*) in ex. (Hy.; *rev. of Salonina*). *R.I.C.* S290   12

1027 Kf. R. — Vesta stg. l., holding simpulum and transverse sceptre (Hy.;
       rev. of Salonina)   12

1027a Kk. R. — As last; P or Q in ex. *R.I.C.* S290   12

1029 Kk(M). R. VESTA FELIX, as last, but S in field or ex. *R.I.C.* S518 ..   14

1029a Kk(M). R. — As last, but Vesta seated l. *R.I.C.* S518 (*Voetter*) ..   14

1030a Df. R. VIC . GAL . AVG., Victory stg. r., inscribing III on shield on palm
       trunk; her foot on small post; T in ex. *R.I.C.* S292   18

1031 Kf. R. VIC. GALL . AVG., as last. *R.I.C.* S293   18

1031a Kf. R. VICT . AET . AVG., Victory walking r.; at foot, captive. *R.I.C.* S291   20

1032a

1032 Kk. R. VICT . GAL . AVG., three Victories facing, hds. l., each raising
       wreath in r. hand and holding palm. *R.I.C.* S294   22

1032a Kk. R. — As last, but V in ex. *R.I.C.* S294   22

1033 Kk (bust). R. — As **1032**. *R.I.C.* S294..   22

1034 Kc and/or f. R. — As **1032** and/or **1032a**. *R.I.C.* S294   ..   22

1034a Kg, with helmet and sp. R. — As last. *R.I.C.* S294 (*Voetter*)   ..   25

1035 **Antoninianus.** Kk. ℞ VICT . GAL . AVG . III, as **1032** £22
1035a Kf. ℞. — As last. *R.I.C.* S295   22
1036 Kg, sp. sh. ℞. — As last   25
1036a Kg. ℞. — As last. *R.I.C.* S295..   22
1037 Kc. ℞. — As last. *R.I.C.* S295   22
1037a Dg, sp. sh. (M). ℞. — As last. *R.I.C.* S519 (*Voetter*)   25
1040 K, rad. bust dr. and cuir. l. ℞. VIC . GALL . AVG, Victory walking l.;
     T in field   14
1041 Df. ℞. — (*R.I.C.* VICT.). As last. *R.I.C.* S296   14
1041a Df. ℞. — — As last, but nothing in field. *R.I.C.* S296   14
1041b Dk. ℞. — — As **1041** and/or last. *R.I.C.* S296 (*Voetter*)   ..   14
1042 Dg, sp. sh. ℞. — — As last. *R.I.C.* S296   15
1042a Dg. ℞. — — As last. *R.I.C.* S296   16
1043 Mf(L). ℞. VICT . GALLIENI AVG., Gallienus, in military dress, stg. r.,
     holding spear and shield, trampling down enemy. *R.I.C.* 38   18
1045 Fc(M). ℞. VICT . GERM., Victory walking l., captive at feet. *R.I.C.* 404   15
1045a Fa(M). ℞. — As last. *R.I.C* 404 (*Voetter*)   15
1045b Ff(M). ℞. — As last. *R.I.C.* 404 (*Voetter*)   15
1045c **Quinarius.** M, laur. bust cuir. l., sp. sh. (L). ℞. VICT . GERMANICA,
     as last, but trampling down enemy. *R.I.C.* 63   140
1046a As last, but no enemy. *R.I.C.* 63   140
1047 (*also* **1050**). **Antoninianus.** Mg, sp. sh. (L). ℞. — As last. *R.I.C* 45   18
1048 Mf(L). ℞. — As last. *R.I.C.* 45   15
1049 Mk(?). ℞. — As last   ..   ..
1051 Df(L). ℞. — Victory running r., holding wreath and trophy. *R.I.C.* 41   15
1052 IMP . GALLIENVS V . AVG. (*sic*), f (L ?). ℞. — As last   16
1053 Ec and/or f (L). ℞. — As last. *R.I.C.* 40   15
1054 Jc and/or f (L). ℞. — As last. *R.I.C.* 39   15

1055 Mg, sp. sh. on which is seen hd. of Medusa (L). ℞. — As last.
     R.I.C. 42   20
1055a As last, but on a thick flan. *R.I.C.* 42 note   30
1056 Ll, sp. sh. (L). ℞. — As last. *R.I.C.* 43   18

1058 **Quinarius.** *Obv.* as **1045c** (L). ℞. — Victory running l., holding
     wreath and trophy, trampling on German captive seated on ground with
     hands behind back. *R.I.C.* 62   140

1059 **Antoninianus.** Mg, sp. sh. (L). ℞. — As last. *R.I.C.* 44   18
1060 Mc(L). ℞. — As last. *R.I.C.* 44   15
1060a As last, but P . L . AVG. (L). *R.I.C.* 44   16
1061 As **1060**, but on heavy flan (5.40 gms.). *R.I.C.* 44 note   30
1061a Mf(L). ℞. — As **1058**. *R.I.C.* 44   15

N.B.—S *before and R.I.C. number indicates that it is a coin from his sole reign.*

1062 Antoninianus. Mf(L). ℞. — Victory, holding wreath and trophy,
walking r. on globe, which is between two German captives sitting
outwards in attitude of sadness. *R.I.C.* 49   ..   ..   £15

1063 As last, but on heavy flan (6·10 gms.). *R.I.C.* 49 note   30

1064 Quinarius. Mp (L). ℞. — As before. *R.I.C.* 61   140

1065 Antoninianus. *Obv.* as **1055** (L). ℞. — As last. *R.I.C.* 49   20

1066 Df(L). ℞. — As last. *R.I.C.* 48   15

1066a Ef(L). ℞. — As last. *R.I.C.* 47 (*Voetter*)   15

1067 Jf(L). ℞. — As last. *R.I.C.* 46   15

1070 Quinarius. Km. ℞. VICTORIA AET., Victory stg. l. *R.I.C.* S373   ..   110

1071 Antoninianus. Kk(S). ℞. — As last. *R.I.C.* S586   8

1071a Kk(S). ℞. — As last, but P, S, SP or SD in field. *R.I.C.* S586 (SP *only*)   8

1071b Kk. ℞. — As last, but Z in field or ex. *R.I.C.* S297 ..   ..   ..

1072 Kf(S). ℞. — As **1070**. *R.I.C.* S586   8

1072a Kf(S). ℞. — As **1071a**. *R.I.C.* S586 (SP only)   8

1072b Kf. ℞. — As **1071b**. *R.I.C.* S297   8

1073 Denarius. Dm. ℞. — As **1070**. *R.I.C.* S361   100

1071b   1075b

1074a Quinarius. Kf (*?mistake for* e). ℞. VICTORIA AVG., as **1070**. *R.I.C.*
374 (*Voetter*)   110

1075 Antoninianus. Kk (R and S). ℞. — As last. *R.I.C.* S299 and S587   8

1075a Kk(S). ℞. — As last, but star, S or B in field. *R.I.C.* S587   8

1075b Kk. ℞. — As last, but Z in field   9

1076 Kf(R and S). ℞. — As **1075**. *R.I.C.* S299   8

1076a Kf(S). ℞. — As **1075a**. *R.I.C.* S587   8

N.B.—*R.I.C.* S587 (*Siscia mint*) *also gives obv. l. and h. with rev of* **1075**
or **1076**. *It also says* Victory sometimes running.

1079 Df(R). ℞. — As **1070**. *R.I.C.* S298   8

1079a Df(S). ℞. — As **1075a**. *R.I.C.* S587   8

1084 Medallion. Cm and/or e. ℞. — Victory stg. l., leaning on shield and
holding palm (diam. 31 mm.). *R.I.C.* S148   ..   ..   ..   *Very rare*

1085 Antoninianus. Ka(A). ℞. — Victory walking l., placing shield on
pedestal; SPQR in ex. *R.I.C.* S665   16

1085a Kf(A). ℞. — As last. *R.I.C.* S665   16

1085b Mf(A). ℞. — As last. *R.I.C.* S664   16

1086 K (or M, *R.I.C.*) f (A). ℞. — Victory stg. l., holding wreath, trophy
and shield inscribed CA; in ex., SPQR. *R.I.C.* S666 (*description doubtful*)

1087 Dc(M). ℞. — Victory stg. l., attaching to palm tree a shield inscribed
III. *R.I.C.* S521   14

1088 Kc and/or f (M). ℞. — As last. *R.I.C.* S522   14

1088a Kk(M). ℞. — As last. *R.I.C* S522   14

1093 Denarius. Km. ℞. VICTORIA AVG., Victory walking l. *R.I.C.* S362 £100
1094 Antoninianus. Kk(M). ℞. — As last; T in field. *R.I.C.* S523 .. 9
1094a Ka ℞. — As last; nothing or S in field. *R.I.C.* S301 10
1094b Ka(A). ℞. — As last; star or crescent in field. *R.I.C.* S663 10
1094c Ka(A). ℞. — As last; star or SPQR in ex. *R.I.C.* S663 10
1094d Kf. ℞. — As **1094a.** *R.I.C.* S301 10
1094e Kf(A). ℞. — As **1094b** or **1094c.** *R.I.C.* S663 10
1094f Kc. ℞. — As **1094a.** *R.I.C.* S301 10
1094g Kc(M). ℞. — As **1094.** *R.I.C.* S523 10
1094h Kc(A). ℞. — As **1094b** or **1094c** *R.I.C.* S663 10
1095 Kg(?A). ℞. — As last (?) .. ..

1096 Quinarius. Ke. ℞. — As before; nothing in field or ex. *R.I.C.* S375 110
1096a Kb. ℞. — As last. *R.I.C.* S375.. 110
1097 IMP . GALLIENVS F . AVG., laur. bust cuir. l., sp. sh. ℞. — As last.
   R.I.C. S376 130

1098c

1098 Antoninianus. Mf(A). ℞. VICTORIA AVG., Victory stg. or walking l.;
   star in field. *R.I.C.* S662 9
1098a Mf(A). ℞. — As last; nothing in field; SPQR in ex. *R.I.C.* S662 .. 10
1098b Ma(A). ℞. — As **1098** or last. *R.I.C.* S662 10
1098c Mf(A). ℞. — As **1098,** but nothing in field 10
1099 Mg, sp. sh. ℞. — As before; anything in field or ex.? (*possibly a
   mistake for* **1100a**) .. ..
1100 Df. ℞. — Victory walking l.; T in field. *R.I.C.* S300.. 9
1100a Dg, sp. sh. ℞. — A last. *R.I.C.* S300 (*Voetter*) 12
1106 Kf(A). ℞. — Victory walking l., holding diadem in both hands; to l.,
   shield on cippus; in ex., VIIC. *R.I.C.* S622 12
1106a Ka(A). ℞. — As last. *R.I.C.* S622 12
1107 Kf. ℞. — Victory running r. *R.I.C.* S303 12
1107a Kf(S). ℞. — As last, or **1107c.** *R.I.C.* S587 10
1107b Kk(S). ℞. — Victory walking r. *R.I.C.* S588 (*Voetter*) .. 10
1107c Kk(S). ℞. — As last, but star, S or B in field. *R.I.C.* S588 (*Voetter*) 10
1107d Kf, with scaled armour. ℞. — Three Victories stg. l. *R.I.C.* S302
   (*Voetter*) 20
1108 Kk(M). ℞. — Victory stg. on globe between two captives. *R.I.C.* S520 14
1109 Ca(A). ℞. — Victory, holding palm stg. l., presenting wreath to
   Gallienus, in military dress, stg. r. and holding spear. *R.I.C.* 450 .. 14
1109a As last, but with star or wreath in field. *R.I.C.* 450 14
1109b Cc(A). ℞. — As **1109** and/or last. *R.I.C.* 450.. 14

1113 Denarius. Mr. ℞. — Gallienus, in military dress, stg. l., holding
   globe and transverse sceptre, crowned by Victory, holding palm.
   R.I.C. S363 150

1115　Antoninianus. Kk(M). ℞. VICTORIA AVG . II, Victory walking l.;
　　　T in ex. *R.I.C.* S524 .. 　　.. 　.. 　.. 　.. 　.. 　.. 　£9
1115a Kf(M). ℞. — As last. *R.I.C.* 524 　.. 　.. 　.. 　.. 　10
1118 Kk(M). ℞. VICTORIA AVG . III, as last, but ex. clear. *R.I.C.* S525 　.. 　8
1118a Kk. ℞. — As last, but T in ex. *R.I.C.* S305 　.. 　.. 　.. 　9
1119 Kf(M). ℞. — As **1118**. *R.I.C.* S525 　.. 　.. 　.. 　.. 　8
1119a Kf. ℞. — As **1118a**. *R.I.C.* S305 　.. 　.. 　.. 　.. 　9
1120 Kl(M). ℞. — As **1118**. *R.I.C.* S525 　.. 　.. 　.. 　.. 　9
1120a Kl. ℞. — As **1118a**. *R.I.C.* S305 　.. 　.. 　.. 　.. 　10
1121 Kg, rad. helmet, w. sp. sh. ornate with hd. of Medusa (M). ℞. — As
　　　1118. *R.I.C.* S525 　.. 　.. 　.. 　.. 　.. 　.. 　.. 　18
1121a *Obv.* as last. ℞. — As **1118a**. *R.I.C.* S305 　.. 　.. 　.. 　18
1122 As **1121,** but instead of to waist, aegis on breast (M). ℞. — As **1118**.
　　　R.I.C. S525 　.. 　.. 　.. 　.. 　.. 　.. 　.. 　18
1122a *Obv.* as last. ℞. — As **1118a**. *R.I.C.* S305 　.. 　.. 　.. 　18
1122b Dk. ℞. — As last. *R.I.C.* S304 (*Voetter*) 　.. 　.. 　.. 　10
1122c GALLIENVM AVG . SENATVS, c. ℞. — As last. *R.I.C.* S306 (*Vierordt*) .. 　35
1129 Kg (*Cohen,* viewed from behind; *R.I.C.* to waist), rad. helmet, sp. sh. as
　　　1121 (M). ℞. VICTORIA AVG . VII, as last, but at her feet, German captive
　　　seated with hands tied behind back. *R.I.C.* S526 　　.. 　.. 　.. 　18
1131 Kl(M). ℞. — As last. *R.I.C.* S526 　.. 　.. 　.. 　.. 　▲ 　12
　　　N.B.—*R.I.C. indicates that some or all of* **1129-1136** *exist without the
　　　captive.*
1132 Kc(M). ℞. — As last. *R.I.C.* S526 　.. 　.. 　.. 　.. 　9
1133 Kk(M). ℞. — As last. *R.I.C.* S526 　.. 　.. 　.. 　.. 　9
1134 Kl(M). ℞. VICTORIA AVG . VIII, as last. *R.I.C.* S527 　.. 　.. 　14
1135 Kk(M). ℞. — As last. *R.I.C.* S527 　.. 　.. 　.. 　.. 　12
1135a Kf(M). ℞. — As last. *R.I.C.* S527 　.. 　.. 　.. 　.. 　12
1135b One or more of the last three with s in *rev.* field. *R.I.C.* S527.. 　.. 　12

1135c Kl(M). ℞. — As **1134,** but Ƨ in *rev.* field 　.. 　.. 　.. 　.. 　18
1136 Kk(M). ℞. VICTORIA AVG . VIIII, as before. *R.I.C.* S528 　.. 　.. 　16
1138 Bf. ℞. VICTORIA AVGG., Victory stg. l. *R.I.C.* 170 　.. 　.. 　12
1138a Ba(R and V). ℞. — As last. *R.I.C.* 170 and 299 　.. 　.. 　12
1138b Cf. ℞. — As last. *R.I.C.* 171 (*Voetter*) .. 　.. 　.. 　.. 　14
1139　Quinarius. Ce. ℞. — As last. *R.I.C.* 192 　.. 　.. 　.. 　125
1142a Bb. ℞. — Victory stg. l., leaning on shield and holding palm. *R.I.C.*
　　　193 　.. 　.. 　.. 　.. 　.. 　.. 　.. 　.. 　.. 　125
1143　Antoninianus. Ck. ℞. — As last. 　.. 　.. 　.. 　.. 　.. 　12
1146a Gf. ℞. — As before, but also holds wreath. *R.I.C.* 169 　.. 　.. 　12
1148 Df(M). ℞. — Flying Victory l., holding diadem in both hands, between
　　　two shields. *R.I.C.* 405 　.. 　.. 　.. 　.. 　.. 　.. 　14
1149 Dl(M). ℞. — As last. *R.I.C.* 405 　.. 　.. 　.. 　.. 　15
1150 The same, but of heavy weight (6.72 gms.) 　.. 　.. 　.. 　.. 　30
1151 Dg, sp. sh. (M). ℞. — As last. *R.I.C.* 405 　.. 　.. 　.. 　16
1152 Mg, w. sc. sh. (M ?). ℞. — As last 　.. 　.. 　.. 　.. 　.. 　16

1152a Quinarius. Ke(M). R. VICTORIA AVGG., as last, but Victory facing, wings outspread. *R.I.C.* 415 (*Voetter*) £125
1154 Antoninianus. Bc. R. — Victory walking l. *R.I.C.* 172 12
1154a Ba(V). R. — As last. *R.I.C.* 299 12
1154b Ba(V). R. — Victory stg. l. *R.I.C.* 299 (*Voetter*) 14
1160 Cf. R. VICTORIA GERM., Victory stg. l., at her feet, seated German captive with hands tied behind back. *R.I.C.* 174 15
1161 Ca. R. — As last. *R.I.C.* 174 15
1162 Gf. R. — As last. *R.I.C.* 175 15
1163 Hf. R. — As last. *R.I.C.* 175 15
1164 Bc. R. — As last. *R.I.C.* 173 15
1165 Ff(M). R. — As last. *R.I.C.* 406 15
1166 Quinarius. Be. R. — As last. *R.I.C.* 194 140
1166a IMP . GALLIENVS AVG . GERM., e. R. — As last, without captive. *R.I.C.* 196 140
1173 Antoninianus. Df(A). R. VICTORIA GERMAN., Victory stg. r., holding palm, presenting wreath to Gallienus, in military dress, stg. l., holding globe and sceptre (*Cohen*, spear). *R.I.C.* 452 17
1173a Df(A). R. — As last, but with star in field. *R.I.C.* 452 17
1174 Fc and/or f (A). R. — As **1173**. *R.I.C.* 451 17
1174a As last, but with star in field. *R.I.C.* 451 17
1175 Ga. R. VICTORIA GERMANICA, as **1160**. *R.I.C.* 180 16
1176/7 GALLIENVS AVG . GERM., g, sp. sh. (L). R. — Flying Victory on globe r., between two seated German captives. *R.I.C.* 52 18

1176a Lg, sp. sh. (L). R. — As last. (*Dorchester*) 18
1178 Gk. R. — As last. *R.I.C.* 180a 15
1179 Jf(L). R. — As last. *R.I.C.* 50 15
1180 Kf. R. — As last. *R.I.C.* S308 15
1181 Mf(L). R. — As last. *R.I.C.* 51 15
1182 Quinarius. Mq, sp. sh. R. — Victory running l. *R.I.C.* S377 .. 150
1185 Antoninianus. Gf. (*R.I.C.* e) R. VICTORIA G . M., as **1160**. *R.I.C.* 176 (*but says*, without captive) 14
1186 Quinarius. Ge. R. — As last. *R.I.C.* 195 130
1187 Antoninianus. Hk (*R.I.C.* e). R. — As last. *R.I.C.* 176 (*but says*, without captive) 14
1187a Dk. R. — Victory stg. l.; at feet, two captives. *R.I.C.* S307 14
1189 Hf. R. — Trophy between two captives. *R.I.C.* 177 16

N.B.—*R.I.C.* 177 *gives* G *and/or* H f *and* k. R. VICTORIA GERM *or* G. M. *or* GERMANICA, *trophy between captives.*

N.B.—S *before an R.I.C. number indicates that it is a coin from his sole reign.*

1190 **Antoninianus.** Kf. ℞. VICTORIA PART., Victory stg. l.; s in field.
R.I.C. S310 .. .. £35

1191 Kc and/or f. ℞. — Victory crowning emperor. *R.I.C.* S310.. .. 40

1192 Df(A). ℞. — Gallienus stg. l., holding globe and spear, receiving
wreath from Victory stg. r., holding palm. *R.I.C.* 453 40

1193 Dk. ℞. VICTORIAE AVG., two Victories holding globe surmounted by a
third Victory. *R.I.C.* S311.. 50

1196 Ba (*Cohen*, c)(V). ℞. VICTORIAE AVGG., soldier stg. r., holding spear, and
leaning on shield. *R.I.C.* 300 15

1198a

1198 Ck. ℞ VICTORIAE AVGG . IT . GERM., Victory stg. l.; at feet, captive with
hands tied behind back 15

1198a Cf. ℞. — As last 15

1198b Cf. ℞. — As last, but without captive. *R.I.C.* 178 15

1199 Gf. ℞. — As **1198**.. 15

1199a Gf. ℞, — As **1198a**. *R.I.C.* 179 15

1199b Kk(S). ℞ VIRT . AVG., Gallienus riding down enemy r. *R.I.C.* S589
(*Voetter*) 25

1204 Ka(M). ℞. VIRT . GALLIENI AVG., Gallienus galloping r., spearing fallen
enemy. *R.I.C.* S529 20

1204a Kf(R and M). ℞. — As last. *R.I.C.* S312 and S529 20

1204b Kc. ℞. — As last. *R.I.C.* S312.. 20

1205 Kl or g, with rad. helmet, seen from behind, sp. ℞. — As last.
R.I.C. S312 25

1205a *Obv.* as last, but also sh. (M). ℞. — As last. *R.I.C.* S529 .. 25

1206 Mf(L and R). ℞. — Gallienus, in military dress, walking r., holding
spear and shield, trampling down enemy. *R.I.C.* 54 and S314 15

1207 **Quinarius.** Mq, sp. ℞. — As last. (*Probably an error for next*) ..

1207a Mq, sp. and sh. (L and R). ℞ — As last (*R.I.C.* 64 (cuir.) and S378 150

1208 **Antoninianus.** Mg(or l.), sp. sh. (L). ℞. As last. *R.I.C.* 54 .. 18

1209 Df(L and R). ℞. — As last. *R.I.C.* 53 and S313) 15

1210 Dl. ℞. — As last. *R.I.C.* S313 12

1211 Mc. ℞. — As before, but Gallienus walking l. *R.I.C.* S315.. .. 10

1211a Mf(L). ℞. — As last. *R.I.C.* 55 15

1211b Ml(M). ℞. — As before, but Gallienus stg. r. *R.I.C.* S530a .. 12

1211c Dl(M). ℞. — As before, but Gallienus running r. (no enemy ?).
R.I.C. 530 (*Voetter*) 14

1214 **Denarius.** Km. ℞. VIRTVS AVG., helmeted hd. of Mars l. *R.I.C.* S364
(*wrong rev. legend*) 250

1216 **Quinarius.** Cb. ℞. — Mars walking r., holding spear and trophy ..

1216a **Antoninianus.** Kh. ℞. — As last. *R.I.C.* S319 12

1216b Kl (or g) seen from back, sp. sh. (S). ℞. — As last, but also trampling
down enemy. *R.I.C.* S591 (*Voetter*) 18

1221 **Antoninianus.** Kc. ℞. VIRTVS AVG., Mars stg. l., holding globe and
spear (*Cohen*, sceptre) £9
1221a Kc. ℞. — As last, P or Q in field. *R.I.C.* S317 8
1221b Kf. ℞. — As **1221** 9
1221c Kf. ℞. — As **1221a.** *R.I.C.* S317 8
1222 K retrograde l. ℞. — As **1221** or **1221a.** *R.I.C.* S317, *obv.* k, *in error* ?) 10
1223 Df. ℞. — As **1221,** but with foot on helmet. *R.I.C.* S316 8
1223a Dc. ℞. — As last. *R.I.C.* S316 8
1224 Dl(or g), sp. sh. ℞. — As last. *R.I.C.* S316 12
1225 Kk. ℞. — As last 8
1225a Kk. ℞. — As last, but P or Q in field. *R.I.C.* S317 8
1225b Kf. ℞. — As **1221,** but at feet, shield or globe; P, S or Q in field.
R.I.C. S321 10
1231 Hk. ℞. — Mars stg. r., holding spear and trophy 10
1231a Hc. ℞. — As last. *R.I.C.* S318 10
1231b Kh. ℞. — As last, but Mars walking. *R.I.C.* S319 12

1221c

1232 Kc. ℞. — Mars stg. l., holding branch and spear; at feet, shield (or
globe) 10
1232a Kc. ℞. — As last, but X in field. *R.I.C.* S320 10
1232b Kc. ℞. — As last, but V or XII in field. *R.I.C.* S329 10
1232c Kl. ℞. — As **1232a.** *R.I.C.* S320 12
1232d Ak. ℞. — As last. *R.I.C.* S320 (*Voetter*) 12

VALUES

We would remind readers that the values here (from
p. 48) are for billon or silver-washed coins in average
state. Most that are found today are just Æ and
worth very considerably less.

1233 Quinarius. Km. ℞. VIRTVS AVG., Mars (or soldier) stg. l., leaning on
shield and holding spear. *R.I.C.* S379 .. .. £110

1237b

1235 Antoninianus. Mf(A). ℞. — Virtus (or soldier) as last. *R.I.C.* S667   8
1235a Mf(A). ℞. — As last; star in field. *R.I.C.* S667   9
1236 Kk(M and A). ℞. — As **1235.** *R.I.C.* S534 and S668   8
1236a Kk(M). ℞. — As last; s (*Cohen,* P) in field. *R.I.C.* S534   8
1236b Kk. ℞. — As last; VI or N in field. *R.I.C.* S325   8
1236c Kk(R and M). ℞. — As **1235,** but P or S in ex. *R.I.C.* S325 and S534   8
1236d Kk(A). ℞. — As last, but star in field or ex. *R.I.C.* S668   9
1237 Ka(A). ℞. — As **1235.** *R.I.C.* S668   8
1237a Ka. ℞. — As **1236b** and/or **c.** *R.I.C.* S325   8
1237b Ka(A). ℞. — As **1236d.** *R.I.C.* S668   8
1237c Kf(M and A). ℞. — As **1235.** *R.I.C.* S534 and S668   8
1237d Kf. ℞. — As **1236b** and/or **c.** *R.I.C.* S325   8
1237e Kf(A). ℞. — As **1236d.** *R.I.C.* S668   8
1237f Kf(M). ℞. — As **1236a** and/or **c.** *R.I.C.* S534   8
1238 Kg with rad. helmet, w. sp. sh. (M). ℞. — As **1235.** *R.I.C.* S534 ..   14
1238a Kg, w. sp. sh. ℞. — As **1236b** and/or **c.** *R.I.C.* S325 (perhaps a
mistake for *obv.* as last)   14
1238b Kg as **1238** (M). ℞. — As **1236a** and/or **c.** *R.I.C.* S534   12
1239 Kl(M). ℞. — As **1235.** *R.I.C.* S534   10
1239a Kl(M). ℞. — As **1236a** and/or **c.** *R.I.C.* S534   10
1239b Kl. ℞. — As **1236b** and/or **c.** *R.I.C.* S325   10
1240 Kg. ℞. — As last. *R.I.C.* S325   10
1241 Kg, sp. sh. ℞. — As last. *R.I.C.* S325   12
1241a Kg, sp. sh. (M). ℞. — As **1236a** and/or **c.** *R.I.C.* S534   12
1241b Dg, sp. square sh. (M). ℞. — As **1235.** *R.I.C.* S532 (*Voetter*) ..   14
1241c Fg, sp. sh. (M). ℞. — As **1236c.** *R.I.C.* S531 (*Voetter*) ..   12
1241d Mk (M). ℞. — As last. *R.I.C.* S533 (*Voetter*)   12
1241e GALLIENVS P . AVG., l(M). ℞. — As **1236c.** *R.I.C.* S536 (*Voetter*) ..   14
1242 Bc. ℞. — As **1235** or one of the others .. ..
1243 IMP . GALLIENVS AVG . GER., l(M). ℞. — As **1236c**   12
1243a — g, r. hand upraised (M). ℞. — As last. *R.I.C.* S535 (*Voetter*) ..   14
1244 IMP . GALLIENVS AVG . COS II, l, sc. ea. ℞. — As **1235.** *R.I.C.* 114a ..   30
1245 Ka(A). ℞. — As last, but stg. r. and P XV in ex. *R.I.C.* S612   10
1245a Kf (A). ℞. — As last. *R.I.C.* S612   10
1246 Ka(A). ℞. — Virtus (or soldier) stg. r., holding shield and spear.
R.I.C. S669   8
1246a Kf(A). ℞. — As last. *R.I.C.* S669   8
1246b Kl(A). ℞. — As last, but walking r. *R.I.C.* S669 (*Voetter*)   10
1247 Mf. ℞. — As **1246** but r. hand resting on shield, l. holding spear.
R.I.C. S326   8

1249 **Antoninianus.** Ka(A). R. VIRTVS AVG., Hercules stg. facing, hd. r., holding club and lion's skin; SPQR in ex. *R.I.C.* S671 ..   ..   ..   £12

1249a Kf(A). R. — As last. *R.I.C.* S671   12

1249b Kh(A). R. — As last. *R.I.C.* S671   12

1249c Ka(S). R. — Hercules stg. r., holding club, bow and lion's skin. *R.I.C.* S595   12

1249d Kf(S). R. — As last. *R.I.C.* S595   12

1250 Ka(A). R. — Hercules, naked, stg. facing, hd. l., leaning on club and holding apple; VIIC in ex. *R.I.C.* S623 (stg. r.)   12

1250a Kf(A). R. — As last. *R.I.C.* S623 (stg. r.)   12

1251 Df(A and R). R. — As last, but nothing in ex. *R.I.C.* 454 and S327   12

1252 Kl(R and S). R. — Hercules, as before, but holding branch, club and lion's skin. *R.I.C.* S328 and S537   14

1253 Kk(R and S). R. — As last. *R.I.C.* S328 and S537   12

1254 Kf(S). R. — As last. *R.I.C.* S537   12

1255 Kl(S). R. — As last, with s in field. *R.I.C.* S537   14

1256 Kk(A). R. — Gallienus, laur. and in military dress, stg. r., holding transverse spear and globe; branch in ex. *R.I.C.* S670   10

1257 Ka(A). R. — As last. *R.I.C.* S670   10

1258 Kc and/or f(A). R. — As last. *R.I.C.* S670   10

Cohen gives these last three also without the branch in ex.

1259 Ml, sp. sh.(M ?). R. — As last ..   ..

1259a Mc. R. — Gallienus stg. r., holding transverse spear and ensign. *R.I.C.* S324   12

1260 **Quinarius.** Ke. R. — Gallienus stg. l., in military dress, holding globe and spear. *R.I.C.* S380   120

1260a Denarius. Ke. R. — As last. *R.I.C.* S365 (given in error ?)   ..

1261 **Quinarius.** Ke. R. — As before, but holding spear and trophy. *R.I.C.* S380   120

1262 **Antoninianus.** Kk (*Cohen*, laur. in error) (S). R. — Gallienus stg. l., crowning a trophy; at foot, captive and shield. *R.I.C.* S592   15

1262a Kf(S). R. — As last. *R.I.C.* S592   15

1262b Cc(A). R. — Gallienus stg., l. crowning trophy. *R.I.C.* 458 (*Voetter*)   16

1263 Ka(M). R. — Gallienus galloping r., spearing fallen enemy. *R.I.C.* S538   18

1263a Kf(S). R. — As last. *R.I.C.* S593   18

1264 Kf(S). R. — As before, but spearing lion. *R.I.C.* S594   20

1265 Kf(R and S). R. — Gallienus as **1260,** but between suppliant female and seated captive. *R.I.C.* S323 and S590   18

1265a Kk(R and S). R. — As last. *R.I.C.* S323 and S590   18

1265b Ka(S). R. — As last. *R.I.C.* S590   18

1266 Cc(A). R. — Gallienus stg. r., holding transverse spear and receiving a Victory from Roma stg. l., who leans on shield and has a spear resting against l. arm; sometimes in the field, star or wreath (*not given by Cohen*). *R.I.C.* 457   14

1267 Kc. R. — As last, but nothing in field. *R.I.C.* S322   12

N.B.—S *before an R.I.C. number indicates that it is a coin from his sole reign.*

1271a Quinarius. Cb or e. ℞. VIRTVS AVGG., soldier walking r., holding spear and trophy. *R.I.C.* 197 (*Voetter*) £125
1271b Ge. ℞. — As last. *R.I.C.* 198 (*Voetter*) 125
1272 Antoninianus. Gf. ℞. — As last. *R.I.C.* 186 14
1272a Hf. ℞. — As last. *R.I.C.* 186 14
1273 Bc. ℞. — As last. *R.I.C.* 184 12
1273a Ba. ℞. — As last. *R.I.C.* 184 12
1273b Cf. ℞. — As last. *R.I.C.* 185 (*Voetter*) 12
1273c Kf. ℞. — As last (Hy.). *R.I.C.* S344 12
1274 Mk. ℞. — As last 12
1274a Mf or c. (L). ℞. — As last. *R.I.C.* 56 12

1271a   1288

1276 Ha. ℞. — Soldier stg. r., holding spear and leaning on shield .. 14
1276a Gf. ℞. — As last. *R.I.C.* 183 14
1283 Quinarius. Cd. ℞. — As before, but stg. l. *R.I.C.* 199 125
1284 Antoninianus. Cf. ℞. — As last. *R.I.C.* 182 12
1288 Ba(R and V). ℞. — As last. *R.I.C.* 181 and 301 12
1288a Bf. ℞. — As last. *R.I.C.* 181 12
1289 Ef(M). ℞. — As last. *R.I.C.* 410 12
1290 Ec and/or a(M). ℞. — As last. *R.I.C.* 410 12
1291 IMP . GALLIENVS P . F . AVG . OERS, f. ℞. — As last 14
1292 Mk. ℞. — As last (probably meant for one of the next two) .. ..
1292a Mc(L). ℞. — As last. *R.I.C.* 59 12
1292b Mf(L). ℞. — As last. *R.I.C.* 59 12
1299 Kg with helmet, w. seen from behind, sp. sh. (M). ℞. — Hercules, naked, stg. l., holding olive-branch and club with lion's skin. (*B.M.*) .. 18
1299a As last, with VIIC in ex. (A). *R.I.C.* S624 18
1301 Gf. ℞. — Romulus (or Gallienus), bare-headed, walking r., holding spear and trophy. *R.I.C.* 187a 15
1303 GALLIENVS P . F . AVG . GERM., f. ℞. — As last. *R.I.C.* 187 15
1304 IMP . C . GALLIENVS P . F . AVG., f. ℞. — As last 15
1305 Fa(M). ℞. — As last. *R.I.C.* 408 15
1305a Ef(M). ℞. — As last. *R.I.C.* 409 (*Voetter*) 15
1306 Ff(M). ℞. — Gallienus, bare-headed and in military dress, stg. l., holding spear in both hands; to r., ensign. *R.I.C.* 407 14
1307 Mc(L). ℞. — As last. *R.I.C.* 57 14
1307a Mf(L). ℞. — As last. *R.I.C.* 57 14
1309 Mc(L). ℞. — Gallienus, stg. r., holding spear and ensign. *R.I.C.* 58 12
1309a Mf(L). ℞. — As last. *R.I.C.* 58 12
1310 Cc(A). ℞. — Valerian and Gallienus stg. face to face, one holds spear and globe, the other Victory and reversed spear. *R.I.C.* 456 12
1310a Cc(A). ℞. — As last, with wreath or star in field. *R.I.C.* 456 .. 12
1310b Cc(A). ℞. — As last. *R.I.C.* 456 12
1311 Bc and/or a(A). ℞. — As **1310.** *R.I.C.* 455 12
1312 Bf(A). ℞. — As last. *R.I.C.* 455 12
1312a Bg. ℞. — As last. *R.I.C.* 455 14

1317 Denarius. Kn(A). ℞. VIRTVS AVGVSTI, Hercules, naked, stg. r., holding lion's skin and club resting on rock. *R.I.C.* S678 .. .. £110

1318 Antoninianus. Kl(M). ℞. — As last. *R.I.C.* S539 12

1319 Kl or g with helmet, sp. sh. (M). ℞. — As last. *R.I.C.* S539 .. 15

1320 Kf(M). ℞. — As last. *R.I.C.* S539 10

1320a Kf(A). ℞. — As last, but star in field or ex. *R.I.C.* S673 .. 10

1320b Kk(M). ℞. — As **1317**. *R.I.C.* S539 10

1320c Ka(A). ℞. — As **1320a**. *R.I.C.* S673 10

1320d Kc. ℞. — As last. *Best style* 12

1321 Mf(A). ℞. — As **1317**. *R.I.C.* S672 10

1322 Kk. ℞. — Mars stg. l., foot on helmet, holding branch and sceptre; x in field 12

1322a Ak. ℞. — Mars stg. l., holding branch and spear; x in field. *R.I.C.* S330 (*Voetter*) 12

1322b Kl. ℞. VIRTVS or VIRTVTIS AVGVSTI, Hercules stg. r., holding club and lion's skin. *R.I.C.* S331 14

1324 Medallion. IMP GALLIENVS PIVS FEL . AVG., laur. bust cuir. l., w., sp. sh. with hd. of Medusa. ℞. VIRTVS AVGVSTORVM, Gallienus seated l. on cuirass, crowned by Victory who stands behind him, and receiving olive-branch from soldier or Virtus stg. r. before him; in the background, two ensigns (diam. 37 mm. weight, 27·00 gms.). *R.I.C.* 114 *Excessively rare*

1320d   1326

1325 Antoninianus. Kf(S). ℞. VIRTVS FALERI, quiver, lion's skin, club, vase and bow. *R.I.C.* S596 100

1326 K rad. bust r. draped with lion's skin (S). ℞. — As last. *R.I.C.* S596 125

1326a Medallion. GALLIENVS PIVS FEL . AVG . GERM, laur. cuir. bust l., sp. sh. ℞. VIRTVS GALLIENI AVG., Gallienus riding r., preceded by soldier; beneath horse, two enemies. (24 mm., 4·73 gms.) *R.I.C.* S149 (*Gnecchi*)
Extremely rare

1328 Antoninianus. Dk. ℞. VIRTVS MIL., soldier stg. l., holding spear and leaning on shield. *R.I.C.* S332 15

1328a Df(M). ℞. — As last. *R.I.C.* 411 15

1329 Ka(A). ℞. VIRTVTI AVG., Gallienus walking r., holding bipennis and pelta; SPQR in ex. *R.I.C.* S676 35

1330 Da ?(A). ℞. — Trophy between two captives; SPQR in ex. *R.I.C.* S674

1331 Ka(A). ℞. — As last. *R.I.C.* S675 25

1331a Kf(A). ℞. — As last. *R.I.C.* S675 25

1331b Kh(A). ℞. — As last. *R.I.C.* S675 25

1332 Kk. ℞. VOTA DECENALIA, Victory stg. r., writing on shield attached to palm-tree (*Cohen*); affixing shield on palm-tree. (*R.I.C.*) 20

1332a Ka(R and M). ℞. — As last. *R.I.C.* S333 and S540 20

1332b Kf(R and M). ℞. — As last. *R.I.C.* S333 and S540 20

1332c Kc. ℞ — As last. *R.I.C.* S333 20

1333 Kl(R and M). ℞. — As last. *R.I.C.* S333 and S540 22

1334 Kl, helmet, SR. (R and M). ℞. — As last. *R.I.C.* S333 and S540 .. 25

1335 Antoninianus. Bf(A). ℞. VOTA ORBIS, two Victories attaching to
palm-tree a shield inscribed SC £18
1335a Ba(A). ℞. — As last. *R.I.C.* 459 18
1335b Bc(A). ℞ — As last. *R.I.C.* 459 18
1335c Bg(A). ℞. — As last. *R.I.C.* 459 (*Voetter*) 20
1336 Cf(A). ℞ — As last. 18
1336a Ca(A). ℞. — As last. *R.I.C.* 460 18
1336b Cc(A). ℞. — As last. *R.I.C.* 460 18
1336c Ka(M). ℞. VOTA VICENNALIA, as last or with P in field. *R.I.C.* S541
(*Voetter*) 20
1336d Kf(M). ℞. — As last. *R.I.C.* S541 (*Voetter*) 20
1336e Kh imperial mantle, sc. ea. ℞. — As last. *R.I.C.* S541 (*Voetter*) .. 25

1335b   1352

1336f Kk. ℞. VOT or VOTIS in laurel-wreath. *R.I.C.* S335 (*in error for* **1355** ?) 22
1338 Kc. ℞. VOTIS DECANNALIB., in laurel-wreath. *R.I.C.* S334 18
1339 Kk(S). ℞. VOTIS DECENNALIBVS in laurel-wreath. *R.I.C.* S597 .. 18
1339a Kf. ℞. — As last. *R.I.C.* S334 18
1340 Kl, sp. sh. ℞. — As last. *R.I.C.* S334 20
1340a Kh(S). ℞. — As last. *R.I.C.* S597 (*Voetter*) 20
1340b Kh, sp. sh. (S). ℞. — As last. *R.I.C.* S597 20
1350 Kf(S). ℞. VOTIS X in laurel-wreath. *R.I.C.* S598 22
1351 Kk(S). ℞. — As last. *R.I.C.* S598 22
1352 K rad. bust dr. and cuir. l. (S). ℞. — As last. *R.I.C.* S598 25
1355 Kk(S). ℞. VOT. or VOTIS X ET XX in laurel-wreath. *R.I.C.* S599 .. 30

GALLIENUS and SALONINA

5a Denarius. CONCORDIA AVGG., diad. dr. bust of Sal, r. facing laur. dr.
bust of Gal. l. ℞. FELICITATIS, Victory seated l.; at her feet, empress (?)
and two children stg. l.; third child stg. by chair. *R.I.C.* S6 (*B.M.*)
Excessively rare

9 Medallion. — — ℞. PIETAS FALERI, goat stg. r. under tree, suckling
child; another child seated; to r., eagle; in ex., thunderbolt (28 mm.;
28·00 gms.). *R.I.C.* 2 .. .. *Extremely rare*

11 Antoninianus. Kk or l. ℞. SALONINA AVG., diad. bust r. on crescent.
R.I.C. S4 .. .. *Extremely rare*

12 Medallion. Fk. ℞. — her diad. bust dr. r. (27 mm.; 7·50 gms.).
R.I.C. 3 .. .. *Extremely rare*

15 Antoninianus. SALONINA AVG., her diad. bust r. ℞. VIRTVS AVG.,
helmeted hd. of Gal. l. *R.I.C.* S5 .. .. *Very rare*

GALLIENUS and SALONINUS

2 Medallion. CONCORDIA AVGVSTORVM, bare-headed bust of Saloninus dr.
and cuir. r., facing laur. bust of Gal. dr. and cuir. l. ℞. ADVENTVS AVGG.,
Valerian, Gallienus and Saloninus or Valerian II riding l., preceded by
Victory and accompanied by soldiers; beneath two enemies; in background,
three ensigns (35 mm.; 32·60 gms.). *R.I.C.* 1 .. .. .. *Extremely rare*

SALONINA

Cornelia Salonina was married to Gallienus about 243 A.D. *and was the mother of Valerian II and Saloninus. She was murdered with her husband in* 268 A.D.

Obverse legends and types.

A. CORNELIA SALONINA AVG.
B. CORN. SALONINA AVG.
C. SALONINA AVG.
a. Diademed bust draped right, on crescent.
b. Diademed bust draped right.

References.

S before *R.I.C.* reference indicates that they were struck in the sole reign of Gallienus and start on p. 192. They are numbered separately from those struck during the lifetime of Valerian, which start in that work on p. 108.

1	**Antoninianus.** Ca. ℞. ABVNDANTIA AVG., Abundantia stg. l., emptying cornucopiae; B in field. *R.I.C.* S1 ..	£16
1a	Ca(A). ℞. — Abundantia walking r., holding two torches; SPQR in ex. *R.I.C.* S89 (*Voetter*) ..	20
4	Ca(A). ℞. ABQVITAS AVG., Aequitas stg. l.; crescent in field, VIIC in ex. *R.I.C.* S87 ..	14
4a	Ca(A). ℞. — As last, but without the crescent in field ..	
4b	Ca(S). ℞. — As **4,** but nothing in field or ex. *R.I.C.* S70 ..	14
5	Cb. ℞. — As **4**	
7	**Medallion.** Cb. ℞. AEQVITAS PVBLICA, the three Monetae stg. half-left, piles of metal at their feet (31-30 mm.; 27-24·30 gms.). *R.I.C.* 16	*Extremely rare*
8	Bb. ℞. — As last (37-20 mm.; 30-16 gms.). *R.I.C.* 18	.. *Extremely rare*
9/10	Ab (sometimes w.). ℞. — As last (38-37 mm.; 33·04-33·88 gms.). *R.I.C.* 17	.. *Extremely rare*
10a	CORNELIA SALONINA AVGVSTA, b. ℞. — As last (36 mm.; 27·20 gms.). *R.I.C.* 19	.. *Excessively rare*

4a   22a

16	**Antoninianus.** Ca. ℞. ANNONA AVG., Abundantia stg. l. before modius, holding ears of corn and anchor (Hy.; *rev. of Gallienus*) ..	15
17	Ca(M). ℞. AVG . IN PACE, Salonina seated l., holding olive-branch and sceptre; P, S, MP or MS in ex. *R.I.C.* S58 ..	20
17a	Ca(S). ℞. — As last; SI in ex. ..	20
17b	Ca(M). ℞. — As last, nothing in ex. *R.I.C.* 58 ..	20
18	Ba(M). ℞. — As last. *R.I.C.* S57 ..	20
19	COR . SALONINA P . F . AVG., a (M). ℞. — As last. *R.I.C.* S59 ..	22
20	Ca(M). ℞. AVGVSTA IN PACE, as **17b.** *R.I.C.* S60 ..	20
20a	Ca(M). ℞. — As last, but P or S in ex. *R.I.C.* S60 ..	20
20b	Ca(M). ℞. — As **17b,** but P in field. *R.I.C.* S60 ..	20
21	Ba(M). ℞. BENERI GENETRICI, Venus stg. l., holding apple and sceptre. *R.I.C.* 61 note ..	14
22	Ca(A). ℞. CEREI AVG., Ceres seated l., holding corn-ears and torch. *R.I.C.* S90 ..	22
22a	Ca(A). ℞. — As last, but with branch in ex. ..	22

23   **Antoninianus.** Ca(L). ℞. CERES SEGESTAE, goddess in four-columned temple (Hy.; *or misreading of* **36**). *R.I.C.* 1 note ..   ..

24   Ca(S). ℞. CONCOR. AVG., Concordia seated l., holding patera and double-cornucopiae £10

24a   Ca(S). ℞. — As last, but A or II in ex. *R.I.C.* S71.   10

25   Ca. ℞. CONCORD. AET., as **24**, but RP in ex. *R.I.C.* S2..   ..   10

25a   Ca(M). ℞. — As last, but MP in ex.   ..   ..   ..

26   **Denarius.** Cb. ℞. — As **24**. *R.I.C.* S34   100

27   **Antoninianus.** Ca. ℞. CONCORDIA AET., as last   ..   ..

28   Ca(S). ℞. CONCORDIA AVG., as last. *R.I.C.* S72   10

29   Cb (?denarius ?A). ℞. CONCORDIA AVGG., as last   ..   ..

30   Ba(?A). ℞. — As last   ..   ..

31   Ba(A). ℞. — Gal. and Sal. clasping hands. *R.I.C.* 63   12

31a   Ba(A). ℞. — As last, with star or wreath in field. *R.I.C.* 63 ..   12

32   *Obv.*? ℞. — Two joined hands (Hy.?) ..   ..   ..

36   Ca(L). ℞. DEAE SEGETIAE, goddess in four-columned temple. *R.I.C.* 5   20

37   Ca. ℞. DIANAE CONS. AVG, hind walking r.   ..   ..   ..

37a   Ca. ℞. — Doe walking r., Δ in ex. *R.I.C.* S4   12

38   Ca. ℞. DIANA LVCIFERA, Diana stg., holding lighted torch. *R.I.C.* 53..   14

36   50

39   Ca. ℞. FECVNDITAS AVG., Fecunditas stg. l., holding cornucopiae and extending hand to child   10

39a   Ca. ℞. — As last, but Δ or ϵ in field. *R.I.C.* S5   10

39b   Ca. ℞. — As last, but Δ in ex. *R.I.C.* S5   10

40   COR. SALONINA AVG., a. ℞. — As **39, 39a,** or **39b.** *R.I.C.* S5ᵃ   ..   16

41   CORNEL. SALONINA AVG., a. ℞. — As last. *R.I.C.* S5ᵃ   16

41a   **Denarius.** Cb. ℞. — As **39**. *R.I.C.* 35 (*Voetter*)   125

43   **Quinarius.** Cb. ℞. — Fecunditas stg. r., infant on l. arm and extending hand to child. *R.I.C.* S42   125

44   **Antoninianus.** Ca (R and M). ℞. — As last. *R.I.C.* 26 and 57 ..   10

44a   Ca. ℞. — As last, but with Δ or N in field (*Cohen*) or in ex. (*R.I.C.*). *R.I.C.* S6   10

47   Ca. ℞. FELICITAS AVGG., Felicitas stg. l. *R.I.C.* 27   12

50   Ca(L). ℞. FELICITAS PVBLICA, Felicitas seated l. *R.I.C.* 6   ..   10

50a   Ca(S). ℞. FELICITAS SAECVLI, Felicitas stg. l. (Hy.; *rev of Gallienus*). *R.I.C.* S73 (*Voetter*)   15

51   Ca(M). ℞. FELICIT. PVBL., Felicitas stg. l., legs crossed, leaning on column, holding caduceus. *R.I.C.* S61   10

51a   **Denarius.** Cb. ℞. FIDES MILITVM, Fides stg., holding ensign and sceptre. *R.I.C.* S36 (*Voetter*)   125

51b   **Antoninianus.** Ca. ℞. — As last, but IV in field. *R.I.C.* S7 (*Voetter*)   16

51c   Ca. ℞. FORTVNA AVG., Fortuna stg. l. and sacrificing from patera over altar. *R.I.C.* S8   16

51d Antoninianus. Ca(A). ℞. FORTVNA AVG., Fortuna stg. l. by altar, holding patera and cornucopiae; SPQR in ex. *R.I.C.* S91 (*Voetter*) .. £16

51e Ca(S). ℞. FORTVNA RED., Fortuna stg. l. *R.I.C.* S74 (*Voetter*).. .. 14

52 Ca(S). ℞. FORTVNA REDVX, Fortuna seated l. *R.I.C.* S75 12

52a Denarius. Cb. ℞. — As **51e.** *R.I.C.* S37 (*Voetter*) 125

53 Antoninianus. Ca. ℞, — Salonina? stg. l., holding cornucopiae and giving hand to child (*probably misdescription of next piece*) 20

53a Ca. ℞. — As **51e,** but S in field. *R.I.C.* S9 20

54 Ca. ℞. INDVLGENT . AVG., Indulgentia seated l. 12

54a Ca. ℞. — As last, but P in ex. *R.I.C.* S10 12

54b Bb(Spain). ℞. IOVI VLTORI, Jupiter stg. facing, hd. r., holding thunderbolt, cloak on arm; V or S in field? (Hy.; *rev. of Gallienus*). *Cohen* 54 note

55 Ca(M). ℞. IVNO AVG., Juno seated l., holding infant and flower; MS in ex. *R.I.C.* S62 10

56 Ca. ℞. IVNO CONSERVAT, Juno stg. l., peacock at feet; H or N in field. *R.I.C.* S11 (*does not give* peacock) 14

60   67b

58 Ba (R and M). ℞. IVNO REGINA, Juno stg. l. *R.I.C.* 28 and 58 .. 10

59 Medallion. Ab. ℞. — As last (40-32 mm.; 42-27·10 gms.). *R.I.C.* 20
Extremely rare

60 Antoninianus. Ca (R and A). ℞. — As last. *R.I.C.* 29 and 64 .. 10

60a Ca. ℞. — As last, but Q in field. *R.I.C.* S13 10

60b Ca(S). ℞. — As last, but star in field. *R.I.C.* S76 10

61 Quinarius. Cb. ℞. — As **58.** *R.I.C.* 40 125

67 Antoninianus. Ca. ℞. — As **56,** but nothing in field. *R.I.C.* 30 (eagle for peacock, *in error?*).. 10

67a Ca. ℞. — As last, but Q in field. *R.I.C.* 30 and S12 10

67b Ca(A). ℞. — As **56,** but star or crescent in field, or star in ex. *R.I.C.* S92 10

68 Ca. ℞. IVNO VICTRIX, Juno stg. l. *R.I.C.* 31 10

69 COR . SALONINA AVG., a. ℞. IVNONI CONS . AVG., hind (*C.*) or doe (*R.I.C.*) walking r.; Δ in ex. 10

69a Ba. ℞. — As last. *R.I.C.* S14 10

70 COR . SALONINA AVG., a. ℞. — Similar, but walking l.; Δ (*C.* A or Δ) in ex. *R.I.C.* S16 12

70a Ba. ℞. — As last. *R.I.C.* S16 10

71 Ca. ℞. — As last, but A or Δ in ex. *R.I.C.* S15 10

72 Medallion. Bb. ℞. IVNONI REGINAE, peacock in splendour. *R.I.C.* 21
Excessively rare

73 Antoninianus. Ca. ℞, LAETITIA AVG., Laetitia stg. l. *R.I.C.* S17 .. 18

73a Ca(S). ℞. LIBERAL . AVG., Liberalitas stg. l., I in field (Hy.?; *possibly a die intended for Gallienus and not used*). *R.I.C.* S77 16

73b Ca(M). ℞. LVNA LVCIF., Luna in biga l. *R.I.C.* S63 (*Voetter*).. .. 35

73c Ca(A). ℞. MINERVA AVG., Minerva stg. l., holding spear and leaning on shield; SPQR in ex. *R.I.C.* S93 18

74 Medallion. Bb. ℞. MONETA AVGG., the three Monetae, usual type (33 mm.; 27·00 gms.). *R.I.C.* 22 .. .. *Extremely rare*

74a Antoninianus. Ca. ℞. ORIENS AVGG., Apollo stg. l., holding globe. *R.I.C.* 32 (*Voetter; rev. of Gallienus*) £18

74b Ca. ℞. — Sol stg. l., holding globe (Hy.). *R.I.C.* S18 (*Voetter*) .. 14

75 Ca. ℞. PAX AVG., Pax stg. l. 12

75a Ca. ℞. — As last, but T in field. *R.I.C.* S19 12

76 Ca. ℞. PAX PVBLICA, Pax seated l.; V in ex. *R.I.C.* S20.. 12

77 Ca. ℞. PIETAS AVG., Pietas stg. l., holding box of perfumes and raising r. hand; P in field or ex. *R.I.C.* S22 10

77a Ca(S). ℞. — As last, but P or P II (*C. PH*) in field or P in ex. *R.I.C.* S78 10

78 Ba. ℞. — As before, with P in field. *R.I.C.* S21 10

79 Ca(S). ℞. — As last, but sacrificing before altar, no mark. *R.I.C.* S79 10

79a Ca(S). ℞. — As last, but II in field (*Cohen*), in ex. (*R.I.C.*). *R.I.C.* S79 10

79b Ca(M). ℞. — Pietas stg. l., before altar, both hands raised. *R.I.C.* S64 (*Voetter*) 14

81 Ca. ℞. PIETAS AVGG., Pietas stg. l., holding box of perfumes. *R.I.C.* 33 .. 12

82 Ca. ℞. — As last, but Pietas sacrificing before altar. *R.I.C.* 34 .. 12

83 Medallion. Ab. ℞. — Pietas seated l., holding sceptre; in front, two children, another at the side of her chair (36-32 mm.; 35·92-22·00 gms.). *R.I.C.* 23 .. .. *Extremely rare*

84 Antoninianus. Ca. ℞. — As last. *R.I.C.* 35 12

84a   92a

84a Ca(M). ℞. — As last, but perhaps no child by chair. *R.I.C.* 59 .. 12

85 Quinarius. Cb (R and A). ℞. — As **83**. *R.I.C.* 41 and 72 125

88 Antoninianus. Ca(S). ℞. PIETAS AVGVST., as **77**, but P II in ex. *R.I.C.* S78 12

88a Ca(S). ℞. PROVI . AVG., Providentia stg. l., holding baton and cornucopiae; at foot, globe. *R.I.C.* S80 (*Voetter*) 14

89 Ba. ℞. PROVID . AVG., Providentia stg. l., holding globe and transverse sceptre 14

89a Ca. ℞. — As last or as next. *R.I.C.* S23 (*Voetter*) 14

90 Ba. ℞. — As **89**, but patera for globe 14

N.B.—*Probably* **89** *and* **90** *are the same coin variously described and they may be the same as* **89a**, *having a misdescribed obv.*

91 Ca(S). ℞. PROVIDENTIA AVG., as last (or **89**). *R.I.C.* S81.. 14

92 Ca. ℞. PVDICITIA, Pudicitia stg. l., raising veil and holding sceptre. *R.I.C.* S24 10

92a Ca. ℞. — As last, but Q or VI in field. *R.I.C.* S24 10

92b Ca. ℞. — As **92**, but Q in ex. *R.I.C.* S24 10

92c Denarius. Cb. ℞. — As **92**. *R.I.C.* S38 (*Voetter*) 110

94 Antoninianus. Ca. ℞. — As last, but Pudicitia seated. *R.I.C.* S25.. 10

94a Ca. ℞. — As last Q, IV or VI in ex. *R.I.C.* S25 10

95 Quinarius. Cb. ℞. — As **94**. *R.I.C.* S43 110

95a Cb. ℞. PVDICITIAM, as last. *R.I.C.* S43 (*Hamburger*, 1925) 140

97 Medallion. Bb. ℞. PVDICITIA AVG., as last. (31 mm.; 21·83 gms.).
R.I.C. 24 .. .. *Extremely rare*

98 Antoninianus. Ba(A). ℞. — As last. R.I.C. 66 .. .. .. £10

99 Ca(S). ℞. — As last. 10

99a Ca(S). ℞. — Similar, but SI or B in ex. R.I.C. S82 10

99b Ca(A). ℞. — As **92.** R.I.C. 65 (*Voetter*) 12

101 Ca. ℞. PVDICITIA AVGG., as **94** 10

102 Medallion. Bb. ℞. PVDICITIA AVGVSTAE, Pudicitias seated as **94**; in front, Salus stg. l., feeding serpent in arms; behind, Felicitas stg. l., leaning against column with legs crossed (35-32 mm.; 25·86-24·00 gms.).
R.I.C. 25 .. .. *Extremely rare*

102a Antoninianus. Ca(S). ℞. RESTITVTOR ORBIS, Gallienus stg. l., holding patera and spear, sacrificing at altar (Hy.; *rev. of Gallienus*). R.I.C. S83 (*Voetter*) 15

103 Ca(A). ℞. ROMAE AETERNAE, Gallienus stg. r., receiving a Victory from Roma, holding spear seated l.; behind her, a shield. R.I.C. 67 12

103a Ca(A). ℞. — As last, but in field, star or wreath. R.I.C. 67 12

105 Ca(A). ℞. SALVS AVG., Salus stg. r., feeding serpent in arms. R.I.C. S88 15

106a Ca(S). ℞. — Salus stg. l., holding sceptre, feeding serpent rising from altar. R.I.C. S84 (*Voetter*) 15

106b Ca(M). ℞. SALVS AVGG., as last, but perhaps without sceptre. R.I.C. 60 (*Voetter*) 15

107 Ca. ℞. SECVRIT . ORBIS, Securitas seated l., holding sceptre, l. hand raised to hd. (Hy.; *late obv.; joint reign rev. of Gallienus*). R.I.C. S26 .. 15

107a — ℞. — As last, but VI in ex. R.I.C. S26 15

108 Ca. ℞. SECVRIT . PERPET., Securitas stg. l., legs crossed, leaning on column and holding sceptre. R.I.C. S27 14

108a Ca. ℞. — As last, but H in field. R.I.C. S27 14

108b Denarius. Cb. ℞. — As **108.** R.I.C. S39 (*Voetter*) 110

108c Antoninianus. Ca. ℞. SECVRIT . PVBL., as **107a.** R.I.C. S28 (*Voetter*) .. 15

108d Ca. ℞. VBERITAS AVG., Uberitas stg. l. R.I.C. S29 (*Voetter*) 16

108e Denarius. Cb. ℞. — As last. R.I.C. S40 (*Voetter*) 110

109 Antoninianus. Ca. ℞. VBERTAS AVG., as last. R.I.C. S29 16

109a Ca. ℞. — As **108d** and/or as last, with E in field. R.I.C. S29 (*Voetter*) .. 16

110 Ba(M). ℞. VENEREM GENETRICEM, Venus stg. l., holding apple and sceptre. R.I.C. 61 20

111a Ba(M). ℞. VENERI GENETRICI, as last. R.I.C. 61 10

112 Ba(A). ℞. — As last, star in field 12

113 Ca(A). ℞. VENVS AVG., Venus stg. l., holding helmet and spear; beside her, shield; PXV in ex. R.I.C. S86 12

113   115

115 Ca(L). ℞. VENVS FELIX, Venus seated l., holding sceptre and stretching out hand to child. R.I.C. 7 (captive *for* child, *in error ?*) 14

116 As last, on a heavy flan. R.I.C. 7 note 30

117 Antoninianus. Ca(M). ℞. VENVS FELIX, Venus stg. l., holding sceptre
 and infant £10
117a Ca(M). ℞. — As last, P in field; *R.I.C.* S65   10
118 Ca(M). ℞. — Venus stg. l., holding apple and sceptre, Cupid at her feet 10
118a Ca(M). ℞. — As last, but P in field. *R.I.C.* S65   10
120 Quinarius. Cc. ℞. VENVS GENETRIX, as **118.** *R.I.C.* 42 and S44   ..   125
121 Antoninianus. Ca. ℞. — As last. *R.I.C.* 36   10
121a Ca. ℞. — As last, but S, V, VI or N in field. *R.I.C.* S30 (helmet or apple) 10
126 Ca(M). ℞. VENVS VICT., as before, but holding helmet and sceptre   ..   10
126a Ca(M). ℞. — As last, but P in field. *R.I.C.* S66   10
126b Ca(M). ℞. — As **126,** but P in ex. *R.I.C.* S66   10
127 Ca(M). ℞. — Venus stg. l., leaning on shield and holding helmet and
 transverse spear (*R.I.C.* sceptre).   10
127a Ca(M). ℞. — As last, but MS in ex. *R.I.C.* S67   10
129 Ca. ℞. VENVS VICTRIX, Venus stg. l., holding helmet and sceptre, shield
 at her side. *R.I.C.* 37 (seated *in error*)   10
129a Ca. ℞. — As last, but H or VI or IV in field. *R.I.C.* S31   10

130   146

130 Ca (A and R). ℞. — As last, but holding apple and palm. *R.I.C.* 68
 and S31   10
130a Ca. ℞. — As last, but H or VI or IV in field. *R.I.C.* S31   10
131 Ca (A and R). ℞. — As **130,** but with captive at feet. *R.I.C.* 68 and S31 12
132 Ca. ℞. — As last, but H or VI or IV in field. *R.I.C.* S31   10
134 Ca(L). ℞. — Venus, half-naked, seen from the rear, stg. r. and leaning
 on column, holding palm and helmet. *R.I.C.* 8 (stg. l.)   14
137 Ba. ℞. VESTA, Vesta stg. l., holding patera and transverse sceptre.
 R.I.C. 39   10
138 Aa. ℞. — As last. *R.I.C.* 38   10
139 Ca(M). ℞. — As last. *R.I.C.* S68   10
139a Ca(M). ℞. — As last, but S in field. *R.I.C.* S68   10
140 Ba(A). ℞. — As **137,** but lighted torch for sceptre. *R.I.C.* 69..   ..   10
141 Quinarius. Ba. ℞. — As last. *R.I.C.* 43   125
141a Ba. ℞. — As **137.** *R.I.C.* 43 (*Voetter*)   125
141b Ba. ℞. — As one of the last two, but Vesta seated. *R.I.C.* 43   125
142 Antoninianus. Ca(A). ℞. — Vesta seated l., holding palladium (*R.I.C.*
 Victory) and transverse sceptre. *R.I.C.* 70   10
142a Ca(L.) ℞. — As last, but holds Victory and palm. *R.I.C.* 9   14
143 Ca. ℞. — As last, but holds patera and transverse sceptre; Q in ex.
 R.I.C. S32   10
144 Quinarius. Cb. ℞. — As last, but nothing in ex. *R.I.C.* S45   ..   125
146 Antoninianus. Ba(A). ℞. VESTA AETERNAE, Vesta stg. l., holding
 palladium (Victory, *R.I.C.*) and sceptre. *R.I.C.* 71   12
147 Ca(M). ℞. VESTA FELIX, as **143,** but S in field or S or MS in ex. (*Cohen also
 gives* T . S *in field or ex.*). *R.I.C.* S69   10
148a Ca. ℞. VICTORIA AET., Victory stg. l.; Z in field. *R.I.C.* S33 (*Voetter*) 15
148b Denarius. Cb. ℞. VICTORIA AVG., Victory stg. l. *R.I.C.* S41   110
148c Antoninianus. Ca(S). ℞. VICTORIA . . ., Victoria seated l., holding
 shield or helmet and palm; beside her, shield. *R.I.C.* S85 (*Voetter*)   ..   18

VALERIAN II or JUNIOR

P. Cornelius Licinius Valerianus was the elder son of Gallienus and Salonina. On his father's elevation he was given the rank of Caesar and died about two years later.

N.B.—*All but one of the coins of this prince in* Cohen *have the obverse legend* VALERIANVS P . F . AVG. *and are now attributed to Valerian I.*

2   Ɍ.   DEO VOLKANO, see Valerian I **50c**
3   Ɍ.   DEO VOLKANO, see Valerian I **50d**
5   Ɍ.   ORIENS AVGG., see Valerian I **140b**
6   Ɍ.   ORIENS AVGG., see Valerian I **143a**
7   Ɍ.   PAX AVGG., see Valerian I **150b**
8   Ɍ.   PROVIDENTIA AVG., see Valerian I **176a**
9   Ɍ.   SECVRIT . PERPET, see Valerian I **207a**
10   Ɍ.   VENVS VICTRIX, see Valerian I **212a**
11   Ɍ.   VICT . AVGG., see Valerian I **214a**
12   Ɍ.   VICT . PARTICA, see Valerian I **255b**
13   Ɍ.   VICT . PARTICA, see Valerian I **255c**
15   Ɍ.   VIRTVS AVGG., see Valerian I **278b**
16   Ɍ.   VIRTVS AVGG., see Valerian I **278c**

Also one with *obv.* IMP . P . LIC . VALERIANO AVG.

14   Ɍ.   VIRTVS AVG., see Valerian I **278a**

Obverse legends.

A.   COR . LIC . VALERIANVS CAES.
B.   COR . VALERIANVS CAESAR.
C.   C . P . L . VALREIANVS CAES.
D.   LIC . VALERIANVS NOB . CAES.
E.   P . C . L . VALERIANVS NOB . CAES.
F.   P . LIC . COR . VALERIANVS CAES.
G.   P . LIC . VALERIANVS CAES.
H.   VALERIANVS CAES.
J.   VALERIANVS NOBIL . CAES.
  Posthumous Coins.
PA.   DIVO CAES VALERIANO.
PB.   DIVO VALERIANO CAES.

Obverse types.
All are to right.
a.   Radiate bust draped.
b.   Bare-headed bust draped.
c.   Radiate bust draped and cuirassed.
d.   Bare-headed bust draped and cuirassed.
e.   Bare head.
f.   Radiate head.

Mints.
L—Lugdunum; A—Antioch; R—Rome.

The following coins were given by *Cohen* to Saloninus but are now attributed to Valerian II.

N.B.—*The numbers we give below are* Cohen's *Saloninus nos. with one or two additions.*

2 **Antoninianus.** PBa(L). ℞. CONSACRATIO, eagle stg. l., turning hd. r. *R.I.C.* 8 .. .. £25

4 PBa(L). ℞. — As last, but eagle on globe. *R.I.C.* 8 25

5 PBa(L). ℞. — Eagle bearing prince to heaven. *R.I.C.* 9 30

6 PBa(L). ℞. — Funeral pyre in four stages; on top, Valerian II in quad. facing. *R.I.C.* 10 40

7 PAf. ℞. CONSECRATIO, eagle stg. r., turning hd. l.; s in ex. *R.I.C.* 27 .. 25

8 PAa. ℞. — As last. *R.I.C.* 27 25

9 PAf. ℞. — As 2. *R.I.C.* 27 25

10 **Quinarius.** PAe. ℞. — As last. *R.I.C.* 31 200

12 **Antoninianus.** PAf. ℞. — Lighted altar. *R.I.C.* 24 25

13 PAc. ℞. — As last. *R.I.C.* 24 25

13a PAa. ℞. — As last. *R.I.C.* 24 25

14 As last, but on heavy flan (*wt.*, 7·60 gms.). *R.I.C.* 24 note 40

14a Ea. ℞. — As last (Hy.). *R.I.C.* 25 (*Voetter*) 35

14b Da. ℞. — As last (Hy.). *R.I.C.* 26 35

15 PAa. ℞. — As 6, but five stages and biga. *R.I.C.* 28 (bare-headed, dr.) 40

20 Ha(L). ℞. DEO VOLKANO, Vulcan in temple of four columns, holding hammers and pincers. *R.I.C.* 2 50

24 Ja(A). ℞. FIDES MILITVM, legionary eagle between two ensigns. *R.I.C.* 46 35

26 Ha(L). ℞. IOVI CRESENTI, child Jupiter seated facing on goat walking r. *R.I.C.* 3 30

27 As last on heavy flan (6 gms.) 40

28 Ea. ℞. — As last. *R.I.C.* 14 30

28a Ea. ℞. — As before, but goat walking l. *R.I.C.* 14 .. .. ..

29 Gc. ℞. — As 26, but child facing r. *R.I.C.* 13 30

29a Ga. ℞. — As last, and/or goat walking l. *R.I.C.* 13 30

30 Ea. ℞. — As 29a. *R.I.C.* 14 30

31 Bc. ℞. — As last. *R.I.C.* 16 30

32 Ac. ℞. — As last. *R.I.C.* 15 30

32a Ha. ℞. — As 29, but with z in ex. *R.I.C.* 17 30

34 Ec. ℞. LIBERALITAS AVGG., Liberalitas stg. l. *R.I.C.* 18 60

34a Ea. ℞. — As last. *R.I.C.* 18 60

36a Medallion. Ed. ℞. MONETA AVGG., the three Monetae as usual on these medallions (*wt.*, 18·11 gms; *diam.* 31 mm.). *R.I.C.* 12 (*Gnecchi*)

Excessively rare

37 Antoninianus. Jk and/or a (A). ℞. ORIENS, prince leaning on shield and crowning trophy. *R.I.C.* 47 .. .. £60

45 Ga. ℞. PIETAS AVGG., sprinkler, simpulum, vase, sacrificial knife and augur's wand. *R.I.C.* 19 25

46 Ga. ℞. — Sprinkler, knife, vase, wand on simpulum. *R.I.C.* 19 .. 25

47 Ga. ℞. — Wand on simpulum, vase, knife and sprinkler. *R.I.C.* 19.. 25

50 Ea. ℞. — Wand, knife, patera, vase, simpulum and sprinkler. *R.I.C.* 20 25

51 Ca. ℞. — As last. *R.I.C.* 21 25

52 Ha(L). ℞ — As last. *R.I.C.* 4 25

56 Ea. ℞. — Wand, knife, vase, simpulum and sprinkler. *R.I.C.* 20 .. 25
R.I.C., page 118 note, says that some of the above read AGG for AVGG.

56a Fa(A). ℞. — Sacrificial implements. *R.I.C.* 48 (*Voetter*) 30

59 Ea. ℞. P . M . TR . P . V . COS . IIII P . P., Gallienus seated l. in curule chair, holding globe and sceptre (Hy.; *mule with rev. of Gallienus*). *R.I.C.* 22 35

66 Ha(L). ℞. PRINC . IVVENTVTIS, prince in military dress, stg. l., holding baton and reversed spear; on r., two ensigns. *R.I.C.* 5 25

67 Ja(A). ℞. — Prince, as last, crowning trophy and holding spear and shield. *R.I.C.* 49 30

67a Jc(A). ℞. — As last. *R.I.C.* 49 30

67b Jc (A). ℞. PRINC . IVVETVTIS, as last. (*David R. Sear*) 30

70 Ea. ℞. PRINCIPI IVVENT., prince, in military dress, stg. l., holding globe and reversed spear. *R.I.C.* 23 25

74 Ea. ℞. — As last, but holding ensign and spear. *R.I.C.* 23 25

78 Fa(A). ℞. PRINCIPI IVBENTVTIS. As **67.** *R.I.C.* 50 30

80 Quinarius. Eb. ℞. PRINCIPI IVVENTVTIS, as **74,** but holding ensign and sceptre. *R.I.C.* 30 200

80a Denarius. As last. *R.I.C.* 29 (*Voetter*) 250

81 Antoninianus. Ec. ℞. — As last. *R.I.C.* 23 25

81a PAa, c or k. ℞. As 70,74 or 80 (Hy. *or mule*) 25

84 Fa(A). ℞. As **70,** but baton for globe. *R.I.C.* 51 30

91 Ha(L). ℞. RESTITV . . . . GALLIAR., Gallienus, in military dress, stg. l., raising kneeling female (Gaul) and holding spear. (Hy.; *mule with rev. of Gallienus*). *R.I.C.* 6 40

92 Ja(A). ℞, SPES PVBLICA, Spes walking l. *R.I.C.* 52 25

96 Fa(A). ℞. VICTORIA GERMAN., Victory stg. r., holding palm, presenting wreath to prince, in military dress, stg., holding spear *R.I.C.* 53 .. 60

97 Fa(A). ℞. VICTORIA PART., as last. *R.I.C.* 54 50

SALONINUS

*P. Licinius Cornelius Saloninus Valerianus was the second son of Gallienus and Salonina.
On the death of his brother in 255 A.D. he received the title of Caesar, and four years later
was elevated to the rank of Augustus. Soon after his elevation he was put to death by
Postumus, commander of the Rhine legions.*

Obverse legends.

A.   LIC . COR . SAL . VALERIANVS N . CAES.
B.   SALON . VALERIANVS CAES.
C.   SAL . VALERIANVS C.
D.   SAL . VALERIANVS CS.

As Augustus.

E.   IMP . SALON . VALERIANVS AVG.

Obverse types and mints as Valerian Junior (p. 117).

1 **Antoninianus.** Da(L). ℞. ADVENTVS AVGG., prince riding l., raising
r. hand and holding spear. *R.I.C.* 6   ..   ..   £125

1a P. COR. SAL. GALLIENVS NOB. CAES., rad and cuir. bust r. (A). ℞. CONCORDIA
MILITVM, three standards. (*British Museum*)   ..   ..   *Very rare*

2 ℞. CONSECRATIO, see Valerian Junior   ..   ..   ..

3 Ba(K). ℞. — Eagle stg. l., looking back. *R.I.C.* 15   30

4 to 10, 12 to 15 ℞. — See Valerian Junior..   ..   ..

19 P . COR . SAL . VALERIANO CES., f(L). ℞. DEO MARTI, Mars in temple of
four columns. *R.I.C.* 7   50

20 ℞. DEO VOLKANO, see Valerian Junior   ..   ..

21 P . COR . SAL . VALERAINVS CAES., a(A). ℞. DII . NVTRITORES, Jupiter,
naked, mantle on arm, stg. l., holding sceptre and presenting to prince
a small Victory. *R.I.C.* 35   40

23 Ba(L). ℞. FELICITAS AVGG., Felicitas stg. l. *R.I.C.* 8   30

23a Ea(L). ℞. As last. (*British Museum*)   250

24 ℞. FIDES MILITVM, see Valerian Junior   ..   ..

26 to 32 ℞. IOVI CRESCENTI, see Valerian Junior   ..   ..

33a Aa. ℞, LERIGIO AVGG., Diana stg. l., holding bow; Q in field. *R.I.C.* 29
(*Voetter*)   40

34 ℞. LIBERALITAS AVGG., see Valerian Junior..   ..   ..   ..

35 **Medallion.** Ad. ℞. MONETA AVGG., the three Monetae, as usual on
these pieces. (Diam. 38-37 mm.; wt. 33·12-22·15 gms.). *R.I.C.* 22 *Extremely rare*

35a Ad seen from the back. ℞. — As last (31 mm.; 18 gms.). *R.I.C.* 23
(*Gnecchi*)   ..   ..   *Extremely rare*

37 **Antoninianus.** ℞. ORIENS, see Valerian Junior ..   ..

38 Aa. ℞. ORIENS AVGG., Sol stg. l. *R.I.C.* 24   30

39 Aa. ℞. PAX AVGG., Pax stg. l. *R.I.C.* 25   35

41 Ba(L). ℞. PIETAS AVG., augur's wand, sacrificial knife, vase, simpulum
and sprinkler. *R.I.C.* 9   25

45 to 47 ℞. PIETAS AVGG., see Valerian Junior..   ..   ..

49 Aa. ℞. — wand, knife, patera, vase, simpulum and sprinkler. *R.I.C.* 26   25

50 to 52, 56 — See Valerian Junior   ..   ..

59 ℞. P . M . TR . P . V . COS . IIII P . P., see Valerian Junior   ..   ..

49   63

60 Antoninianus. Aa. ℞. PRINC . IVVENT., prince, in military dress, stg. l., holding ensign and spear. *R.I.C.* 27 .. .. £25

61 Da(L). ℞. — As last, but holds baton and transverse spear; to r., ensign. *R.I.C.* 10 25

62 As last, but on r. two ensigns. *R.I.C.* 10 .. ..

62a Quinarius. Cb. ℞. — As before but without ensigns. *R.I.C.* 30 .. 200

63 Antoninianus. Aa. ℞. — As **60,** but holds globe and spear; at his feet, captive; P in field. *R.I.C.* 28 (holds ensign and spear or sceptre). *Illustrated on p.* 120 30

64 Da(L). ℞. — As **61,** but no ensigns; on l., trophy, below which are two captives with the hands tied behind their backs. *R.I.C.* 11 30

66, 67 ℞. PRINC . IVVENTVTIS, see Valerian Junior .. ..

70 ℞. PRINCIPI IVVENT., see Valerian Junior .. ..

73 Aa. ℞. — As **60.** *R.I.C.* 27 25

74 ℞. — — see Valerian Junior .. ..

78 ℞. PRINCIPI IVBENTVTIS, see Valerian Junior .. .. ..

80, 81, 84 ℞. PRINCIPI IVVENTVTIS, see Valerian Junior .. .. ..

85 Quinarius. A (or perhaps C) b. ℞. — Prince, as **60,** but holds ensign in each hand. *R.I.C.* 31 200

87 Antoninianus. Ba(L). ℞. — As **64,** but shield at base of trophy instead of captives. *R.I.C.* 12 25

90a Aa. ℞. RELIGIO AVGG., Diana stg. l., holding bow; Q in field. *R.I.C.* 29 (*Voetter*) 40

91 ℞. RESTITV . . . . GALLIAR., see Valerian Junior .. .. ..

92 ℞. SPES PVBLICA, see Valerian Junior .. ..

93 Ba(L). ℞. — Spes stg. l. *R.I.C.* 13 25

94 Ea(L). ℞. — As last. *R.I.C.* 14 250

95 SALON . VALERIANVS NOB . CAES, a(A). ℞. — Spes stg. l. presenting flower to prince stg. r., holding spear. *R.I.C.* 36 30

95a As last, with star or wreath in field. *R.I.C.* 36 30

96 ℞. VICTORIA GERMAN., see Valerian Junior .. ..

97 ℞. VICTORIA PART., see Valerian Junior .. ..

Saloninus 95a   Julius Gallienus 1a

JULIUS GALLIENUS

Quintus Julius Gallienus may have been another son of Gallienus.

1 Denarius. DIVO CAES . GALLIENO, laur. hd. r. ℞. CONSECRATIO, eagle looking upwards. *R.I.C.* 2 (*very doubtful*) .. ..

1a Antoninianus. DIVO CAES . Q . GALLIENO, rad. bust r. ℞. — Altar. *R.I.C.* 1 (*doubtful, but possibly genuine*) .. .. *Extremely rare*

122

MACRIANUS (JUNIOR)

260-261 A.D.

Fulvius Julius Macrianus was the elder son of T. Fulvius Macrianus, one of Valerian's generals, who rallied the remanants of the Roman army after Valerian's capture by the Persians. The younger Macrianus and his brother, Quietas, were proclaimed emperors. The general took vigorous action and halted the advance of the Persians and gained a notable victory over Sapor at Corycus, and the latter was obliged to retreat to the Euphrates. Flushed with victory the two Macriani set out for Europe to challenge Gallienus, they were however utterly defeated in Illyricum and both slain.

Obverse legend.

IMP . C . FVL . MACRIANVS P . F . AVG.

Obverse types as given in *R.I.C.*

D.   Radiate bust draped right.
DC. Radiate bust draped and cuirassed r.
C.   Radiate bust cuirassed r. (many of these have slight drapery on l. shoulder).
R.I.C. gives all coins to Antioch mint.

1 **Antoniniani.** C. ℞. AEQVTAS AVG., Aequitas stg. l., star in field.
  R.I.C. 5   .. .. £100
1a C. ℞. AEQVITAS AVG., as last. *R.I.C.* 5 110
1b C. ℞. As **1** or **1a,** but with nothing in field. *R.I.C.* 5 100

2   8a

2 C. ℞. APOLINI CONSERVA, Apollo naked but mantle showing behind
  him, stg. half left, holding branch and leaning on lyre. *R.I.C.* 6 .. 100
2a C. ℞. — As last; star in field. *R.I.C.* 6 100
4 MACRIANVS NOBIL . CAES., rad. bust dr. r. ℞. FIDES MILITVM, legionary
  eagle between two standards. *A forgery, probably a Valerian II* **24** *altered*
5 C. ℞. FORT . REDVX, Fortuna seated l., wheel at her feet. *R.I.C.* 7 .. 120
5a As last, without wheel. *R.I.C.* 7 120
5b As one or both of the last, with star in field and pellet in ex. *R.I.C.* 7 .. 120
6 C. ℞. INDVLGENTIAE AVG., Indulgentia seated l. *R.I.C.* 8 100
6a C. ℞. — As last, with star in field. *R.I.C.* 8 100
7 C. ℞. INDVLGENTIAE AVE., as one of the last two. *R.I.C.* 8 110
7a C. ℞. INDVLGENTIA AVG., as last. *R.I.C.* 8 note 110
7b DC. As one or more of the last four. *R.I.C.* 8 110
8 C. ℞. IOVI CONSERVATORI, Jupiter seated l., holding patera and sceptre;
  eagle at feet. *R.I.C.* 9 100
8a As last, with star in field. *R.I.C.* 9.. 100
9 C. ℞. MARTI PROPVGNATORI, Mars walking or running r., holding spear
  and shield. *R.I.C.* 10 120
9a As last, but with star in field. *R.I.C.* 10 120
  Cohen gives a similar coin, on p. 3, with a bearded face and says some
  authorities attribute this to Macrianus Senior. *R.I.C.* p. 581, note 2.
10a C. ℞. PIETAS AVGG., Mercury stg. l., holding purse and caduceus.
  (*British Museum*) 150

11 Antoninianus. C. ℞. ROMAE AETERNAE, Roma seated l. on shield, holding Victory and spear. *R.I.C.* 11 .. .. £100

11a As last, but with star in field. *R.I.C.* 11 100

11b As **11a**, but also two pellets in ex. *R.I.C.* 11 100

11c As one of the last three, but *obv.* commences IMP . CAE . FVLV. *R.I.C.* note

11a   12a

12 C. ℞. SOL. INVICTO, Sol, half-naked, stg. l. *R.I.C.* 12 100

12a As last, but star in field. *R.I.C.* 12 100

12b D. ℞. — As one or both of the last. *R.I.C.* 12 110

13 C. ℞. SPES PVBLICA, Spes walking l. *R.I.C.* 13 100

13a As last, but star in field. *R.I.C.* 13 100

13b D. ℞. — As one or both of the last. *R.I.C.* 13 110

15 C. ℞. VICTORIA AVGG., Victory walking r. *R.I.C.* 14 120

QUIETUS

260-261 A.D.

Fulvius Julius Quietus was the younger son of T. Fulvius Macrianus and proclaimed joint-emperor with his brother Macrianus. After the defeat of his father and brother he was besieged by Odenathus, the king of Palmyra, and eventually captured and killed.

Obverse legend and type.

IMP . C . FVL . QVIETVS P . F . AVG.

All have his radiate bust draped r., except where otherwise stated.

R.I.C. attribute all his coinage to Antioch.

1 ℞. AEQVITAS AVG., Aequitas stg. l. *R.I.C.* 2 110

1a ℞. AEQVITAS AVGG., as last. *R.I.C.* 2 110

1b ℞. AEQVTAS AVG. or AVGG, as last. *R.I.C.* 2 100

1c One or more of the last three with star in field. *R.I.C.* 2 100

1d One or more of the last four with his rad. bust dr. and cuir. r. *R.I.C.* 2 100

3 ℞. APOLLINI CONSERVA., Apollo, naked but for mantle on r. shoulder, stg. l., holding laurel-branch, l. hand on lyre. *R.I.C.* 3 100

4 ℞. APOLINI CONSERVA, as before but with mantle behind. *R.I.C* 3 .. 100

4a One or both of the last two with star in field *R.I.C.* 3 100

5 ℞. FORT . REDVX seated l., wheel below seat; star in field before. *R.I.C.* 4 120

5a As before, but seated on wheel. *R.I.C.* 4 120

6   8a

6 ℞. INDVLGENTIA AVG., Indulgentia seated l.; star in the field. *R.I.C.* 5   £100
6a As last. but also with pellet in ex. *R.I.C.* 5   100
6b As before, but nothing in field or ex. *R.I.C.* 5   100
7 As **6** and/or possibly one of the last two, but INDVLGNTIAE AVG. *R.I.C.* 5
note   110
8 ℞. IOVI CONSERVATORI, Jupiter seated l., holding patera and sceptre,
eagle at feet. *R.I.C.* 6   100
8a As last, but with star in field. *R.I.C.* 6   100
9 ℞. MARTI PROPVGNATORI, Mars walking r., holding spear and shield.
R.I.C. 7..   150
10 ℞. PIETAS AVG., Mercury stg. l.; star in field. *R.I.C.* 8   ..   ..
10a As last, but without star. *R.I.C.* 8   120
11 ℞. ROMAE AETERNAE, Roma seated l. on shield, holding Victory and spear.
R.I.C. 9..   100
11a As last, but with star in field. *R.I.C.* 9   100
11b As last, but also two pellets in ex. *R.I.C.* 9   100

11a   12

12 ℞. SOL . INVICTO, Sol stg. l. *R.I.C.* 10   100
12a As last, but with star in field. *R.I.C.* 10   100
12b As **12**, but with two pellets in ex. *R.I.C.* 10   100
12c As one or more of the last three with the bust cuir. as well as dr. *R.I.C.* 10   100
14 ℞. SPES PVBLICA, Spes walking l. *R.I.C.* 11   100

14a ℞. As last, but with star in field. *R.I.C.* 11   100
16 ℞. VICTORIA AVGG., Victory walking r. (*Seaby stock, September, 1969.
Cohen says laur. bust, in error ?*)   120
16a ℞. — Victory walking l. *R.I.C.* 12. (*Unusual style; the product of another
mint ?*)   150

REGALIANUS

ca. 260-261 A.D.

Publius Caius Regalianus was a Dacian and one of Valerian's generals. He seized power on the latter's capture, but was murdered by his own soldiers after a short reign.

R.I.C. attributes his coins to a mint at Carnuntum.

All have radiate bust draped r.

1 Antoninianus. IMP . C . RE . . . . R̃ . CONCORᴅIA, emperor and empress stg. face to face, altar between them. *R.I.C.* 1 .. .. £3000

1a IMP . C . P . C . RE . . . . R̃ . — As last. *R.I.C.* 2 (*Rohde*) 3000

2 . . . C . P . C . REGALIAV[TORI]. R̃ . . . VICO[ANTONINVS], Jupiter stg. l. *R.I.C.* 4 (*considers the rev. legend,* IOVI CONSERVATORI). This coin was struck on a coin of Caracalla (MARTI PACATORI; *C.* 149) and the portions of the legend shown here in brackets are letters from the earlier piece .. 3000

2a IMP . C . P . . . . . . [III COSI]VS AVG. R̃ . LIBERALITA[ERM], Liberalitas stg. l., holding purse (?) and sceptre. *R.I.C.* 5 (*Rohde*). This coin was struck on a coin of Maximinus I (probably *C.* 64) and the legend in brackets are letters from the earlier piece 3000

3 IMP . C . P . C . REGALIANVS AVG. R̃ . LIBERLAS AVGG, Libertas stg. l. *R.I.C.* 6 (p. 586) 3000

4 IMP . C . P . C . REGALIANV . . . . R̃ . ORIENS AVG., Sol stg. facing, r. hand raised, l. hand holding whip. *R.I.C.* 6 (p. 587) 3000

4a IMP . C . P . C . REGALIANVS AVG. R̃ . ORIENS AVGG., as last. *R.I.C.* 7 (*B.M.*). Overstruck on a coin of Caracalla with VICTORIA *rev.* 3000

5 . . . . . . REGALIAN . . . . . R̃ . PROVIDENTIA AVG., Providentia stg. l., holding ears of corn and cornucopiae, before modius filled with corn-ears. *R.I.C.* 8 3000

DRYANTILLA

Sulpicia Dryantilla, daughter of Sulpicius Pollio and Claudia Ammiana Dryantilla, was most probably the wife of Regalian.

1 bis SVLP . DRYANTILLA AVG., diad. bust dr. on crescent r. R̃ . AEQVITAS AVGG., Aequitas stg. l., holding scales and double cornucopiae. *R.I.C.* 1 (*B.M.*). A specimen of the type was struck over a coin of Severus Alexander 3000

1, 2, 3 — — R̃ . IVNO or IVNONI REGINA, Juno stg. l., holding uncertain object and sceptre. *R.I.C.* 2. These coins are found struck on coins of Sev. Alexander, Julia Domna and Julia Maesa 3000

POSTUMUS
259-268 A.D.

Marcus Cassianius Latinius Postumus was a man of humble origin and was a soldier of great merit who Valerian had put in charge of the Rhine legions. In 259 he rebelled against Gallienus and ruled Gaul, Spain and Britain firmly and wisely for nearly ten years. In 268, Laelianus rebelled against Postumus, the latter quickly overcame the former. The refusal of Postumus to allow his troops to sack Moguntiacum (Mainz), which had supported the rebels, led to his own assissination.

Obverse legends.

A.   IMP . C . POSTVMVS P . F . AVG.
B.   IMP . POSTVMVS AVG.
C.   POSTVMVS AVG.
D.   POSTVMVS PIVS AVG.
E.   POSTVMVS PIVS FELIX AVG.
F.   VIRTVS POSTVMI AVG.

Obverse types.

a.   Radiate bust draped right.
b.   Laureate bust draped r.
c.   Radiate bust draped and cuirassed r.
d.   Laureate bust draped and cuirassed r.
e.   Radiate head or bust r.
f.   Laureate head or bust r.
g.   Radiate head left, with club and lion's skin.
h.   Radiate bust left, with club and lion's skin.
i.   Jugate laur. heads of emperor and Hercules r.
j.   Jugate laur. heads of emperor and Hercules left.
k.   Jugate laur. busts of emperor and Hercules r.
l.   Jugate laur. busts of emperor and Hercules left.
m.   Laur. hd. of emp. and laur. bust of Her. jugate r.
n.   Laur. bust of emp. and laur. head of Her. jugate r.

N.B.—*Where we put a or c the former is given by Cohen and the latter by R.I.C.; probably just a different person's description of the same bust.*

Mints
(L)   Lugdunum.
(C)   Cologne (Colonia Claudia Agrippina Augusta).
(M)   Mediolanum.

8 Antoninianus. De(C). ℞. CASTOR, Castor stg., l. by horse, holding spear. (*Probably an error for next*) .. ..

8a Ac(C). ℞. — As last. *R.I.C.* 297.. .. .. £125

10 Denarius. El(C). ℞. — As last. *R.I.C.* 335 .. .. .. *Very rare*

11 Antoninianus. Ac(C). ℞. C . C . A . A. COS . IIII, Aequitas, stg. l. *R.I.C.* 285 150

13 Denarius. Ek(C). ℞. CLARITAS AVG., jugate, drap. bust of Sol and Luna r. *R.I.C.* 336 .. .. *Very rare*

14a   19

14 Antoninianus. Ae(C). ℞. COL . CL . AGRIP . COS . IIII, Aequitas stg. l.
R.I.C. 286 ..   ..   *Very rare*
14a Aa(C). ℞. — As last (*B.M.*) ..   ..   *Very rare*
17 IMP . C . POSTVMVS AVG., a (M). ℞. CONCORD . AEQVIT, Fortuna stg. l.,
foot on prow, holding patera and rudder. R.I.C. 370 ..   ..   ..   £20
17a — — ℞. — As last, but with s in ex. R.I.C. 370   20
18 Ba (M). ℞. — As last. R.I.C. 371   20
18a — — ℞. — As 17. R.I.C. 371   20
18b Bc (M). ℞. — As last and/or **17a**. R.I.C. 371   20
19 Ba(M). ℞. CONCORD . EQVIT., as **17**. R.I.C. 373   22
19a — — ℞. — As **17a**. R.I.C. 373   22
19b Bc(M). ℞. — As last and/or **17**. R.I.C. 373   22
20 Aa (*Cohen*, b *in error*) (M.) ℞. — As **17**. R.I.C. 372   22
20a — — — ℞. — As **17a**. R.I.C. 372   22
20b Ac (M). ℞. — As last and/or **17**. R.I.C. 372   22
21 Aa (M). ℞. CONCORD . EQVITVM, as **17a**. R.I.C. 374   20
21a — — ℞. — As **17**. R.I.C. 374   20
22 Ba(M). ℞. CONCORDIA EQVIT., as last. R.I.C. 375   25
24 Denarius. Em(C). ℞. CONSERVATORES AVG., jugate busts of Mars, cuir.,
and Victory; the latter holding wreath and palm. R.I.C. 337 ..   *Very rare*
25 Antoninianus. Aa or c(C). ℞. — As last. R.I.C. 298 ..   ..   *Very rare*
27 Denarius. Em(C). ℞. — jugate busts of Apollo, laur. and with mantle,
and Diana holding bow. R.I.C. 338 ..   ..   *Very rare*
30 Antoninianus. Ae(L). ℞. COS . III, Victory, half-naked, stg. r...   ..   16
30a Aa(L). ℞. — As last. R.I.C. 52   16
30b Ac(L). ℞. — As last. R.I.C. 52   16
31 Aa(C). ℞. COS . IIII, as last. R.I.C. 287   16
31a Ac(C). ℞. — As last. R.I.C. 287   16
32 Aa(C). ℞. COS . V, as last. R.I.C. 288   16
32a Ac(C). ℞. — As last. R.I.C. 288   16
33 Aa or c(C). ℞. DIANAE LVCIFERAE, Diana walking r., quiver on shoulder,
holding lighted torch in both hands. R.I.C. 299   20
34 Aa or c(C). ℞. DIANAE LVCIFERE, as before, but with stag before Diana.
R.I.C. 299   35

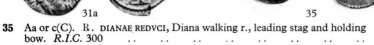

31a   35

35 Aa or c(C). ℞. DIANAE REDVCI, Diana walking r., leading stag and holding
bow. R.I.C. 300   45

39 Antoninianus. Aa(L). ℞. FELICITAS AVG., Felicitas stg. l.   *R.I.C.* 58   £15
39a Ac(L). ℞. — As last.   *R.I.C.* 58   15
55 Em(C). ℞. FELICITAS TEMP., galley l., with four rowers and standard.
    R.I.C. 301   .. .. *Very rare*
55a Denarius. As last.   *R.I.C.* 339   .. .. *Very rare*
57 Antoninianus. Ba(M). ℞. FIDES AEQVIT., Fides seated l., holding
    patera and ensign.   *R.I.C.* 376   20
57a Ba(M). ℞. — As last, but P in ex.   *R.I.C.* 376   20
59 Ae(M). ℞. FIDES EQVIT, as last   .. ..
59a Aa(M). ℞. — As last.   *R.I.C.* 377   20
59b Aa(M). ℞. — As **57**.   *R.I.C.* 377   20
60 Ba(M). ℞. — As **57a**   20
60a Ba(M). ℞. — As **57**.   *R.I.C.* 378   20
61 Be(M). ℞. FIDES EQVITVM, as last   .. ..
61a Ba(M). ℞. — As last.   *R.I.C.* 379   25

60   65

63 Aa or c(C). ℞. FIDES EXERCITI, four ensigns, the two in the middle sur-
    mounted by eagles.   *R.I.C.* 302   30
65 Aa or c(C). ℞. FIDES EXERCITVS, as last, but hand in place of one eagle.
    R.I.C. 303   22
65a As last, but EXERCITAS.   *R.I.C.* 303 22
67 Aa *(Cohen* b *in error)* (L). ℞. FIDES MILITVM, Fides stg. l., holding two
    ensigns.   *R.I.C.* 59   15
67a Ac (L and M). ℞. — As last.   *R.I.C.* 59 and 380   15
68 Quinarius, Ab(L). ℞. — As last.   *R.I.C.* 105   .. *Very rare*
80 Antoninianus. Aa or c(L). ℞. FORTVNA AVG., Fortuna stg. l.   *R.I.C.*
    60   15
81 Aa or c (L and C). ℞. — Fortuna seated l.   *R.I.C.* 61 and 304   .. 18
82a Ac(L). ℞. FORTVNA RAEDVX, Fortuna seated l. in temple with two
    columns; beside her, a wheel.   *R.I.C.* 62   45
83 Aa or c(L). ℞. FORTVNA REDVX, as last.   *R.I.C.* 62   45
84 Aa or c(L). ℞. GERMANICVS MAX . V, trophy between two captives with
    their hands behind their backs.   *R.I.C.* 63 40
91 Aa(L). ℞. HERC . DEVSONIENSI, Hercules stg. r., leaning on club, holding
    bow and lion's skin.   *R.I.C.* 64   18
91a Ac(L). ℞. — As last.   *R.I.C.* 64   18
92 Aa and/or c(L). ℞. — As last, but of heavy weight (6 gms.).   *R.I.C.* 64
    note   35
92a Aa(L). ℞. — As **91,** but club on rock and no bow.   *R.I.C.* 65   .. 22
92b Ac(L). ℞. — As last.   *R.I.C.* 65   22
93 Denarius. Ab(L). ℞. — As last.   *R.I.C.* 98   .. .. *Very rare*

98a   101a

98 Antoninianus. Aa(L). ℞. HERC. DEVSONIENSI, temple of four columns, within which Hercules stg. half-left, leaning on club and holding lion's skin. *R.I.C.* 66 .. .. £25

98a Ac(L). ℞. — As last. *R.I.C.* 66 25

100a Denarius. Af(L). ℞. HERCVLI DEVSONIENSI, laur. bust l. of Postumus as Hercules. *R.I.C.* 99 (*B.M.;* diam. 24 mm.; wt., 3.46 gms.) .. *Very rare*

101 Antoninianus. Aa(L). ℞. HERC. PACIFERO, Hercules stg. l., holding olive-branch, club and lion's skin. *R.I.C.* 67 16

101a Ac(L). ℞. — As last. *R.I.C.* 67 16

102 Aa and/or c(L). ℞. — As last, but heavy weight (6 gms.). *R.I.C.* 67 note 35

103 IMP. C. POSTVMVS, a. ℞. HERC. PACIFERI, as **101** (*barbarous*) .. ..

104 Aa. ℞. HERC. PACIFECI, as last (*barbarous*) .. ..

109 Denarius. Ei(C). ℞. HERCVLI ARCADIO, Hercules stg. r., capturing stag. *R.I.C.* 340 .. .. *Extremely rare*

110 En(C). ℞. HERCVLI ARGIVO, Hercules walking l., slaying hydra with club. *R.I.C.* 341 (2.98 gms.).. .. .. *Extremely rare*

111 Ej(C). ℞. — As last. *R.I.C.* 342 .. .. *Extremely rare*

116 Ek(C). ℞. HERCVLI DEVSONIENSI, bust of Hercules to waist l., lion's skin on hd., holding club. *R.I.C.* 343 .. .. *Extremely rare*

119 Ek(C). ℞. HERCVLI ERVMANTINO, Hercules walking r., carrying boar on his shoulder; wine-jar on r., *R.I.C.* 344 .. .. .. *Extremely rare*

120 Ej(C). ℞. — As last. *R.I.C.* 345 .. .. *Extremely rare*

121 Ek(C). ℞. HERCVLI GADITANO, Hercules stg. r., with lion's skin on l. arm, in combat with three soldiers, representing the triple monster Geryon. *R.I.C.* 346 .. .. *Extremely rare*

122 Ek(C). ℞. HERCVLI INMORTALI, Hercules walking r., with lion's skin over shoulder and holding club, dragging Cerberus r. *R.I.C.* 347 *Very rare*

122a Ek(C). ℞. HERCVLI IMMORTALI, as last. *R.I.C.* 347 .. *Very rare*

123 Ek(C). ℞. HERCVLI INVICTO, Hercules stg. l., treading down Amazon, holding her girdle, club and lion's skin. *R.I.C.* 348 .. .. *Very rare*

124 Antoninianus. A, rad. bust cuir. r. (C). ℞. — As last. *R.I.C.* 305 *Very rare*

129 Aa(L). ℞. HERCVLI MAGVSANO, Hercules stg. r., leaning on club enveloped in lion's skin and on rock. *R.I.C.* 129 .. .. .. *Very rare*

129a Ac(L). ℞. — As last. *R.I.C.* 129 .. .. *Very rare*

120   132

132 Denarius. Ek(C). ℞. HERCVLI NEMAEO, Hercules stg. l., strangling the Nemaean lion. *R.I.C.* 349 .. .. *Extremely rare*

134 Denarius. El(C). R. HERC(VLI) PISAEO, Hercules walking l., holding mattock; at his feet, water-jar (for cleansing the Augean stables). *R.I.C.* 350

Extremely rare

135 Ek(C). R. HERCVLI ROM., ROMA. or ROMANO, Hercules, holding lion's skin and club, stg. l. by tree in the garden of Hesperides; around tree, three nymphs. (Wt. 3.30 gms.). *R.I.C.* 351 .. .. *Extremely rare*

136 Antoninianus. Aa(C). R. HERCVLI ROMANO AVG., bow, club and quiver. *R.I.C.* 306 .. .. £35

136a Ac(C). R. — As last. *R.I.C.* 306 35

137   160

137 Ch(C). R. — As last. *R.I.C.* 307 90

139 Denarius. C, laur. bust l. with lion's skin and club (C). R. HERCVLI THRACIO, Hercules stg. overcoming the horses of Diomedes. *R.I.C.* 353 *Very rare*

140 Ek(C). R. — As last. *R.I.C.* 352 .. .. *Very rare*

141 Ek(C). R. HILARITAS AVG., Hilaritas stg. l. between two young children, holding long palm and cornucopiae. *R.I.C.* 354 .. .. .. *Very rare*

142 Antoninianus. Aa(L). R. IM . C . POSTVMVS P . F . AVG., a. *R.I.C.* 69 *Very rare*

144 Aa(C). R. IMP . X COS . V., Victory, half-naked, stg. r. *R.I.C.* 289 20

144a Ac(C). R. — As last. *R.I.C.* 289 20

144b A, rad. bust cuir. r. (C). R. — As last. *R.I.C.* 289 22

145a Ac(C). R. INTERNVTIVS (*sic*) DEORVM, Mercury stg. l., holding purse and caduceus. (*British Museum*) .. .. *Very rare*

148 Denarius. Ad(L). R. INVICTO AVG., rad. bust of Postumus cuir. to waist l., holding sceptre or spear on shoulder (wt. 2.86 gms.). *R.I.C.* 100

Very rare

149 Antoninianus. Ae. R. (INVIC)TV . AVG., Sol, rad. and half-naked, walking r., holding thunderbolt .. ..

151 Aa(C). R. IOVI CONSERVAT., Jupiter, naked but with mantle flowing behind him, stg. l.; at feet, a child. *R.I.C.* 308 24

152 Aa(C). R. IOVI CONSERVATORI, as last. *R.I.C.* 308 26

153 Aa(L). R. IOVI PROPVGNAT, Jupiter, as last, walking l., looking back, holding thunderbolt and outstretching l. hand. *R.I.C.* 70 16

153a Ac(L). R. — As last. *R.I.C.* 70 16

154 Aa(L). R. — As last, but with seven stars in field and an eagle between Jupiter's legs. *R.I.C.* 71 40

154a Ac(L). R. — As last. *R.I.C.* 71 40

155 Aa(L). R. IOVI PROPVGNATORI, Jupiter, as **151,** but walking l., looking back, no child. *R.I.C.* 72 15

155a Ac(L). R. — As last. *R.I.C.* 72 15

159 Aa(C). R. IOVI STATORI, Jupiter, naked, stg. facing, looking r. *R.I.C.* 309 15

159a Ac(C). R. — As last. *R.I.C.* 309 15

160 Ch or g (C). — As last. *R.I.C.* 310 75

161 Aa(C). R. IOVI VICTORI, Jupiter, naked, walking l., looking back. *R.I.C.* 311 18

161a Ac(C). R. — As last. *R.I.C.* 311 18

162 Aa(C). R. — As before, but with seven stars in field and an eagle between Jupiter's legs. *R.I.C.* 311a 40

162a Ac(C). R. — As last. *R.I.C.* 311a 40

163 Aa(C). R. — As **161** (*Cohen has as last, probably in error*), with CA in field. *R.I.C.* 311 note .. .. *Very rare*

167 **Antoninianus.** Aa(L). ℞. LAETITIA around, AVG. in ex., galley to l., with three or four (*R.I.C.* four or five) rowers and a pilot. *R.I.C.* 73 .. £25

167a Ac(L). ℞. — As last. *R.I.C.* 73 25

168 Aa and/or c(L). ℞. — Similar, but with sail. *R.I.C.* 73 40

187 **Denarius.** Df(C). ℞. LIBERALITAS AVG., Liberalitas stg. l. *R.I.C.* 355 125

190 Ab(C). ℞. LIBERTAS AVG., Libertas stg. l., holding pileus and cornu-copiae. *R.I.C.* 356 125

167   195a

191 **Antoninianus.** Aa (*Cohen,* b *in error*) (C). ℞. MARS VICTOR, Mars stg., l., leaning on shield and holding spear. *R.I.C.* 312 25
R.I.C. 356 *and* 357 (*obv.* b *and* d) *also show* **191** *and* **192** *as denarii, but cannot verify this.*

192 Aa (*Cohen,* b *in error*) (C). ℞. MERCVRIO FELICI, Mercury, half-naked, stg. facing, looking r. *R.I.C.* 313 25

195 Aa(L). ℞. MINER FAVTR., Minerva running l., holding olive branch, spear and shield. *R.I.C.* 74 20

195a Ac(L). ℞. — As last. *R.I.C.* 74 20

199 Aa(L and C). ℞. MONETA AVG., Moneta stg. l. *R.I.C.* 75 and 315 .. 15

199a Ac(L and C). ℞. — As last. *R.I.C.* 75 and 315 15

200 Aa and/or c. ℞. — As last, but of heavy weight (7.10 gms). *R.I.C.* 75 note 35

202a Bc(C). ℞. MONET AVG., Hercules stg. l., holding club. *R.I.C.* 314 .. 30

199   213c

205 Aa(L). ℞. NEPTVNO REDVCI, Neptune stg. l., naked, but mantle behind l. arm; to l., forepart of vessel. *R.I.C.* 76 22

205a Ac(L). ℞. — As last. *R.I.C.* 76 22

206 Aa(L). ℞. — As last, but without the vessel. *R.I.C.* 76 22

206a Ac(L). ℞. — As last. *R.I.C.* 76 22

213 Ae(C). ℞. ORIENS AVG., Sol walking l., holding whip and r. hand raised

213a Ae(C). ℞. — As last, but P in field ..

213b Aa(L and C). ℞. — As **213**. *R.I.C.* 77 and 316 16

213c Ac(L and C). ℞. — As last. *R.I.C.* 77 and 316 16

213d Aa and/or c (C). ℞. — As **213a**. *R.I.C.* 216 note 16

214 Antoninianus. Ae(C). ℞. PACATOR ORBIS, rad. bust of Sol dr. r. ..

214a Aa(C). ℞. — As last. *R.I.C.* 317 .. .. £45

214b Ac(C). ℞. —As last. *R.I.C.* 317 45

215 Ae(C). ℞. PAX AVG., Pax stg. l. ..

215a Aa(C). ℞. —As last. *R.I.C.* 318 15

215b Ac(C). ℞. —As last. *R.I.C.* 318 15

215c Aa and/or c (C). ℞. — As last, but P or V and star in field. *R.I.C.* 318
note 18

216 Denarius. Ek, but Hercules bare-headed (C). ℞. — Pax stg. l.
R.I.C. 359 .. .. *Very rare*

217 Quinarius. D, as last (C). ℞. — As last. *R.I.C.* 371 .. *Very rare*

218 Antoninianus. Ch(C). ℞. — As last. *R.I.C.* 319 75

219 As last, but spear for club on *obv.* *R.I.C.* 319 75

219a As **218** and/or **219**. ℞. — As **215c**. *R.I.C.* 319 note 75

220 Aa(L). ℞. — Pax walking l. *R.I.C.* 78 15

227 Aa(L). ℞. PAX AVGVSTI, Pax stg. l. *R.I.C.* 79 15

227a Ac(L). ℞. —As last. *R.I.C.* 79 16

228 Aa(M). ℞. PAX EQVITVM, as last; T in field. *R.I.C.* 381 20

228a Ac(M). ℞. —As last. *R.I.C.* 381 20

228b Aa and/or c (M). ℞. —As last, but nothing in ex. *R.I.C.* 381 .. 20

215a   243

230 Aa(C). ℞. PIETAS AVG., Pietas stg. l. between two children, another two
in her arms. *R.I.C.* 320 22

230a Ac(C). ℞. —As last. *R.I.C.* 320 22

231 Aa(C). ℞. —Pietas stg. facing, raising both arms. *R.I.C.* 321 .. 35

238 Denarius. A, laur. bust cuir. r. (L). ℞. P . M . TR . P . COS . P . P.,
lion walking l., thunderbolt in its mouth. *R.I.C.* 95 150

239 Antoninianus. Aa(L). ℞. P . M . TR . P . COS . I P . P., emperor in
military dress stg. l., holding globe and spear. *R.I.C.* 53 45

239a Ac(L). ℞. —As last. *R.I.C.* 53 45

239b Aa(L). ℞. V . M. etc., as last. (*Paris*) 45

241 Quinarius. Ab(L). ℞. P . M . TR . P . COS . II P . P., as last. *R.I.C.*
104 .. .. *Very rare*

242 IMP . POSTVMVS P . F . AVG., b (L). ℞. —As last. *R.I.C.* 104 .. *Very rare*

243 Antoninianus. Aa(L). ℞. — As last. *R.I.C.* 54 18

243a Ac(L). ℞. —As last. *R.I.C.* 54 18

244 Aa and/or c (L). As before, but heavy weight (6.40 gms.). *R.I.C.* 54
note 35

261 Ae(L). ℞. P . M . TR . P . COS . III P . P., as before. *R.I.C.* 55 20

261a Aa(L). ℞. —As last. *R.I.C.* 55 20

266 Aa(C). ℞. P . M . TR . P . COS . III P . P., as last. *R.I.C.* 290 40

269 Aa(L). ℞. P . M . TR . P . III COS . III P . P., Mars, naked but mantle
floating, walking r., holding spear and trophy. *R.I.C.* 56 18

273 Aa(L). ℞. P . M . TR . P . III COS . III P . P., as last. *R.I.C.* 57 20

273a Ac(L). ℞. —As last. *R.I.C.* 57 20

276 Antoninianus. Aa(C). ℞. P . M . TR . P . V COS . V P . P., emperor or
Genius of the Senate (?) stg. l., holding branch and sceptre (*an error for
C.* 286) .. ..

281 Aa(C). ℞. P . M . TR . P . VIIII COS . IIII P . P., bow, club and flat quiver.
R.I.C. 291 .. .. £30

282 Ch(C). ℞. — As last. *R.I.C.* 292 75

283 As **281,** but cylindrical quiver. *R.I.C.* 291 30

283a Ac(C). ℞. — As **281** and/or **283.** *R.I.C.* 291 30

284a Denarius. Dk(C). ℞. P . M . TR . P . X COS . V . P . P., winged bust to
waist of Victory r., inscribing VOT . XX (?) on shield. *R.I.C.* 334 (*Levis
coll.*) .. .. *Extremely rare*

285 Antoninianus. Aa(C). ℞. — Victory, half-naked, stg., r. foot on globe
(or helmet); holding on knee, shield inscribed VO . XX. *R.I.C.* 295 .. 40

285a Aa(C). ℞. — Victory stg. r. *R.I.C.* 293 (*Vierordt*) 40

286 Aa(C). ℞. — As **276.** *R.I.C.* 294 25

290 Denarius. El(C). ℞. POSTVMVS AVGVSTVS, bust of emperor r., lion's
skin on head, paws around neck; all in laurel-wreath. *R.I.C.* 360 *Extremely rare*

291 Antoninianus. Ac(C). ℞. POSTVMVS P . F . AVG., his bare hd. r.
R.I.C. 322 .. .. *Very rare*

295 Aa (L and C). ℞. PROVIDENTIA AVG., Providentia stg. l., holding globe
and transverse sceptre. *R.I.C.* 80 and 323 15

295a Ac (L and C). ℞. — As last. *R.I.C.* 80 and 323 15

296 Aa and/or c (L). ℞. As before but of heavy weight (6.75 gms.). *R.I.C.*
80 note) 35

297 Quinarius. A, bare-headed full-faced bust, draped (C). ℞. — As
before. *R.I.C.* 362 .. .. *Extremely rare*

301 Denarius. Df (L). ℞. — Providentia, legs crossed, stg. l. leaning on
column, holding cornucopiae and baton, which she points to globe at her
feet. *R.I.C.* 101 (wt. 2.76 gms). 125

303 Antoninianus. Aa(L). ℞. — As last. *R.I.C.* 81 22

304 Denarius. IMP . C . POSTVMVS P . F . AVG . COS . III, b (L). ℞. — As last.
R.I.C. 96 .. .. *Very rare*

311 Antoninianus. Aa (L). ℞. REST . GALLIAR., Postumus, in military
dress, stg. l., foot on captive, holding spear and raising Gallia who
before him. *R.I.C.* 82 25

312 Aa (L). ℞. — As before, but Postumus is laur. and Gallia wears mural
crown and holds cornucopiae. *R.I.C.* 82 25

313 Aa (L). ℞. RESTIT . GALLIARVM, as last. *R.I.C.* 82 25

313a Ac (L). ℞. As **311, 312, 313** and/or **319.** *R.I.C.* 82 25

319 Aa (L). ℞. RESTITVTOR GALLIAR., as **311,** but Gallia wears mural crown.
R.I.C. 82 22

295a   323

323 Aa (C). ℞. REST . ORBIS, Postumus, laur. and in military dress, holding
spear and raising kneeling female who holds cornucopiae. *R.I.C.* 324 .. 22

325 Aa (C). ℞. — As before, but female wears mural crown. *R.I.C.* 324 .. 22

325a Aa (C). ℞. RESTIT . ORBIS, as **323** or **325.** *R.I.C.* 324 22

325b Ac (C). ℞. As **323, 325, 325a** and/or **326.** *R.I.C.* 324 22

326 Aa (C). ℞. RESTITVTOR ORBIS. As **323** and/or **325.** *R.I.C.* 324 .. 25

330   Antoninianus. Obv. ? (L ?).   ℞. ROMAE AETERNAE, Roma seated l., holding Victory and sceptre; shield under chair ..   ..

331   Aa (L).   ℞. SAECVLI FELICITAS, emperor, in military dress, stg. r., holding spear and globe. *R.I.C.* 83 ..   ..   £18

331a Ac (L and C).   ℞. — As last. *R.I.C.* 83 and 325   18

332a Aa and/or c (L).   ℞. SAECVLI FRVGIFERO, winged caduceus. *R.I.C.* 84   22

333   Aa (L).   ℞. SAECVLO FRVGIFERO, as last. *R.I.C.* 84   22

333a Ac (L).   ℞. — As last. *R.I.C.* 84   22

336   Aa (L and C).   ℞. SALVS AVG., Aesculapius stg. facing, hd. l., leaning on his serpent-entwined staff. *R.I.C.* 86 and 326   20

336a Aa (L and C).   ℞. — As last, but globe at feet. *R.I.C.* 86 and 326   ..   20

336b Aa (M).   ℞. — As last, but P in ex. *R.I.C.* 382   20

336c Aa (M).   ℞. — As last, but without globe. *R.I.C.* 382   20

336d Ac (L, C and M).   ℞. — As any or all of the last four. *R.I.C.* 86, 326 and 382   20

337   Quinarius. Ci(C).   ℞. — As **336.** *R.I.C.* 363   350

339   Aa (L).   ℞. — Salus stg. l., holding rudder and feeding serpent arising from altar. *R.I.C.* 85   15

339a Ac (L).   ℞. — As last. *R.I.C.* 85   15

348   Aa (*Cohen* b *in error*) (M).   ℞. SALVS EXERCITI, as **336b.** *R.I.C.* 383   ..   25

348a Ac (M).   ℞. — As last. *R.I.C.* 383   25

348b Ac (C).   ℞. — As last, but without P in ex. *R.I.C.* 327   25

350   Aa (C).   ℞. SALVS POSTVMI AVG., Salus stg. r., feeding serpent in her arms. *R.I.C.* 328   20

350a Ac (C).   ℞. — As last. *R.I.C.* 328..   20

355   Aa (L).   ℞. SALVS PROVINCIARVM, Rhine reclining l., resting on urn, r. hand on forepart of boat, l. holding anchor (?), horns on his head. *R.I.C.* 87   35

355a Aa (L).   ℞. — As before, but without horns. (? *C.* 353). *R.I.C.* 87   ..   35

355b Ac (L).   ℞. — As **355** and/or **355a.** *R.I.C.* 87   35

356   As one of the last three, but heavy (wt. 5.60 gms.). *R.I.C.* 87 note   ..   50

355b   360a

357   Aa (C).   ℞. SARAPIDI COMITI AVG., Serapis stg. l., holding sceptre and raising r. hand.; in lower background, vessel. *R.I.C.* 329   25

358   Aa (C).   ℞. SERAPI or SARAPI . COMITI AVG., as last. *R.I.C.* 329   ..   22

358a Ac (C).   ℞. As **357** and/or **358.** *R.I.C.* 329   22

360   Aa (C).   ℞. As **358,** but without vessel. *R.I.C.* 329   22

360a Ac (C).   ℞. As last   22

361 Antoninianus. Aa(L). R. SPEI . PERPETVAE, Spes walking l. *R.I.C.* 88   £25
361a Ac (L). R. — As last. *R.I.C.* 88   25
363 Aa (M). R. SPES PVBLICA, as last, but with P in ex. *R.I.C.* 384   ..   25
363a Aa (M). R. — As last, but ex. clear. *R.I.C.* 384   25
364 Aa (C). R. TP . P . X COS . V P . P ., Victory stg. r., l. foot on helmet (or globe), writing VO. or VOT . XX on shield which she holds on her knee. *R.I.C.* 296   40
364a Ac (C). R. — As last. *R.I.C.* 296   40
365 Aa (C). R. VBERTAS AVG., Uberitas stg. l. *R.I.C.* 330   20
366 Aa (C). R. VBERITAS AVG., as last. *R.I.C.* 330   20
366a Ac (C). R. As **365** and/or **366.** *R.I.C.* 330   20
368 Denarius. C, helmeted bust cuir. r. (L). R. VICT . GERM . TR . P . V COS . III P . P ., emperor stg. l., holding globe and spear, being crowned by Victory stg., who holds palm. *R.I.C.* 97 ..   ..   *Very rare*
371 Af (L). R. VICT . GERMANICA, Victory walking l. *R.I.C.* 102   150
371a Ab (L). R. — As last. *R.I.C.* 102..   150
376 F, helmeted bust cuir. r. (L). R. VICTORIA AVG, as last, but with captive at her feet. *R.I.C.* 103   150

377 Antoninianus. Aa (L). R. — As last. *R.I.C.* 89   16
377a Ac (L). R. — As last. *R.I.C.* 89   16
378 As **377,** but heavy (wt. 5.00 and 5.70 gms.). *R.I.C.* 89 note   ..   35
     N.B. *A Becker forgery exists between the size of a* den. *and a* quin. IMP . C . POSTVMVS PIVS AVG., f. R. As above, but Victory running r.
390 Aa (L). R — As **376,** but without captive. *R.I.C.* 90   18
405 Fa (L). R. VICTORIA GERMANICA, Victory running r. *R.I.C.* 91   90
412 IMP . C . POSTVMVS AVG., c (M). R. VIRTVS AEQVIT., soldier or Mars walking r., holding spear and trophy. *R.I.C.* 385   20
412a As last, but with T in *rev.* ex. *R.I.C.* 385   20
413 Bc (M). R. — As **412.** *R.I.C.* 386   20
413a Bc (M.) R. — As **412a.** *R.I.C.* 386   20
418 Aa (L). R. VIRTVS AVG., Hercules stg. r., holding club, lion's skin and bow. *R.I.C.* 92   22
418a Ac (L). R. — As last. *R.I.C.* 92   22
418b Aa and/or c (L). R. — As last, but four apples for bow. *R.I.C.* 92 (B.M.)   25
419 Aa (L). R. — Mars stg. r., leaning on shield and holding spear. *R.I.C.* 93   15

419a   443

419a Ac (L). R. — As last. *R.I.C.* 93   15
420 As **419,** but heavy (wt. 5.50 and 5.20 gms.). *R.I.C.* 93   35

427 Antoninianus. Aa(C). ℞. VIRTVS AVG., emperor, bare-headed, in military dress, walking r., holding spear and shield, at his feet a captive. *R.I.C.* 331 ..   ..   £18

428 Aa (C). ℞. — As last, but without captive. *R.I.C.* 331..   18

428a Ac (C). ℞. — As **427** and/or **428**. *R.I.C.* 331   18

434 Aa (L and C). ℞. — Emperor, in military dress, stg. l., holding spear and placing r. hand on trophy between two captives. *R.I.C.* 94 and 332 ..   75

441 Ba or c (M). ℞. VIRTVS EQVIT., soldier or Mars walking r., holding spear and trophy; T in ex. *R.I.C.* 388 ..   ..:   22

442 Ac (M). ℞. — As last. *R.I.C.* 387   20

442a Ac (M). ℞. — As last, but ex. clear. *R.I.C.* 387   20

442b Aa (M). ℞. — As **442** and/or **442a**. *R.I.C.* 387   22

443 Aa (M). ℞. VIRTVS EQVITVM, Hercules stg. r., leaning on club with lion's skin on rock; S (*Cohen* or Z) in ex. *R.I.C.* 389   25

443a Aa (M). ℞. — As last, but ex clear   25

443b Aa (M). ℞. — As **443**. *R.I.C.* 389   25

452 Aa or c (C). ℞. VIRTVTI AVGVSTI, as **443**, but without rock. *R.I.C.* 333 ..   20

INDEX

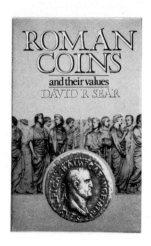

ROMAN COINS
and Their Values

by D. R. Sear
3rd Revised Edition 1981
£10·00 $25·00

A general catalogue of Roman coins, with values, containing biographical and historical details, and descriptions of over 4300 coins

376 pages, with chronological tables, twelve plates and many half tone illustrations in text.

ROMAN SILVER COINS

by H. A. Seaby

New editions revised by
D. R. Sear and Robert Loosley

Vol. I. Republic to Augustus
£7·50 $16·00
Vol. II. Tiberius to Commodus
£12·00 $30·00
Vol. III. Pertinax to Balbinus and Pupienus
£10·00 $22·50
Vol. IV. Gordian III to Postumus
£10·00 $22·50

The text of the above volumes has been revised to include the latest valuations, new coins and the latest research, and contains new photographic illustrations.

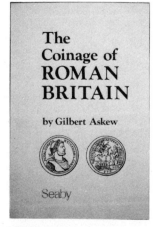

THE COINAGE OF ROMAN BRITAIN

by Gilbert Askew
£4·75 $12·00

Second edition with new introduction. The most compact listing of the Roman coins relating to the Province of Britannia.

A DICTIONARY OF ROMAN COINS

by S. W. Stevenson

£16·00 $35·00

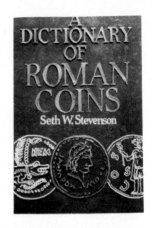

First published in 1889, this is a reprint of the most comprehensive dictionary of Roman coin types, legends, emperors, etc., ever published in a single volume and contains much information for students of Roman coinage not assembled elsewhere.

929 pages, several hundred illustrations.

GREEK IMPERIAL COINS and Their Values

The Local Coinages of the Roman Empire

by David R. Sear

£27·50 $55·00

Arranged chronologically by emperors, this catalogue is unique in providing the collector with the only comprehensive and authoritative guide devoted specifically to the local coinages of the Roman Empire. Includes the "quasi-autonomous" series and completes the listing of contemporary coinages begun in "Greek Coins and their Values".

Over 6000 coins described and valued with 1750 photographs and 10 maps.

THE EMPERORS OF ROME AND BYZANTIUM

Chronological and Genealogical Tables for History Students and Coin Collectors

by David R. Sear

£5·00 $12·50

An introduction, plus 75 tabulated sheets giving dates, relationships, cause of death, and many other life details of all the Roman and Byzantine emperors.

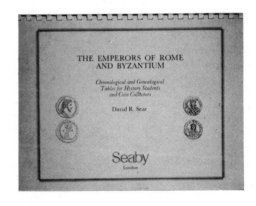

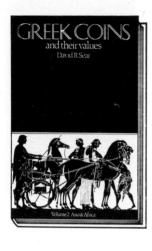

GREEK COINS
and Their Values
by D. R. Sear

Vol I. **Europe**
£12·50 $27·50

Vol. II. **Asia & Africa,**
including the Hellenistic
Monarchies.
£14·00 $35·00

The most comprehensive priced guide to Greek coins ever published. The average collector should be able to locate all the types he is likely to encounter in one denomination or another. Useful historical notes and illustrated preface. Altogether 7956 coins listed with 3356 photographs of coins in the British Museum.

GREEK COIN TYPES AND THEIR IDENTIFICATION

by Richard Plant
£10·00 $24·00

Nearly 3000 Greek coins are listed and illustrated, concentrating on types not immediately identifiable from their inscriptions or subjects represented. Place of issue, date, denomination, metal and size are given. An invaluable aid to the identification of Greek and 'Greek Imperial' coins.

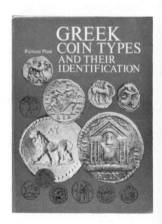

Please send for a complete list of our numismatic publications and current book and accessory catalogue.

Seaby Coin and Medal Bulletin. A monthly magazine for all interested in numismatics. Specimen copy upon request.